PEARSON

ALWAYS LEARNING

J. R. Tony Arnold • Stephen N. Chapman • Lloyd M. Clive

Introduction to Materials Management

Custom Edition

The Association for
Operations Management®

Cover Art: Courtesy of Photodisc/Getty Images.

Taken from:

Introduction to Materials Management, Seventh Edition
by J. R. Tony Arnold, Stephen N. Chapman, and Lloyd M. Clive
Copyright © 2012 by Pearson Education, Inc.
Published by Prentice Hall
Upper Saddler River, New Jersey 07458

Pearson Learning Solutions, 501 Boylston Street, Suite 900, Boston, MA 02116
A Pearson Education Company
www.pearsoned.com

Printed in the United States of America

11 12 13 14 15 V092 16 15

000200010270805228

RG

ISBN 10: 1-256-49733-9
ISBN 13: 978-1-256-49733-2

LETTER FROM THE CHAIRS OF APICS EXAM COMMITTEES

APICS The Association for Operations Management, the global leader and premier source for the body of knowledge in supply chain and operations management, has had a more than 30 year association with the *Introduction to Materials Management* text. The book is tightly integrated into the organization's two well-respected certification programs, the APICS Certified in Production and Inventory Management (CPIM) designation and the APICS Certified Supply Chain Professional designation (CSCP).

Introduction to Materials Management remains an important reference for three of the five APICS CPIM modules, and underpins the new APICS Principles of Operations Management education courses, due to its excellent overall coverage, straightforward approach, and readability. It is recommended to all candidates for APICS certifications or anyone wishing to gain a better understanding of operations planning and control in the production and distribution environments.

In particular, the book has had a major role in the development of the APICS CPIM Basics of Supply Chain Management (Basics) module, which provides exam candidates with a common, fundamental understanding of production planning and control processes. It has been the primary reference for this module since Basics was first offered.

Introduction to Materials Management provides comprehensive coverage of most of the essential foundation content of the body of knowledge and was written with the intention of helping learners understand the subject matter covered by APICS certification programs and exams. This approach has been very effective in assisting those pursuing APICS certification. More than 90,000 professionals have completed the APICS CPIM program since it began in 1973 and many more have completed the Basics course.

The scope of the book has evolved over time to remain current in its explanation of the fundamental principles in the supply chain and operations management fields. We hope you will enjoy this special, APICS edition of *Introduction to Materials Management*. The longevity and relevance of the text is not only a testament to its quality, it is also an indication of what it has meant to the careers of the people who have learned from it and obtained their certifications as a result.

Ann K. Gatewood, CFPIM, CIRM, CSCP, Chair of the APICS Certification Committee
Paul H. Pittman, Ph.D., CFPIM, CSCP, Jonah, Chair of the CPIM committees

CONTENTS

Preface   ix

1 Introduction to Materials Management   1

Introduction   1 / Operating Environment   1 / The Supply Chain Concept   4 / What Is Materials Management?   9 / Summary   13 / Key Terms   13 / Questions   13 / Problems   14

2 Production Planning System   16

Introduction   16 / Manufacturing Planning and Control System   17 / Sales and Operations Planning   20 / Manufacturing Resource Planning   22 / Enterprise Resource Planning   23 / Making the Production Plan   24 / Summary   33 / Key Terms   33 / Questions   33 / Problems   34 / Case Study: Meridian Water Pumps   39

3 Master Scheduling   41

Introduction   41 / Relationship to Production Plan   42 / Developing a Master Production Schedule   44 / Production Planning, Master Scheduling, and Sales   49 / Summary   54 / Key Terms   55 / Questions   55 / Problems   56 / Case Study: Acme Water Pumps   61

4 Material Requirements Planning   62

Introduction   62 / Bills of Material   64 / Material Requirements Planning Process   70 / Using the Material Requirements Plan   81 / Summary   84 / Key Terms   84 / Questions   84 / Problems   85 / Case Study: Apix Polybob Company   95

5 Capacity Management   98

Introduction   98 / Definition of Capacity   98 / Capacity Planning   99 / Capacity Requirements Planning   100 / Capacity Available   102 / Capacity Required (Load)   105 / Scheduling Orders   107 / Making the Plan   109 / Summary   109 / Key Terms   110 / Questions   111 / Problems   111 / Case Study: Wescott Products   114

6 Production Activity Control   117

Introduction   117 / Data Requirements   120 / Order Preparation   121 / Scheduling   122 / Load Leveling   127 / Scheduling Bottlenecks   128 / Theory of Constraints and Drum-Buffer-Rope   130 / Implementation   132 / Control   133 / Production Reporting   138 / Product Tracking   139 / Summary   139 / Key Terms   139 / Questions   140 / Problems   141 / Case Study: Johnston Products   145

7 Purchasing   147

Introduction   147 / Establishing Specifications   150 / Functional Specification Description   152 / Selecting Suppliers   154 / Price Determination   157 / Impact of Material Requirements Planning on Purchasing   159 / Environmentally Responsible Purchasing   161 / Expansion of Purchasing into Supply Chain Management   162 / Some Organizational Implications of Supply Chain Management   163 / Summary   164 / Key Terms   164 / Questions   165 / Problems   165 / Case Study: Let's Party!   166

8 Forecasting   167

Introduction 167 / Demand Management 167 / Demand Forecasting 168 / Characteristics of Demand 168 / Principles of Forecasting 170 / Collection and Preparation of Data 171 / Forecasting Techniques 172 / Some Important Intrinsic Techniques 173 / Seasonality 176 / Tracking the Forecast 179 / Summary 185 / Key Terms 186 / Questions 186 / Problems 186 / Case Study: Northcutt Bikes: the Forecasting Problem 193

9 Inventory Fundamentals   196

Introduction 196 / Aggregate Inventory Management 196 / Item Inventory Management 196 / Inventory and the Flow of Material 197 / Supply and Demand Patterns 198 / Functions of Inventories 198 / Objectives of Inventory Management 199 / Inventory Costs 201 / Financial Statements and Inventory 203 / ABC Inventory Control 207 / Summary 210 / Key Terms 211 / Questions 211 / Problems 212 / Case Study: Randy Smith, Inventory Control Manager 216

10 Order Quantities   218

Introduction 218 / Economic-Order Quantity (EOQ) 219 / Variations of the EOQ Model 223 / Quantity Discounts 224 / Order Quantities for Families of Product When Costs are Not Known 225 / Period-Order Quantity (POQ) 226 / Summary 229 / Key Terms 229 / Questions 229 / Problems 230 / Case Study: Carl's Computers 234

11 Independent Demand Ordering Systems   237

Introduction 237 / Order Point System 237 / Determining Safety Stock 239 / Determining Service Levels 245 / Different Forecast and Lead-Time Intervals 247 / Determining When the Order Point Is Reached 247 / Periodic Review System 249 / Distribution Inventory 251 / Summary 254 / Key Terms 254 / Questions 255 / Problems 255

12 Physical Inventory and Warehouse Management   262

Introduction 262 / Warehousing Management 262 / Physical Control and Security 267 / Inventory Record Accuracy 268 / Technology Applications 273 / Summary 274 / Key Terms 274 / Questions 275 / Problems 275 / Case Study: CostMart Warehouse 278

13 Physical Distribution   282

Introduction 282 / Physical Distribution System 285 / Interfaces 287 / Transportation 288 / Legal Types of Carriage 290 / Transportation Cost Elements 291 / Warehousing 296 / Packaging 301 / Materials Handling 302 / Multi-Warehouse Systems 303 / Summary 305 / Key Terms 306 / Questions 306 / Problems 308 / Case Study: Metal Specialties, Inc. 309

14 Products and Processes   310

Introduction 310 / Need for New Products 310 / Product Development Principles 311 / Product Specification and Design 313 / Process Design 315 / Factors Influencing Process Design 316 / Processing Equipment 317 / Process Systems 318 / Selecting the Process 320 / Continuous Process Improvement (CPI) 322 / Key Terms 332 / Questions 333 / Problems 334 / Case Study: Cheryl Franklin, Production Manager 337

15 Lean Production   339

Introduction 339 / Lean Production 339 / Waste 341 / The Lean Production Environment 343 / Manufacturing Planning and Control in a Lean Production Environment: JIT Production 350 / Which to Choose: MRP (ERP), Kanban, or Theory of Constraints? 359 / Summary 361 / Key Terms 361 / Questions 362 / Problems 363 / Case Study: Murphy Manufacturing 364

16 Total Quality Management   367

Introduction   367 / What Is Quality?   367 / Total Quality Management (TQM)   369 / Quality Cost Concepts   372 / Variation as a Way of Life   373 / Process Capability   375 / Process Control   379 / Sample Inspection   382 / ISO 9000:2008   383 / Benchmarking   385 / Six Sigma   386 / Quality Function Deployment   387 / JIT, TQM, and MRP   389 / Summary   390 / Key Terms   390 / Questions   390 / Problems   391 / Case Study: Accent Oak Furniture Company   393

Readings   397
Index   401

PREFACE

Introduction to Materials Management is an introductory text written for students in community colleges and universities. It is used in technical programs, such as industrial engineering and manufacturing engineering; in business programs; and by those already in industry, whether or not they are working in materials management.

This text has been widely adopted by colleges and universities not only in North America but also in other parts of the world. APICS–The Association for Operations Management recommends this text as the reference for certification preparation for various CPIM examinations. In addition, the text is used by production and inventory control societies around the world, including South Africa, Australia, New Zealand, Germany, France, and Brazil, and by consultants who present in-house courses to their customers.

Introduction to Materials Management covers all the basics of supply chain management, manufacturing planning and control systems, purchasing, physical distribution and quality management. The material, examples, questions, and problems lead the student logically through the text. The writing style is simple and user-friendly—both instructors and students who have used the book attest to this.

NEW TO THIS EDITION

- All chapters have been updated to reflect new techniques and technology
- Case studies added to Chapters 2: Production Planning System, 9: Inventory Fundamentals, and 14: Products and Processes
- Re-organized content to emphasize lean production separate from but related to JIT
- Extensive updates to Chapter 15: Lean Production
- End of chapter problems have been altered
- Addition of information on sustainability and "green" production

In addition, we have retained several features from previous editions:

- Margin icons to note key concepts
- Key terms listed at the end of each chapter
- Example problems within the chapters
- Chapter summaries
- Questions and problems at the end of each chapter

APPROACH AND ORGANIZATION

Materials management means different things to different people. In this textbook, materials management includes all activities in the flow of materials from the supplier to the consumer. Such activities include physical supply, operations planning and control, and physical distribution. Other terms sometimes used in this area are *business logistics* and *supply chain management*. Often, the emphasis in business logistics is on transportation and distribution systems with little concern for what occurs in the factory. Whereas some chapters in this text are devoted to transportation and distribution, emphasis is placed on operations planning and control.

Distribution and operations are managed by planning and controlling the flow of materials through them and by using the system's resources to achieve a desired customer service level. These activities are the responsibility of materials management and affect every department in a manufacturing business. If the materials management system is not well designed and managed, the distribution and manufacturing system will be less effective and more costly. Anyone working in manufacturing or distribution should have a good basic understanding of the factors influencing materials flow. This text aims to provide that understanding and also includes a chapter on quality management.

APICS defines the body of knowledge, concepts, and vocabulary used in production and inventory control. Establishing standard knowledge, concepts, and vocabulary is essential both for developing an understanding of production and inventory control and for making clear communication possible. Where applicable, the definitions and concepts in this text subscribe to APICS vocabulary and concepts.

The first six chapters of *Introduction to Materials Management* cover the basics of production planning and control. Chapter 7 discusses important factors in purchasing and supply chain; Chapter 8 discusses forecasting. Chapters 9, 10, and 11 look at the fundamentals of inventory management. Chapter 12 discusses physical inventory and warehouse management, and Chapter 13 examines the elements of distribution systems, including transportation, packaging, and material handling. Chapter 14 covers factors influencing product and process design. Chapter 15 looks at the philosophy and environment of just-in-time and lean production and explains how operations planning and control systems relate to just-in-time and lean production. Chapter 16 examines the elements of total quality management and six sigma quality approaches.

ONLINE INSTRUCTOR RESOURCES

To access supplementary materials online, instructors need to request an instructor access code. Go to **www.pearsonhighered.com**, click the **Instructor Resource Center** link, and then click **Register Today** for an instructor access code. Within 48 hours after registering you will receive a confirming e-mail including an instructor access code. Once you have received your code, go to the site and log on for full instructions on downloading the materials you wish to use.

ACKNOWLEDGMENTS

Help and encouragement have come from a number of valued sources, among them friends, colleagues, and students. We thank the faculty of other colleges and the many members of APICS chapters who continue to offer their support and helpful advice. Many thanks to those who reviewed the sixth edition and provided suggestions for the seventh edition, including members of the APICS Basics of Supply Chain Management Certification Committee: Jim Caruso (Chair) of Tyco Healthcare; Carol Bulfer, Parker Hanninfin Corp.; William Leedale, IFS; and Angel Sosa, University of Puerto Rico at Bayamon. Academic reviewers included Sheila E. Rowe, North Carolina A&T State University; David Lucero, Greenville Technical College; Floyd Olson, Utah Valley State College; Ralph G. Kauffman, University of Houston–Downtown; Ronald J. Baker, Shoreline Community College; and Richard E. Crandall, Appalachian State University.

Tony Arnold thanks his wife, Vicky Arnold, for her assistance throughout the years of writing and revising this text, and Steve Chapman thanks his wife, Jeannine, for her support as well. Lloyd Clive thanks his wife, Kathleen, for her continued support.

Overall, this book is dedicated to those who have taught us the most—our students.

J. R. Tony Arnold, Professor Emeritus, CFPIM, CIRM
Fleming College
Peterborough, Ontario

Stephen N. Chapman, Ph.D., CFPIM, Associate Professor
Department of Business Management, College of Management
North Carolina State University
Raleigh, North Carolina

Lloyd M. Clive, CFPIM
Coordinator Materials Management and Distribution
School of Business
Fleming College
Peterborough, Ontario

INTRODUCTION TO MATERIALS MANAGEMENT

INTRODUCTION

The wealth of a country is measured by its gross national product—the output of goods and services produced by the nation in a given time. Goods are physical objects, something we can touch, feel, or see. Services are the performance of some useful function such as banking, medical care, restaurants, clothing stores, or social services.

But what is the source of wealth? Wealth is measured by the amount of goods and services produced, but where does it come from? Although we may have rich natural resources in our economy such as mineral deposits, farmland, and forests, these are only potential sources of wealth. A production function is needed to transform these resources into useful goods. Production takes place in all forms of transformation—extracting minerals from the earth, farming, lumbering, and fishing and using these resources to manufacture useful products.

There are many stages between the extraction of resource material and the final consumer product. At each stage in the development of the final product, value is added, thus creating more wealth. If ore is extracted from the earth and sold, wealth is gained from our efforts, but those who continue to transform the raw material will gain more and usually far greater wealth. Japan is a prime example of this. It has very few natural resources and buys most of the raw materials it needs. However, the Japanese have developed one of the wealthiest economies in the world by transforming the raw materials they purchase and adding value to them through manufacturing.

Manufacturing companies are in the business of converting raw materials to a form that is of far more value and use to the consumer than the original raw materials. Logs are converted into tables and chairs, iron ore into steel, and steel into cars and refrigerators. This conversion process, called *manufacturing* or *production*, makes a society wealthier and creates a better standard of living.

To get the most value out of our resources, we must design production processes that make products most efficiently. Once the processes exist, we need to manage their operation so they produce goods most economically. Managing the operation means planning for and controlling the resources used in the process: labor, capital, and material. All are important, but the major way in which management plans and controls is through the flow of materials. The flow of materials controls the performance of the process. If the right materials in the right quantities are not available at the right time, the process cannot produce what it should. Labor and machinery will be poorly utilized. The profitability, and even the existence, of the company will be threatened.

OPERATING ENVIRONMENT

Operations management works in a complex environment affected by many factors. Among the most important are government regulation, the economy, competition, customer expectations, and quality.

Government. Regulation of business by the various levels of government is extensive. Regulation applies to such areas as the environment, safety, product liability, and taxation. Government, or the lack of it, affects the way business is conducted.

Economy. General economic conditions influence the demand for a company's products or services and the availability of inputs. During economic recession the demand for many products decreases while demand for others may increase. Materials and labor shortages or surpluses influence the decisions management makes. Shifts in the age of the population, needs of ethnic groups, low population growth, freer trade between countries, and increased global competition all contribute to changes in the marketplace.

Competition. Competition is severe today.

- Manufacturing companies face competition from throughout the world. They find foreign competitors selling in their markets even though they themselves may not be selling in foreign markets. Companies also are resorting more to worldwide sourcing.
- Transportation and the movement of materials are relatively less costly than they used to be.
- Worldwide communications are fast, effective, and cheap. Information and data can be moved almost instantly halfway around the globe. The Internet allows buyers to search out new sources of supply from anywhere in the world as easily as they can from local sources.

Customers. Both consumers and industrial customers have become much more demanding, and suppliers have responded by improving the range of characteristics they offer. Some of the characteristics and selection customers expect in the products and services they buy are

- A fair price.
- Higher-(right) quality products and services.
- Delivery lead time.
- Better presale and after-sale service.
- Product and volume flexibility.

Quality. Since competition is international and aggressive, successful companies provide quality that not only meets customers' high expectations but exceeds them. Chapter 16 discusses quality in detail.

Order Qualifiers and Order Winners

Generally, a supplier must meet set minimum requirements to be considered a viable competitor in the marketplace. Customer requirements may be based on price, quality, delivery, and so forth and are called **order qualifiers**. For example, the price for a certain type of product must fall within a range for the supplier to be considered by potential customers. But being considered does not mean winning the order. To win orders, a supplier must have characteristics that encourage customers to choose its products and services over competitors'. Those competitive characteristics, or combination of characteristics, that persuade a company's customers to choose its products or services are called **order winners**. They provide a competitive advantage for the firm. Order winners change over time and may well be different for different markets. For example, fast delivery may be vital in one market but not in another. Characteristics that are order winners today probably will not remain so, because competition will try to copy winning characteristics, and the needs of customers will change.

It is very important that a firm understands the order winners and order qualifiers for each of its products and in each of its markets because they should drive the manufacturing strategy. Since it is virtually impossible to be the best in every dimension of competition, firms should in general strive to provide at least a minimal level of acceptance for each of the order qualifiers but should try to be the *best* in the market for the order winner(s).

One also should recognize that the order winners and qualifiers for any product/market combination are not static. Not only will customers change perspectives as competitors jockey for position, but the order winners and qualifiers will often change based on the concepts of the product life cycle. The product life cycle implies that most products go through a life cycle, including introduction, growth, maturity, and decline. For example, in the introduction phase, design and availability are often much more important than price. Quality and delivery tend to have increased importance during growth, while price and delivery are often the order winners for mature products. This life cycle approach is complicated in that the duration of the life cycle will be very different for different products. Although some products have life cycles many years long, the life cycle of other products (certain toys or electronics, for example) can be measured in months or even weeks.

Manufacturing Strategy

A highly market-oriented company will focus on meeting or exceeding customer expectations and on order winners. In such a company, all functions must contribute toward a winning strategy. Thus, operations must have a strategy that allows it to supply the needs of the marketplace and provide fast on-time delivery.

Delivery lead time   From the supplier's perspective, delivery lead time is the time from receipt of an order to the delivery of the product. From the customer's perspective, it may also include time for order preparation and transmittal. Customers want delivery lead time to be as short as possible, and manufacturing must design a strategy to achieve this. There are four basic strategies: engineer-to-order, make-to-order, assemble-to-order, and make-to-stock. Customer involvement in the product design, delivery lead time, and inventory state are influenced by each strategy. Figure 1.1 shows the effect of each strategy.

Engineer-to-order means that the customer's specifications require unique engineering design or significant customization. Usually the customer is highly involved in the product design. Inventory will not normally be purchased until needed by manufacturing. Delivery lead time is long because it includes not only purchase lead time but also design lead time.

Make-to-order means that the manufacturer does not start to make the product until a customer's order is received. The final product is usually made from standard items but may include custom-designed components as well. Delivery lead time is reduced because there is little design time required and inventory is held as raw material.

Assemble-to-order means that the product is made from standard components that the manufacturer can inventory and assemble according to a customer order. Delivery lead time is reduced further because there is no design time needed and inventory is held ready for assembly. Customer involvement in the design of the product is limited to selecting the component part options needed.

Make-to-stock means that the supplier manufactures the goods and sells from a finished-goods inventory. Delivery lead time is shortest. The customer has little direct involvement in the product design.

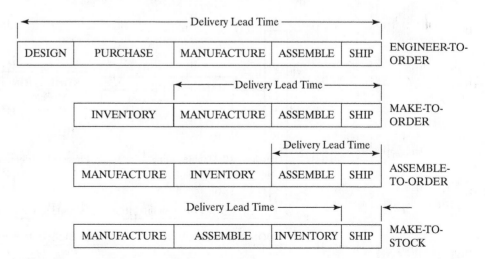

FIGURE 1.1 Manufacturing strategy and lead time.

Postponement is another application of assemble-to-order, described by the Association for Operations Management (APICS) as "a product design strategy that shifts product differentiation closer to the consumer by postponing identity change to the last possible supply chain location." This strategy reduces the number of different items in the supply chain, lowering the amount of in-process inventory.

Computer printers for a global market use universal power supplies that can be switched to different voltages; on receipt of a customer's order, they are packaged with the appropriate cords, instructions, and labeling. This avoids filling an entire supply chain with expensive printers destined for different countries. Some basic postponement can be done in a distribution center and often by third parties. Foreign suppliers of appliances such as vacuum cleaners destined for multiple customers postpone the packaging of their products, applying customer-specific labels, bar codes, boxes, instructions, and so forth until after receipt of the customer order.

THE SUPPLY CHAIN CONCEPT

There are three phases to the flow of materials. Raw materials flow into a manufacturing company from a physical supply system, they are processed by manufacturing, and finally, finished goods are distributed to end consumers through a physical distribution system. Figure 1.2 shows this system graphically. Although this figure shows only one supplier and one customer, usually the supply chain consists of several companies linked in a supply/demand relationship. For example, the customer of one supplier buys a product, adds value to it, and supplies yet another customer. Similarly, one customer may have several suppliers and may in turn supply several customers. As long as there is a chain of supplier/customer relationships, they are all members of the same supply chain.

There are a number of important factors in supply chains:

- The supply chain includes all activities and processes to supply a product or service to a final customer.
- Any number of companies can be linked in the supply chain.
- A customer can be a supplier to another customer so the total chain can have a number of supplier/customer relationships.
- Although the distribution system can be direct from supplier to customer, depending on the products and markets, it can contain a number of intermediaries (distributors) such as wholesalers, warehouses, and retailers.
- Product or services usually flow from supplier to customer; design and demand information usually flows from customer to supplier. Rarely is this not so.

Although these systems vary from industry to industry and company to company, the basic elements are the same: supply, production, and distribution. The relative importance of each depends on the costs of the three elements.

FIGURE 1.2 Supply-production-distribution system.

Supply Chain Concepts

In recent years there has been a great deal of attention given to the concept of supply chain management (SCM). It is important to understand the fundamental issues behind this movement, as well as the impact on materials management.

Historical perspective   In the past, many company managers placed most of their attention on the issues that were internal to their companies. Of course they were aware of the impact of suppliers, customers, and distributors, but those entities were often viewed as business entities only. Specialists in purchasing, sales, and logistics were assigned to "deal" with those outside entities, often through formal legal contracts that were negotiated regularly and represented short-term agreements. For example, suppliers were often viewed as business adversaries. A key responsibility of a purchasing agent was to negotiate the best financial and delivery conditions from a supplier, whose job was to maximize company profit. Organization theorists often called the functions that dealt with outside entities boundary spanners, indicating that for most people in the organization there were well-defined and rigid boundaries between their organization and the rest of the world.

The first major change in that perspective for most companies can be traced to the explosive growth in just-in-time (JIT) concepts, originally developed by Toyota and other Japanese companies in the 1970s. Supplier partnerships were felt to be a major aspect of successful JIT. With that concept, suppliers were viewed as partners as opposed to adversaries. In that sense the supplier and the customer had mutually linked destinies, in that the success of each was linked to the success of the other. Great emphasis was put on trust between the partners, and many of the formal boundary mechanisms, such as the receiving/inspection activity of incoming parts, were changed or eliminated altogether. As the partnership concept grew, there were many other changes in the relationship, including

- **Mutual analysis for cost reduction.** Both parties examined the process used to transmit information and deliver parts, with the idea that cost reductions would be shared between the two parties.
- **Mutual product design.** In the past the customer often submitted complete designs to the supplier, who was obligated to produce according to design. With partnering, both companies worked together. Often the supplier would know more about how to make a specific product, whereas the customer would know more about the application for which the design was intended. Together, they could probably produce a superior design compared to what either could do alone.
- **Enhanced information flow.** With JIT, the concept of greatly reduced inventory in the process and the need for rapid delivery according to need, the speed of accurate information flow became critical. Formal paper-based systems gave way to electronic data interchange and informal communication methods.

The growth of the supply chain concept   As we continue into the new millennium, the world continued to change, forcing additional modifications to the trend:

- There has been explosive growth in computer capability and associated software applications. Highly effective and integrated systems such as enterprise resource planning (ERP) and the ability to link companies electronically (through the Internet, for example) have allowed companies to share large amounts of information quickly and easily. The ability to have the information rapidly has become a competitive necessity for many companies.
- There has been a large growth in global competition. Very few companies can still say they have only local competition, and many of the global competitors are forcing existing companies to find new ways to be successful in the marketplace.
- There has been a growth in technological capabilities for products and processes. Product life cycles for many products are shrinking rapidly, forcing companies to not only become more flexible in design but also to communicate changes and needs to suppliers and distributors.

- The changes prompted by JIT in the 1980s have continued to mature and become more accurately defined as lean production (see Chapter 15). Now many companies have new approaches to interorganizational relationships as a normal form of business.
- Partially in response to the preceding conditions, more and more companies are subcontracting more of their work to suppliers, keeping only their most important core competencies as internal activities.

What is the current supply chain concept? Companies currently adopting the supply chain concept view the entire set of activities from raw material production to final customer purchase to final disposal as a linked chain of activities. To result in optimal performance for customer service and cost, it is felt that the supply chain of activities should be managed as an extension of the partnership. This implies many issues, but three critical ones include

1. Flow of materials.
2. Flow of information and sharing of information, mostly through the Internet.
3. Fund transfers.

In addition, a new trend is to manage the recovery, recycling, and reuse of material.

The primary supply chain management approach is a conceptual one. All portions of the material production, from raw materials to final customer, are considered to be in a linked chain. The most efficient and effective way to manage the activities along the chain is to view each separate organization in the chain as an extension of one's own organization. There can be many organizations in a supply chain. Take as an example the chain of organizations that represents the flow from raw silicon used to make computer chips to the delivery and disposal of the computer itself:

What is illustrated here is but one chain of a set of different component chains that represent a network of suppliers and distributors for a product.

Most companies work with a network of supply chains, obtaining from multiple suppliers a variety of materials and sending them to different customers. Even a grocery store has to deal with suppliers of dry goods, magazines, frozen and fresh products, and small suppliers of local produce or specialty goods.

The many independent businesses that make up a supply chain have individual profit motives and do not naturally cooperate to gain savings. This requires someone to take the initiative. Any member of the supply chain can work with other members to show the benefits of sharing information on forecasts, sales information, or schedules. "Orchestrator" or "channel master" are two emerging terms that describe the individual or company that takes the initiative to integrate both the upstream and downstream supply chain, getting members to work cooperatively to lower total costs. The result is a network of companies who openly share information.

To manage a supply chain, one must not only understand the network of suppliers and customers along the chain but also try to efficiently plan material and information flows along each chain to maximize cost efficiency, effectiveness, delivery, and flexibility. This clearly implies not only taking a different conceptual approach to suppliers and customers but also a highly integrated information system and a different set of performance measures. Overall, the key to managing such a concept is with rapid flows of accurate information and increased organizational flexibility.

Supply Chain Metrics

A **metric** is a verifiable measure stated in either quantitative or qualitative terms defined with respect to a reference point. Without metrics, no firm could expect to function effectively or efficiently on a daily basis. Metrics give us

1. Control by superiors.
2. Reporting of data to superiors and external groups.
3. Communication.
4. Learning.
5. Improvement.

Metrics communicate expectations, identify problems, direct a course of action, and motivate people. Building the right metrics is vital to a company. Problems must be anticipated and corrective action taken before they become severe. Companies cannot risk waiting to react until the order cycle is completed and feedback from customers is received.

Today, production control works in a demanding environment shaped by six major challenges:

1. Customers that are never satisfied.
2. A supply chain that is large and must be managed.
3. A product life cycle that is getting shorter and shorter.
4. A vast amount of data.
5. An emphasis on profit margins that are more squeezed.
6. An increasing number of alternatives.

A firm has a corporate strategy that states how it will treat its customers and what services it will supply. This identifies how a firm will compete in the marketplace. It is the customer who assesses the firm's offering by its decision to buy or not to buy. Metrics link strategy to operations. Finally, the two are brought together by metrics. Figure 1.3 shows this graphically.

The right-hand side of the figure deals with operations and with the implementation and use of metrics. Focus describes the particular activity that is to be measured. Standards are the yardstick that is the basis of comparison on which performance is judged.

There is a difference between measurement and standards. A **performance measure** must be both quantified and objective and contain at least two parameters. For example, the number of orders per day consists of both a quantity and a time measurement.

Transforming company policies into objectives and specific goals creates **performance standards**. Each goal should have target values. An example of this would be to improve

FIGURE 1.3 Metrics context.

order fill rate to 98% measured by number of lines. Performance standards set the goal, while performance measures say how close you came.

Many companies do not realize the potential benefits of performance measurement, nor do they know how to measure performance. It can be used without performance standards. This might occur when the concept of performance measurement and standards is new. When standards are put into use, management can begin to monitor the company. The old saying "What you do not measure, you cannot control" is as valid today as it was when first stated.

The necessary steps in implementing such a program are

1. Establish company goals and objectives.
2. Define performance.
3. State the measurement to be used.
4. Set performance standards.
5. Educate the user.
6. Make sure the program is consistently applied.

Although financial performance has traditionally been the measure of success in most companies, today the focus is on continuous improvement and, with this, an increase in standards. Emphasis should not be placed on a "one-shot" improvement but on such things as the rate of improvement in quality, cost, reliability, innovation, effectiveness, and productivity.

Conflicts in Traditional Systems

In the past, supply, production, and distribution systems were organized into separate functions that reported to different departments of a company. Often, policies and practices of the different departments maximized departmental objectives without considering the effect they would have on other parts of the system. Because the three systems are interrelated, conflicts often occurred. Although each system made decisions that were best for itself, overall company objectives suffered. For example, the transportation department would ship in the largest quantities possible so it could minimize per-unit shipping costs. However, this increased inventory and resulted in higher inventory-carrying costs.

To get the most profit, a company must have at least four main objectives:

1. Provide best customer service.
2. Provide lowest production costs.
3. Provide lowest inventory investment.
4. Provide lowest distribution costs.

These objectives create conflict among the marketing, production, and finance departments because each has different responsibilities in these areas.

Marketing's objective is to maintain and increase revenue; therefore, it must provide the best customer service possible. There are several ways of doing this:

- Maintain high inventories so goods are always available for the customer.
- Interrupt production runs so that a noninventoried item can be manufactured quickly.
- Create an extensive—and consequently costly—distribution system so goods can be shipped to the customer rapidly.

Finance must keep investment and costs low. This can be done in the following ways:

- Reduce inventory so inventory investment is at a minimum.
- Decrease the number of plants and warehouses.
- Produce large quantities using long production runs.
- Manufacture only to customer order.

FIGURE 1.4. Conflicting objectives.

Production must keep its operating costs as low as possible. This can be done in the following ways:

■ Make long production runs of relatively few products. Fewer changeovers will be needed and specialized equipment can be used, thus reducing the cost of making the product.

■ Maintain high inventories of raw materials and work-in-process so production is not disrupted by shortages.

These conflicts among marketing, finance, and production center on customer service, disruption of production flow, and inventory levels. Figure 1.4 shows this relationship.

Today, the concepts of lean production stress the need to supply customers with what they want when they want it and to keep inventories at a minimum. These objectives put further stress on the relationship among production, marketing, and finance. Chapter 15 will discuss the concepts of lean production and how it influences materials management.

One important way to resolve these conflicting objectives is to provide close coordination of the supply, production, and distribution functions. The problem is to balance conflicting objectives to minimize the total of all the costs involved and maximize customer service consistent with the goals of the organization. This requires some type of integrated materials management or logistics organization that is responsible for supply, production, and distribution. Rather than having the planning and control of these functions spread among marketing, production, and distribution, they should occur in a single area of responsibility.

WHAT IS MATERIALS MANAGEMENT?

The concept of having one department responsible for the flow of materials, from supplier through production to consumer, is relatively new. Although many companies have adopted this type of organization, there are still a number that have not. If companies wish to minimize total costs in this area and provide a better level of customer service, they will move in this direction.

The name usually given to this function is **materials management**. Other names include distribution planning and control and logistics management, but the one used in this text is *materials management*. As discussed in Chapter 15, lean production not only requires efficient individual operations but also requires all operations to work together. A materials management department can improve this coordination by having overall responsibility for material.

Materials management is a coordinating function responsible for planning and controlling materials flow. Its objectives are as follows:

■ Maximize the use of the firm's resources.

■ Provide the required level of customer service.

Materials management can do much to improve a company's profit. An income (profit and loss) statement for a manufacturing company might look something like the following:

		Dollars	Percent of Sales
Revenue (sales)		$1,000,000	100
Cost of Goods Sold			
Direct Material	$500,000		50
Direct Labor	$200,000		20
Factory Overhead	$200,000		<u>20</u>
Total Cost of Goods Sold		<u>$900,000</u>	<u>90</u>
Gross Profit		$100,000	10

Direct labor and direct material are costs that increase or decrease with the quantity sold. Overhead (all other costs) does not vary directly with sales. For simplicity this section assumes overhead is constant, even though it is initially expressed as a percentage of sales.

If, through a well-organized materials management department, direct materials can be reduced by 10% and direct labor by 5%, the improvement in profit would be:

	Dollars		Percent of Sales
Revenue (sales)		$1,000,000	100
Cost of Goods Sold			
Direct Material	$450,000		45
Direct Labor	$190,000		19
Overhead	$200,000		20
Total Cost of Goods Sold		$840,000	84
Gross Profit		$160,000	16

Profit has been increased by 60%. To get the same increase in profit ($60,000) by increasing revenue, sales would have to increase to $1.2 million.

	Dollars		Percent of Sales
Revenue (sales)		$1,200,000	100
Cost of Goods Sold			
Direct Material	$600,000		50
Direct Labor	$240,000		20
Overhead	$200,000		17
Total Cost of Goods Sold		$1,040,000	87
Gross Profit		$160,000	13

Example Problem

a. If the cost of direct material is 60%, direct labor is 10%, and overhead is 25% of sales, what will be the improvement in profit if cost of direct material is reduced to 55%?

b. How much will sales have to increase to give the same increase in profit? (Remember, overhead cost is constant.)

ANSWER

a.

	Before Improvement	After Improvement
Revenue (sales)	100%	100%
Cost of Goods Sold		
Direct Material	60%	55%
Direct Labor	10%	10%
Overhead	25%	25%
Total Cost of Goods Sold	95%	90%
Gross Profit	5%	10%

b. Profit = sales − (direct material + direct labor + 0.25)

$$= \text{sales} - (0.6\,\text{sales} + 0.1\,\text{sales} + 0.25)$$

$$= \text{sales} - 0.7\,\text{sales} - 0.25$$

$$0.1 = 0.3\,\text{sales} - 0.25$$

$$0.3\,\text{Sales} = 0.35$$

$$\text{Sales} = \frac{0.35}{0.3} = 1.17$$

Sales must increase 17% to give the same increase in profit.

Work-in-Process

Inventory not only makes up a portion of the cost of goods sold but also has to be purchased at the beginning of production to be processed into finished goods. This type of inventory is called **work-in-process (WIP)**. WIP is a major investment for many companies, and reducing the amount of time that inventory spends in production is a good way to reduce the costs associated with this investment. Labor, materials, and overhead are applied to goods continuously throughout production and the value of the WIP is estimated to be one half the final value. Further discussion on WIP and reducing it is covered in Chapters 9 and 15.

Example Problem

On average, a company has a 12-week production lead time and an annual cost of goods sold of $36 million. Assuming the company works 50 weeks per year:

a. What is the dollar value of the WIP?

b. If the lead time could be reduced to 5 weeks, and the annual cost of carrying inventory was 20% of the inventory value, what would be the annual savings?

ANSWER

Weekly Cost of Goods Sold = $36,000,000 per year/50 weeks per year
= $720,000/week
WIP Value at 12 Weeks LT = 12 weeks × $720,000/week × ½ = $4,320,000
WIP Value at 5 Weeks LT = 5 weeks × $720,000/week × ½ = $1,800,000
Reduction in WIP = $4,320,000 − $1,800,000 = $2,520,000
Annual Savings = $2,520,000 × 20% = $504,000

Reducing cost contributes directly to profit. Increasing sales increases direct costs of labor and materials so profit does not increase in direct proportion. Materials management can reduce costs by being sure that the right materials are in the right place at the right time and the resources of the company are properly used.

There are several ways of classifying this flow of material. A very useful classification, and the one used in this text, is manufacturing planning and control and physical supply/distribution.

Manufacturing Planning and Control

Manufacturing planning and control are responsible for the planning and control of the flow of materials through the manufacturing process. The primary activities carried out are as follows:

1. **Production planning.** Production must be able to meet the demand of the marketplace. Finding the most productive way of doing so is the responsibility of production planning. It must establish correct priorities (what is needed and when) and make certain that capacity is available to meet those priorities. It will involve:
   a. Forecasting.
   b. Master planning.
   c. Material requirements planning.
   d. Capacity planning.

2. **Implementation and control.** These functions are responsible for putting into action and achieving the plans made by production planning. These responsibilities are accomplished through production activity control (often called *shop floor control*) and purchasing.

3. **Inventory management.** Inventories are materials and supplies carried on hand either for sale or to provide material or supplies to the production process. They are part of the planning process and provide a buffer against the differences in demand rates and production rates.

Production planning, implementation, control, and inventory management work together. Inventories in manufacturing are used to support production or are the result of production. Only if items are purchased and resold without further processing can inventory management operate separately from production planning and control. Even then, it cannot operate apart from purchasing.

Inputs to the manufacturing planning and control system   There are five basic inputs to the manufacturing planning and control system:

1. **Product description.**   The product description shows how the product will appear at some stage of production. *Engineering drawings* and *specifications* are methods of describing the product. Another method—and the most important for manufacturing planning and control—is the **bill of material**. As used in materials management, this document does two things:

   - Describes the components used to make the product.
   - Describes the subassemblies at various stages of manufacture.

2. **Process specifications.**   Process specifications describe the steps necessary to make the end product. They are a step-by-step set of instructions describing how the product is made. This information is usually recorded on a route sheet or in a routing file. These are documents or computer files that give information such as the following on the manufacture of a product:

   - Operations required to make the product.
   - Sequence of operations.
   - Equipment and accessories required.
   - Standard time required to perform each operation.

3. **Time.**   The **time needed to perform operations** is usually expressed in standard time, which is the time taken by an average operator, working at a normal pace, to perform a task. It is needed to schedule work through the plant, load the plant, make delivery promises, and cost the product. Usually, standard times for operations are obtained from the routing file.

4. **Available facilities.**   Manufacturing planning and control must know what plant, equipment, and labor will be available to process work. This information is usually found in the work center file.

5. **Quantities required.**   This information will come from forecasts, customer orders, orders to replace finished-goods inventory, and the material requirements plan.

Physical Supply/Distribution

Physical supply/distribution includes all the activities involved in moving goods, from the supplier to the beginning of the production process, and from the end of the production process to the consumer.

The activities involved are as follows:

- Transportation.
- Distribution inventory.
- Warehousing.
- Packaging.
- Materials handling.
- Order entry.

Materials management is a balancing act. The objective is to be able to deliver what customers want, when and where they want it, and do so at minimum cost. To achieve this objective, materials management must make trade-offs between the level of customer service and the cost of providing that service. As a rule, costs rise as the service level increases, and materials management must find that combination of inputs to maximize service and minimize cost. For example, customer service can be improved by establishing warehouses in major markets. However, that causes extra cost in operating the warehouse and in the extra inventory carried. To some extent, these costs will be offset by potential savings in transportation costs if lower-cost transportation can be used.

By grouping all those activities involved in the movement and storage of goods into one department, the firm has a better opportunity to provide maximum service at minimum cost and to increase profit. The overall concern of materials management is the balance between priority and capacity. The marketplace sets demand. Materials management must plan the firm's priorities (what goods to make and when) to meet that demand. Capacity is the ability of the system to produce or deliver goods. Priority and capacity must be planned and controlled to meet customer demand at minimum cost. Materials management is responsible for doing this.

SUMMARY

Manufacturing creates wealth by adding value to goods. To improve productivity and wealth, a company must first design efficient and effective systems for manufacturing. It must then manage these systems to make the best use of labor, capital, and material. One of the most effective ways of doing this is through the planning and control of the flow of materials into, through, and out of manufacturing. There are three elements to a material flow system: supply, manufacturing planning and control, and physical distribution. They are connected, and what happens in one system affects the others.

Traditionally, there are conflicts in the objectives of a company and in the objectives of marketing, finance, and production. The role of materials management is to balance these conflicting objectives by coordinating the flow of materials so customer service is maintained and the resources of the company are properly used.

This text will examine some of the theory and practice considered to be part of the "body of knowledge" as presented by the Association for Operations Management. Chapter 15 will study the concepts of just-in-time manufacturing to see how they affect the practice of materials management.

KEY TERMS

Assemble-to-order 3	Order winners 2
Available facilities 12	Performance measure 7
Bill of material 12	Performance standards 7
Engineer-to-order 3	Postponement 4
Implementation and control 11	Process specifications 12
Inventory management 11	Product description 12
Make-to-order 3	Production planning 11
Make-to-stock 3	Quantities required 12
Materials management 9	Time needed to perform operations 12
Metric 7	
Order qualifiers 2	Work-in-process 11

QUESTIONS

1. What is wealth, and how is it created?
2. What is value added, and how is it achieved?
3. Name and describe four major factors affecting operations management.

4. What are an order qualifier and an order winner?

5. Describe the four primary manufacturing strategies. How does each affect delivery lead time?

6. What is a supply chain? Describe five important factors in supply chains.

7. What must manufacturing management do to manage a process or operation? What is the major way in which management plans and controls?

8. Name and describe the three main divisions of supply, production, and distribution systems.

9. What are the four objectives of a firm wishing to maximize profit?

10. What is the objective of marketing? What three ways will help it achieve this objective?

11. What are the objectives of finance? How can these objectives be met?

12. What are the objectives of production? How can these objectives be met?

13. Describe how the objectives of marketing, production, and finance are in conflict over customer service, disruption to production, and inventories.

14. What is the purpose of materials management?

15. Name and describe the three primary activities of manufacturing planning and control.

16. Name and describe the inputs to a manufacturing planning and control system.

17. What are the six activities involved in the physical supply/distribution system?

18. Why can materials management be considered a balancing act?

19. What are metrics? What are their uses?

20. A computer carrying case and a backpack are familiar items to a student of manufacturing planning and control. Discuss the manufacturing planning and control activities involved in producing a variety of these products. What information from other departments is necessary for manufacturing planning and control to perform its function?

21. Describe at least three supply chains that provide products to your school book store. Do they use cooperative supply chain methods to help reduce their costs?

22. From the bookstore example in question 21, describe how one of the supply chains would use a supply chain "channel master."

23. Which manufacturing strategies are used in a fast-food business? How does this affect the lead time from the customers' point of view?

PROBLEMS

1.1. If the cost of manufacturing (direct material and direct labor) is 60% of sales and profit is 10% of sales, what would be the improvement in profit if, through better planning and control, the cost of manufacturing was reduced from 60% of sales to 50% of sales?

Answer. Profits would improve by 100%.

1.2. In problem 1.1, how much would sales have to increase to provide the same increase in profits?

Answer. Sales would have to increase 25%.

1.3. On the average, a firm has a 10-week lead time for work-in-process, and annual cost of goods sold is $15 million. Assuming that the company works 50 weeks a year:

a. What is the approximate dollar value of the work-in-process?

b. If the lead time could be reduced to 7 weeks and the annual cost of carrying inventory was 20% of the inventory value, what would be the annual saving?

Answer. a. $1,500,000

b. $90,000

1.4. On the average, a company has a work-in-process lead time of 12 weeks and annual cost of goods sold of $40 million. Assuming that the company works 50 weeks a year:

a. What is the dollar value of the work-in-process?

b. If the work-in-process could be reduced to 5 weeks and the annual cost of carrying inventory was 20% of the inventory value, what would be the annual saving?

1.5. Amalgamated Fenderdenter's sales are $10 million. The company spends $3.5 million for purchase of direct materials and $2.5 million for direct labor; overhead is $3.5 million and profit is $500,000. Direct labor and direct material vary directly with sales, but overhead does not. The company wants to double its profit.

a. By how much should the firm increase sales?

b. By how much should the firm decrease material costs?

c. By how much should the firm decrease labor cost?

PRODUCTION PLANNING SYSTEM

INTRODUCTION

This chapter introduces the manufacturing planning and control system. First, it deals with the total system and then with some details involved in production planning. Subsequent chapters discuss master scheduling, material requirements planning, capacity management, production activity control, purchasing, and forecasting.

Manufacturing is complex. Some firms make a few different products, whereas others make many products. However, each uses a variety of processes, machinery, equipment, labor skills, and material. To be profitable, a firm must organize all these factors to make the right goods at the right time at top quality and do so as economically as possible. It is a complex problem, and it is essential to have a good planning and control system.

A good planning system must answer four questions:

1. What are we going to make?
2. What does it take to make it?
3. What do we have?
4. What do we need?

These are questions of priority and capacity.

Priority relates to what products are needed, how many are needed, and when they are needed. The marketplace establishes the priorities. Manufacturing is responsible for devising plans to satisfy the market demand if possible.

Capacity is the capability of manufacturing to produce goods and services. Eventually it depends on the resources of the company—the machinery, labor, and financial resources, and the availability of material from suppliers. In the short run, capacity is the quantity of work that labor and equipment can perform in a given period. The relationship that should exist between priority and capacity is shown graphically in Figure 2.1.

In the long and short run, manufacturing must devise plans to balance the demands of the marketplace with its resources and capacity. For long-range decisions, such as the building of new plants or the purchase of new equipment, the plans must be made for several years. For planning production over the next few weeks, the time span will be days or weeks. This hierarchy of planning, from long range to short range, is covered in the next section.

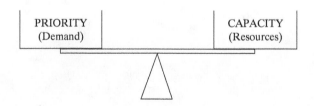

FIGURE 2.1 Priority–capacity relationship.

MANUFACTURING PLANNING AND CONTROL SYSTEM

There are five major levels in the manufacturing planning and control (MPC) system:

- Strategic business plan.
- Production plan (sales and operations plan).
- Master production schedule.
- Material requirements plan.
- Purchasing and production activity control.

Each level varies in purpose, time span, and level of detail. As we move from strategic planning to production activity control, the purpose changes from general direction to specific detailed planning, the time span decreases from years to days, and the level of detail increases from general categories to individual components and workstations.

Since each level is for a different time span and for different purposes, each differs in the following:

- Purpose of the plan.
- Planning horizon—the time span from now to some time in the future for which the plan is created.
- Level of detail—the detail about products required for the plan.
- Planning cycle—the frequency with which the plan is reviewed.

At each level, three questions must be answered:

1. What are the priorities—how much of what is to be produced and when?
2. What is the available capacity—what resources do we have?
3. How can differences between priorities and capacity be resolved?

Figure 2.2 shows the planning hierarchy. The first four levels are planning levels. The result of the plans is authorization to purchase or manufacture what is required. The final level is when the plans are put into action through purchasing and production activity control.

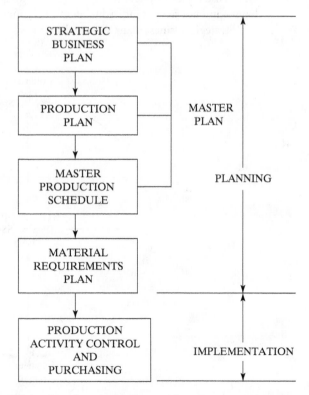

FIGURE 2.2 Manufacturing planning and control system.

The following sections will examine each of the planning levels by purpose, horizon, level of detail, and planning cycle.

The Strategic Business Plan

The strategic business plan is a statement of the major goals and objectives the company expects to achieve over the next 2 to 10 years or more. It is a statement of the broad direction of the firm and shows the kind of business—product lines, markets, and so on—the firm wants to do in the future. The plan gives general direction about how the company hopes to achieve these objectives. It is based on long-range forecasts and includes participation from marketing, finance, production, and engineering. In turn, the plan provides direction and coordination among the marketing, production, financial, and engineering plans.

Marketing is responsible for analyzing the marketplace and deciding the firm's response: the markets to be served, the products supplied, desired levels of customer service, pricing, promotion strategies, and so on.

Finance is responsible for deciding the sources and uses of funds available to the firm, cash flows, profits, return on investment, and budgets.

Production must satisfy the demands of the marketplace. It does so by using plants, machinery, equipment, labor, and materials as efficiently as possible.

Engineering is responsible for research, development, and design of new products or modifications to existing ones. Engineering must work with marketing and production to produce designs for products that will sell in the marketplace and can be made most economically.

The development of the strategic business plan is the responsibility of senior management. Using information from marketing, finance, and production, the strategic business plan provides a framework that sets the goals and objectives for further planning by the marketing, finance, engineering, and production departments. Each department produces its own plans to achieve the objectives set by the strategic business plan. These plans will be coordinated with one another and with the strategic business plan. Figure 2.3 shows this relationship.

The level of detail in the strategic business plan is not high. It is concerned with general market and production requirements—total market for major product groups, perhaps—and not sales of individual items. It is often stated in dollars rather than units.

Strategic business plans are usually reviewed every six months to a year.

FIGURE 2.3 Business plan.

The Production Plan

Given the objectives set by the strategic business plan, production management is concerned with the following:

- The quantities of each product group that must be produced in each period.
- The desired inventory levels.
- The resources of equipment, labor, and material needed in each period.
- The availability of the resources needed.

The level of detail is not high. For example, if a company manufactures children's bicycles, tricycles, and scooters in various models, each with many options, the production plan will show major product groups, or families: bicycles, tricycles, and scooters.

Production planners must devise a plan to satisfy market demand within the resources available to the company. This will involve determining the resources needed to meet market demand, comparing the results to the resources available, and devising a plan to balance requirements and availability.

This process of determining the resources required and comparing them to the available resources takes place at each of the planning levels and is the purpose of capacity management. For effective planning, there must be a balance between priority and capacity.

Along with the market and financial plans, the production plan is concerned with implementing the strategic business plan. The planning horizon is usually 6 to 18 months and is reviewed perhaps each month or quarter.

The Master Production Schedule

The master production schedule (MPS) is a plan for the production of individual end items. It breaks down the production plan to show, for each period, the quantity of each end item to be made. For example, it might show that 200 Model A23 scooters are to be built each week. Inputs to the MPS are the production plan, the forecast for individual end items, sales orders, inventories, and existing capacity.

The level of detail for the MPS is higher than for the production plan. Whereas the production plan was based upon families of products (e.g., tricycles), the master production schedule is developed for individual end items (each model of tricycle). The planning horizon usually extends from 3 to 18 months but primarily depends on the purchasing and manufacturing lead times. This is discussed in Chapter 3 in the section on master scheduling. The term *master scheduling* describes the process of developing a master production schedule. The term *master production schedule* is the end result of this process. Usually, the plans are reviewed and changed weekly or monthly.

The Material Requirements Plan

The material requirements plan (MRP) is a plan for the production and purchase of the components used in making the items in the master production schedule. It shows the quantities needed and when manufacturing intends to make or use them. Purchasing and production activity control use the MRP to decide the purchase or manufacture of specific items.

The level of detail is high. The material requirements plan establishes when the components and parts are needed to make each end item.

The planning horizon is at least as long as the combined purchase and manufacturing lead times. As with the master production schedule, it usually extends from 3 to 18 months.

Purchasing and Production Activity Control

Purchasing and production activity control (PAC) represent the implementation and control phase of the production planning and control system. Purchasing is responsible for establishing and controlling the flow of raw materials into the factory. PAC is responsible for planning and controlling the flow of work through the factory.

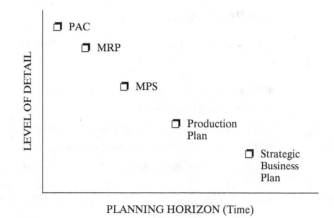

FIGURE 2.4 Level of detail versus planning horizon.

The planning horizon is very short, perhaps from a day to a month. The level of detail is high since it is concerned with individual components, workstations, and orders. Plans are reviewed and revised daily.

Figure 2.4 shows the relationship among the various planning tools, planning horizons, and level of detail.

The levels discussed in the preceding sections are examined in more detail in later chapters. This chapter discusses production planning. Later chapters deal with master scheduling, material requirements planning, and production activity control.

Capacity Management

At each level in the manufacturing planning and control system, the priority plan must be tested against the available resources and capacity of the manufacturing system. Chapter 5 describes some of the details of capacity management. For now, it is sufficient to understand that the basic process in capacity management is one of calculating the capacity needed to manufacture per the requirements of the priority plan and of finding methods to make that capacity available. There can be no valid, workable production plan unless this is done. If the capacity cannot be made available when needed, then the plans must be changed.

Determining the capacity required, comparing it to available capacity, and making adjustments (or changing plans) must occur at all levels of the manufacturing planning and control system.

Over several years, machinery, equipment, and plants can be added to or taken away from manufacturing. However, in the time spans involved from production planning to production activity control, these kinds of changes cannot be made. Some changes, such as changing the number of shifts, working overtime, subcontracting the work, and so on, can be accomplished in these time spans.

SALES AND OPERATIONS PLANNING

The strategic business plan integrates the plans of all the departments in an organization and is normally updated annually. However, these plans should be updated as time progresses so that the latest forecasts and market and economic conditions are taken into account. **Sales and operations planning (SOP)** is a process for continually revising the strategic business plan and coordinating plans of the various departments. SOP is a cross-functional business plan that involves sales and marketing, product development, operations, and senior management. Operations represents supply, whereas marketing represents demand. The SOP is the forum in which the production plan is developed.

FIGURE 2.5 Sales and operations planning.

Although the strategic business plan is updated annually, sales and operations planning is a dynamic process in which the company plans are updated on a regular basis, usually at least monthly. The process starts with the sales and marketing departments, which compare actual demand with the sales plan, assess market potential, and forecast future demand. The updated marketing plan is then communicated to manufacturing, engineering, and finance, which adjust their plans to support the revised marketing plan. If these departments find they cannot accommodate the new marketing plan, then the marketing plan must be adjusted. In this way the strategic business plan is continually revised throughout the year and the activities of the various departments are coordinated. Figure 2.5 shows the relationship between the strategic business plan and the sales and operations plan.

Sales and operations planning is medium range and includes the marketing, production, engineering, and finance plans. Sales and operations planning has several benefits:

- It provides a means of updating the strategic business plan as conditions change.
- It provides a means of managing change. Rather than reacting to changes in market conditions or the economy after they happen, the SOP forces management to look at the economy at least monthly and places it in a better position to plan changes.
- It ensures that the various department plans are realistic and coordinated and support the business plan.
- It provides a realistic plan that can achieve the company objectives.
- It permits better management of production, inventory, and backlog (i.e., unfilled customer orders).

It is important to realize that effective sales and operations planning is an executive-level planning process that involves the potential to make significant trade-offs between the various functions/departments in the company. In this way executives involved in planning can ensure that the best approach to volume and mix are made and that supply and demand are balanced in the best approach possible.

It should be noted that the sales and operations plan does not actually schedule production, but instead focuses on producing a high-level plan for the use of company resources. These resources include not only production resources but also human resources, sales resources, financial resources, and virtually all other functions in the company. The sales and operations plan should reflect the vision and strategies developed in the strategic plan, and should serve as a focused, single plan that provides the approach to running the entire business.

In many companies the resource discussions include some aspects of what is often called **"green" production**. Basically these discussions will focus on issues such as

- Environmental impacts.
- Energy conservation.
- Material usages, such as waste reduction, reuse and recyclability.
- Scarcity of various resources.

The conclusions from these "green" resource discussions can help in both the design of products and process as well as in the most effective uses of production resources. As an example a metal casting manufacturer in Canada which uses a lot of electricity schedules their 'melts' to avoid periods of peak demand. This avoids the local energy supplier from having to increase their capacity and in turn the manufacturer is given a slightly preferred rate.

MANUFACTURING RESOURCE PLANNING

Because of the large amount of data and the number of calculations needed, the manufacturing planning and control system will probably have to be computer based. If a computer is not used, the time and labor required to make calculations manually is extensive and forces a company into compromises. Instead of scheduling requirements through the planning system, the company may have to extend lead times and build inventory to compensate for the inability to schedule quickly what is needed and when.

The system is intended to be a fully integrated planning and control system that works from the top down and has feedback from the bottom up. Strategic business planning integrates the plans and activities of marketing, finance, and production to create plans intended to achieve the overall goals of the company. In turn, master production scheduling, material requirements planning, production activity control, and purchasing are directed toward achieving the goals of the production and strategic business plans and, ultimately, the company. If priority plans have to be adjusted at any of the planning levels because of capacity problems, those changes should be reflected in the levels above. Thus, there must be feedback throughout the system.

The strategic business plan incorporates the plans of marketing, finance, and production. Marketing must agree that its plans are realistic and attainable. Finance must agree that the plans are desirable from a financial point of view, and production must agree that it can meet the required demand. The manufacturing planning and control system, as described here, is a master game plan for all departments in the company. This fully integrated planning and control system is called a **manufacturing resource planning,** or **MRP II** system. The term *MRP II* is used to distinguish the **manufacturing resource plan (MRP II)** from the material requirements plan (MRP).

MRP II provides coordination between marketing and production. Marketing, finance, and production agree on a total workable plan expressed in the production plan. Marketing and production must work together on a weekly and daily basis to adjust the plan as changes occur. Order sizes may need to be changed, orders canceled, and delivery dates adjusted. This kind of change is made through the master production schedule. Marketing managers and production managers may change master production schedules to meet changes in forecast demand. Senior management may adjust the production plan to reflect overall changes in demand or resources. However, they all work through the MRP II system. It provides the mechanism for coordinating the efforts of marketing, finance, production, and other departments in the company. MRP II is a method for the effective planning of all resources of a manufacturing company.

Figure 2.6 shows an MRP II system. Note the feedback loops.

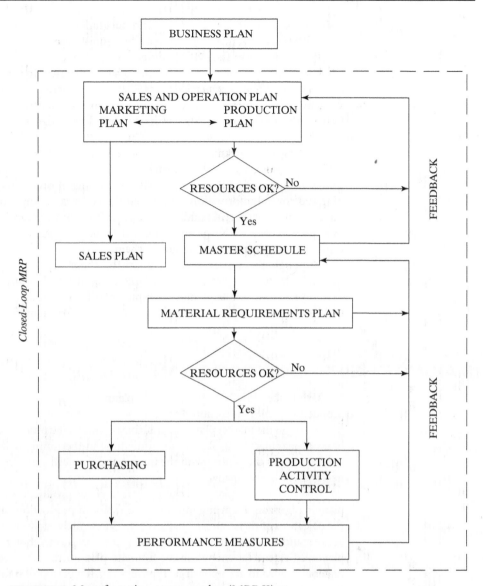

FIGURE 2.6 Manufacturing resource plan (MRP II).

ENTERPRISE RESOURCE PLANNING

As MRP systems evolved, they tended to take advantage of two changing conditions:

1. Computers and information technologies (IT) becoming significantly faster, more reliable, and more powerful. People in most companies had become at least comfortable, but often very familiar, with the advantages in speed, accuracy, and capability of integrated computer-based management systems.

2. Movement toward integration of knowledge and decision making in all aspects of direct and indirect functions and areas that impact materials flow and materials management. This integration not only included internal functions such as marketing, engineering, human resources, accounting, and finance but also included the upstream activities in supplier information and the downstream activities of distribution and delivery. That movement of integration is what is now recognized as supply chain management.

As the needs of the organization grew in the direction of a truly integrated approach toward materials management, the development of IT systems matched that need. As these systems became both larger in scope and integration when compared to the existing MRP and MRP II systems, they were given a new name—**enterprise resource planning (ERP).**

ERP is similar to the MRP II system except it does not dwell on manufacturing. The whole enterprise is taken into account. **The Association for Operations Management,** *APICS 12th Edition Dictionary* defines ERP as a "framework for organizing, defining, and standardizing the business processes necessary to effectively plan and control an organization so the organization can use its internal knowledge to seek external advantage." To fully operate there must be applications for planning, scheduling, costing, and so forth, to all layers in an organization, work centers, sites, divisions, and corporate. Essentially, ERP encompasses the total company whereas MRP II encompasses just manufacturing. The larger scope of ERP systems allows the tracking of orders and other important planning and control information throughout the entire company, from procurement to ultimate customer delivery. In addition, many ERP systems are capable of allowing managers to share data between firms, meaning that these managers can potentially have visibility across the complete span of the supply chain.

Although the power and capability of these highly integrated ERP systems is extremely high, there are also some large costs involved. Many of the best systems are expensive to buy. The large data requirements (for both quantity and accuracy) tend to make the systems expensive, time consuming, and for many firms, generally difficult to implement.

MAKING THE PRODUCTION PLAN

We have looked briefly at the purpose, planning horizon, and level of detail found in a production plan. This section discusses some details involved in making production plans.

Based on the market plan and available resources, the production plan sets the limits or levels of manufacturing activity for some time in the future. It integrates the capabilities and capacity of the factory with the market and financial plans to achieve the overall business goals of the company.

The production plan sets the general levels of production and inventories over the planning horizon. Its prime purpose is to establish production rates that will accomplish the objectives of the strategic business plan. These include inventory levels, backlogs, market demand, customer service, low-cost plant operation, labor relations, and so on. The plan must extend far enough in the future to plan for the labor, equipment, facilities, and material needed to accomplish it. Typically, this is a period of 6 to 18 months and is done in monthly and sometimes weekly periods.

The planning process at this level ignores such details as individual products, colors, styles, or options. With the time spans involved and the uncertainty of demand over long periods, the detail would not be accurate or useful, and the plan would be expensive to create. For planning purposes, a common unit or small number of product groups is what is needed.

Establishing Product Groups

Firms that make a single product, or products that are similar, can measure their output directly by the number of units they produce. A brewery, for instance, might use barrels of beer as a common denominator. Many companies, however, make several different products, and a common denominator for measuring total output may be difficult or impossible to find. Product groups need to be established. Marketing naturally looks at products from the customers' point of view of functionality and application, whereas manufacturing looks at products in terms of processes. Thus, firms need to establish product groups based on the similarity of manufacturing processes.

Manufacturing must provide the capacity to produce the goods needed. It is concerned more with the demand for the specific kinds of capacity needed to make the products than with the demand for the product.

Capacity is the ability to produce goods and services. It means having the resources available to satisfy demand. For the time span of a production plan, it can be expressed as the time available or, sometimes, as the number of units or dollars that can be produced in a given period. The demand for goods must be translated into the demand for capacity. At the production planning level, where little detail is needed, this requires identifying product groups, or families, of individual products *based on the similarity of manufacturing process.* For example, several calculator models might share the same processes and need the same kind of capacity, regardless of the variations in the models. They would be considered as a family group of products.

Over the time span of the production plan, large changes in capacity are usually not possible. Additions or subtractions in plant and equipment are impossible or very difficult to accomplish in this period. However, some things can be altered, and it is the responsibility of manufacturing management to identify and assess them. Usually the following can be varied:

- People can be hired and laid off, overtime and short time can be worked, and shifts can be added or removed.
- Inventory can be built up in slack periods and sold or used in periods of high demand.
- Work can be subcontracted or extra equipment leased.

Each alternative has its associated benefits and costs. Manufacturing management is responsible for finding the least-cost alternative consistent with the goals and objectives of the business.

Basic Strategies

In summary, the production planning problem typically has the following characteristics:

- A time horizon of 12 months is used, with periodic updating perhaps every month or quarter.
- Production demand consists of one or a few product families or common units.
- Demand is fluctuating or seasonal.
- Plant and equipment are fixed within the time horizon.
- A variety of management objectives are set, such as low inventories, efficient plant operation, good customer service, and good labor relations.

Figure 2.7 shows a hypothetical demand forecast for a product group. Note that the demand is seasonal.

There are four basic strategies that can be used in developing a production plan:

1. Chase strategy.
2. Production leveling.
3. Subcontracting.
4. Hybrid strategy

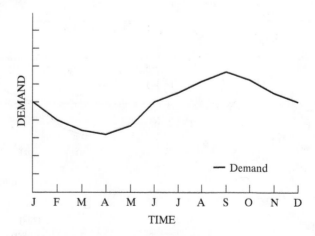

FIGURE 2.7 Hypothetical demand curve.

FIGURE 2.8 Chase (demand matching) strategy.

Chase (demand matching) strategy **Chase strategy** means producing the amounts demanded at any given time. Inventory levels remain stable while production varies to meet demand. Figure 2.8 shows this strategy. The firm manufactures just enough at any one time to meet demand exactly. In some industries, this is the only strategy that can be followed. Farmers, for instance, must produce in the growing season. The post office must process mail over the Christmas rush and in slack seasons. Restaurants have to serve meals when the customers want them. These industries cannot stockpile or inventory their products or services and must be capable of meeting demand as it occurs.

In these cases, the company must have enough capacity to be able to meet the peak demand. Farmers must have sufficient machinery and equipment to harvest in the growing season, although the equipment will lie idle in the winter. Companies have to hire and train people for the peak periods and lay them off when the peak is past. Sometimes they have to add extra shifts and overtime. All these changes add cost.

The advantage to the chase strategy is that inventories can be kept to a minimum. Goods are made when demand occurs and are not stockpiled. Thus, the costs associated with carrying inventories are avoided. Such costs can be quite high, as is shown in Chapter 9, on inventory fundamentals.

Production leveling **Production leveling** is continually producing an amount equal to the average demand. This relationship is shown in Figure 2.9. Companies calculate their total demand over the time span of the plan and, on the average, produce enough to meet it. Sometimes demand is less than the amount produced and an inventory builds up. At other times demand is greater and inventory is used up.

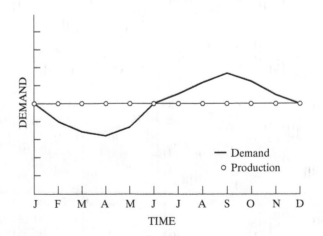

FIGURE 2.9 Production leveling strategy.

The advantage of a production leveling strategy is that it results in a smooth level of operation that avoids the costs of changing production levels. Firms do not need to have excess capacity to meet peak demand. They do not need to hire and train workers and lay them off in slack periods. They can build a stable workforce. The disadvantage is that inventory will build up in low-demand periods. This inventory will cost money to carry and an understated forecast could result in not enough inventory being produced for the peak season.

Production leveling means the company will use its resources at a uniform rate and produce the same amount each day it is operating. The exact amount produced each month (or sometimes each week), however, will not be constant because the number of working days varies from month to month.

Example Problem

A company wants to produce 10,000 units of an item over the next 3 months at a uniform rate. Because of an annual shutdown in the third month, the first month has 20 working days; the second, 21 working days; and the third, 12 working days. On the average, how much should the company produce each day to level production?

ANSWER

$$\text{Total production} = 10{,}000 \text{ units}$$
$$\text{Total working days} = 20 + 21 + 12 = 53 \text{ days}$$
$$\text{Average daily production} = \frac{10{,}000}{53} = 188.7 \text{ units}$$

For some products for which demand is very seasonal, such as Christmas tree lights, some form of production leveling strategy is necessary. The costs of idle capacity—and of hiring, training, and laying off—would be severe if a company employed a chase strategy.

Subcontracting   As a pure strategy, **subcontracting** means always producing at the level of minimum demand and meeting any additional demand through subcontracting. Subcontracting can mean buying the extra amounts demanded or turning away extra demand. The latter can be done by increasing prices when demand is high or by extending lead times. This strategy is shown in Figure 2.10.

The major advantage of this strategy is production cost. Costs associated with excess production capacity are avoided, and because production is leveled, there are no costs associated with changing production levels. The main disadvantage is that the cost of purchasing (item cost, purchasing, transportation, and inspection costs) may be greater than if the item were made in the plant.

Few companies make everything or buy everything they need. The decision about which items to buy and which to manufacture depends mainly on cost, but there are several other factors that may be considered.

Firms may manufacture to keep confidential processes within the company, to maintain quality levels, and to maintain a workforce.

FIGURE 2.10 Subcontracting.

FIGURE 2.11 Hybrid strategy.

They may buy from a supplier who has special expertise in design and manufacture of a component, to allow the firm to concentrate on its own area of expertise, or to provide known and competitive prices.

For many items, such as nuts and bolts or components that the firm does not normally make, the decision is clear. For other items that are within the specialty of the firm, a decision must be made whether to subcontract or not.

Hybrid strategy The three strategies discussed so far are pure strategies. Each has its own set of costs: equipment, hiring/layoff, overtime, inventory, and subcontracting. In reality, there are many possible **hybrid** or combined strategies a company may use. Each will have its own set of cost characteristics. Production management is responsible for finding the combination of strategies that minimizes the sum of all costs involved, providing the level of service required, and meeting the objectives of the financial and marketing plans.

Figure 2.11 shows a possible hybrid plan. Demand is matched to some extent, production is partially smoothed, and in the peak period some subcontracting takes place. The plan is only one of many that could be developed.

Developing a Make-to-Stock Production Plan

In a make-to-stock environment, products are made and put into inventory before an order is received from a customer. Sale and delivery of the goods are made from inventory. Off-the-rack clothing, frozen foods, and bicycles are examples of this kind of manufacturing.

Generally firms make to stock when

- Demand is fairly constant and predictable.
- There are few product options.
- Delivery times demanded by the marketplace are much shorter than the time needed to make the product.
- Product has a long shelf life.

The information needed to make a production plan is as follows:

- Forecast by period for the planning horizon.
- Opening inventory.
- Desired ending inventory.
- Any past-due customer orders. These are orders that are late for delivery and are sometimes called *back orders*.

The objective in developing a production plan is to minimize the costs of carrying inventory, changing production levels, and stocking out (not having the products the customer wants when they are wanted).

The following sections develop a plan for leveling production and one for chase strategy.

Level production plan   Following is the general procedure for developing a plan for level production.

1. Total the forecast demand for the planning horizon.
2. Determine the opening inventory and the desired ending inventory.
3. Calculate the total production required as follows:

$$\text{Total production} = \text{Total forecast} + \text{back orders} \\ + \text{ending inventory} - \text{opening inventory}$$

5. Calculate the production required each period by dividing the total production by the number of periods.
6. Calculate the ending inventory for each period.

Example Problem

Amalgamated Fish Sinkers makes a product group of fresh fish sinkers and wants to develop a production plan for them. The expected opening inventory is 100 cases, and the company wants to reduce that to 80 cases by the end of the planning period. The number of working days is the same for each period. There are no back orders. The expected demand for the fish sinkers is as follows:

Period	1	2	3	4	5	Total
Forecast (cases)	110	120	130	120	120	600

a. How much should be produced each period?
b. What is the ending inventory for each period?
c. If the cost of carrying inventory is $5 per case per period based on ending inventory, what is the total cost of carrying inventory?
d. What will be the total cost of the plan?

ANSWER

a. Total production required = 600 + 80 − 100 = 580 cases

$$\text{Production each period} = \frac{580}{5} = 116 \text{ cases}$$

b. Ending inventory = opening inventory + production − demand

Ending inventory after the first period = 100 + 116 − 110 = 106 cases

Similarly, the ending inventories for each period are calculated as shown in Figure 2.12. The ending inventory for period 1 becomes the opening inventory for period 2:

Ending inventory (period 2) = 106 + 116 − 120 = 102 cases

Period		1	2	3	4	5	Total
Forecast (cases)		110	120	130	120	120	600
Production		116	116	116	116	116	580
Ending Inventory	100	106	102	88	84	80	

FIGURE 2.12 Level production plan: make to stock.

Period	0	1	2	3	4	5	Total
Demand (cases)		110	120	130	120	120	600
Production	100	90	120	130	120	120	580
Change in Production		10	30	10	10	0	60
Ending Inventory	100	80	80	80	80	80	

FIGURE 2.13 Chase strategy: make to stock.

c. The total cost of carrying inventory would be

$$(106 + 102 + 88 + 84 + 80)\$5 = \$2300$$

d. Since there were no stockouts and no changes in the level of production, this would be the total cost of the plan.

Chase strategy Amalgamated Fish Sinkers makes another line of product called fish stinkers. Unfortunately, they are perishable, and the company cannot build inventory for sale later. They must use a chase strategy and make only enough to satisfy demand in each period. Inventory costs will be a minimum, and there should be no stockout costs. However, there will be costs associated with changing production levels.

Let us suppose in the preceding example that changing the production level by one case costs $20. For example, a change from 50 to 60 would cost

$$(60 - 50) \times \$20 = \$200$$

The opening inventory is 100 cases, and the company wishes to bring this down to 80 cases in the first period. The required production in the first period would then be

$$110 - (100 - 80) = 90 \text{ cases}$$

Assuming that production in the period before period 1 was 100 cases, Figure 2.13 shows the changes in production levels and in ending inventory.

The cost of the plan would be

$$\text{Cost of changing production level} = (60)\$20 = \$1200$$

$$\text{Cost of carrying inventory} = (80 \text{ cases})(5 \text{ periods})\$5 = \$2000$$

$$\text{Total cost of the plan} = \$1,200 + \$2,000 = \$3200$$

It should be noted that the previous examples provide a basic understanding of the dollar cost of possible production plans. But before a final selection of a plan is made, there are other considerations that should be evaluated, and some of those are difficult to estimate financially. Some of those issues might include

- Impact on customers if cyclical demand in a level schedule causes shortages.
- Impact on production workers as they are moved into and out of production in a chase strategy. Such an impact will often reduce efficiency of the operation.
- Potential loss of profit if customer impacts cause customers to change buying preferences and seek a competitor's products.

Developing a Make-to-Order Production Plan

In a make-to-order environment, manufacturers wait until an order is received from a customer before starting to make the goods. Examples of this kind of manufacture are custom-tailored clothing, machinery, or any product made to customer specification. Very expensive items are usually made to order. Generally, firms make to order when

- Goods are produced to customer specification.
- The customer is willing to wait while the order is being made.
- The product is expensive to make and to store.
- Several product options are offered.

Assemble to order   Where several product options exist, such as in automobiles, and where the customer is not willing to wait until the product is made, manufacturers produce and stock standard component parts. When manufacturers receive an order from a customer, they assemble the component parts from inventory according to the order. Since the components are stocked, the firm needs only time to assemble before delivering to the customer. Examples of assemble-to-order products include automobiles and computers. Assemble to order is a subset of make to order.

The following information is needed to make a production plan for make-to-order products:

- Forecast by period for the planning horizon.
- Opening backlog of customer orders.
- Desired ending backlog.

Backlog   In a make-to-order environment, a company does not build an inventory of finished goods. Instead, it has a **backlog** of unfilled customer orders. The backlog normally will be for delivery in the future and does not represent orders that are late or past due. A custom woodwork shop might have orders from customers that will keep it busy for several weeks. This will be its backlog. If individuals want some work done, the order will join the queue or backlog. Manufacturers like to control the backlog so that they can provide a good level of customer service.

Level production plan   Following is a general procedure for developing a make-to-order level production plan:

1. Total the forecast demand for the planning horizon.
2. Determine the opening backlog and the desired ending backlog.
3. Calculate the total production required as follows:

    Total production = total forecast + opening backlog − ending backlog
4. Calculate the production required each period by dividing the total production by the number of periods.
5. Spread the existing backlog over the planning horizon according to due date per period.

Example Problem

A local printing company provides a custom printing service. Since each job is different, demand is forecast in hours per week. Over the next 5 weeks, the company expects that demand will be 100 hours per week. There is an existing backlog of 100 hours, and at the end of 5 weeks, the company wants to reduce that to 80 hours. How many hours of work will be needed each week to reduce the backlog? What will be the backlog at the end of each week?

ANSWER

$$\text{Total production} = 500 + 100 - 80 = 520 \text{ hours}$$
$$\text{Weekly production} = \frac{520}{5} = 104 \text{ hours}$$

Period		1	2	3	4	5	Total
Sales Forecast		100	100	100	100	100	500
Planned Production		104	104	104	104	104	520
Projected Backlog	100	96	92	88	84	80	

FIGURE 2.14 Level production plan: make to order.

The backlog for each week can be calculated as

Projected backlog = old backlog + forecast − production
For week 1: Projected backlog = 100 + 100 − 104 = 96 hours
For week 2: Projected backlog = 96 + 100 − 104 = 92 hours

Figure 2.14 shows the resulting production plan.

Resource Planning

Once the preliminary production plan is established, it must be compared to the existing resources of the company. This step is called resource requirements planning or resource planning. Two questions must be answered:

1. Are the resources available to meet the production plan?

2. If not, how will the difference be reconciled?

If enough capacity to meet the production plan cannot be made available, the plan must be changed.

A tool often used is the **resource bill.** This shows the quantity of *critical* resources (materials, labor, and "bottleneck" operations) needed to make one average unit of the product group. Figure 2.15 shows an example of a resource bill for a company that makes tables, chairs, and stools as a three-product family.

If the firm planned to make 500 tables, 300 chairs, and 1500 stools in a particular period, they could calculate the quantity of wood and labor that will be needed. For example, the amount of wood needed is

Tables: $500 \times 20 = 10,000$ board feet
Chairs: $300 \times 10 = 3000$ board feet
Stools: $1500 \times 5 = 7500$ board feet
Total wood required = 20,500 board feet

The amount of labor needed is

Tables: $500 \times 1.31 = 655$ standard hours
Chairs: $300 \times 0.85 = 255$ standard hours
Stools: $1500 \times 0.55 = 825$ standard hours
Total labor required = 1735 standard hours

Product	Wood (board feet)	Labor (standard hours)
Tables	20	1.31
Chairs	10	0.85
Stools	5	0.55

FIGURE 2.15 Resource bill.

The company must now compare the requirements for wood and labor with the availability of these resources. For instance, suppose the labor normally available in this period is 1600 hours. The priority plan requires 1735 hours, a difference of 135 hours, or about 8.4%. Extra capacity must be found, or the priority plan must be adjusted. In this example, it might be possible to work overtime to provide the extra capacity required. If overtime is not possible, the plan must be adjusted to reduce the labor needed. This might involve shifting some production to an earlier period or delaying shipments.

SUMMARY

Production planning is the first step in a manufacturing planning and control system. The planning horizon usually extends for a year. The minimum horizon depends on the lead times to purchase materials and make the product. The level of detail is not high. Usually, the plan is made for families of products based on the similarity of manufacturing process or on some common unit. The production plan is part of the sales and operations planning process, which is an executive-level planning process involving trade-offs across departments or functions in the company.

Three basic strategies can be used to develop a production plan: chase, leveling production, or subcontracting. Each has its operational and cost advantages and disadvantages. It is the responsibility of manufacturing management to select the best combination of these basic plans so total costs are minimized and customer service levels are maintained.

A make-to-stock production plan determines how much to produce in each period to meet the following objectives:

- Achieve the forecast.
- Maintain the required inventory levels.

Although demand must be satisfied, the plan must balance the costs of maintaining inventory with the cost of changing production levels.

A make-to-order production plan determines how much to produce in each period to meet the following objectives:

- Achieve the forecast.
- Maintain the planned backlog.

The cost of a backlog that is too large equals the cost of turning away business. If customers have to wait too long for delivery, they might take their business elsewhere. As with a make-to-stock production plan, demand must be satisfied, and the plan must balance the costs of changing production levels with the cost of a backlog that is larger than desired.

KEY TERMS

Backlog 31

Capacity 16

Chase strategy 26

Enterprise resource planning (ERP) 24

"green" production 22

Hybrid 28

Level production plan 29

Manufacturing resource
plan (MRP II) 22

Priority 16

Production leveling 26

Resource bill 32

Sales and operations planning (SOP) 20

Subcontracting 27

QUESTIONS

1. What are the four questions a good planning system must answer?
2. Define capacity and priority. Why are they important in production planning?

3. Describe each of the following plans in terms of their purpose, planning horizon, level of detail, and planning cycle:
   a. Strategic business plan.
   b. Production plan.
   c. Master production schedule.
   d. Material requirements plan.
   e. Production activity control.

4. Describe the responsibilities and inputs of the marketing, production, finance, and engineering departments to the strategic business plan.

5. Describe the relationship among the production plan, the master production schedule, and the material requirements plan.

6. What is the difference between strategic business planning and sales and operations planning (SOP)? What are the major benefits of SOP?

7. What is MRP II?

8. What is ERP?

9. What two changing conditions led to the development of ERP systems?

10. In the short run, how can capacity be changed?

11. When making a production plan, why is it necessary to select a common unit or to establish product families?

12. On what basis should product groups (families) be established?

13. What are five typical characteristics of the production planning problem?

14. Describe each of the three basic strategies used in developing a production plan. What are the advantages and disadvantages of each?

15. What is a hybrid strategy? Why is it used?

16. Describe four conditions under which a firm would make to stock or make to order.

17. What information is needed to develop a make-to-stock production plan?

18. What are the steps in developing a make-to-stock production plan?

19. What is the difference between make to order and assemble to order? Give an example of each.

20. What information is needed to develop a make-to-order production plan? How does this differ from that needed for a make-to-stock plan?

21. What is the general procedure for developing a level production plan in a make-to-order environment?

22. What is a resource bill? At what level in the planning hierarchy is it used?

23. What kind of production environment would you expect to see if a company uses a chase strategy? What if it uses a level strategy?

24. What does the concept of "green production" mean? How will it potentially impact production planning?

PROBLEMS

2.1. If the opening inventory is 400 units, demand is 900 units, and production is 700 units, what will be the ending inventory?

   Answer.   200 units

2.2. A company wants to produce 500 units over the next 3 months at a uniform rate. The months have 19, 20, and 21 working days, respectively. On the average, how much should the company produce each day to level production?

   Answer.   Average daily production = 8.3 units

2.3. A company plans to produce 25,000 units in a 3-month period. The months have 22, 21, and 20 working days respectively. What should the average daily production be?

2.4. In problem 2.2, how much will be produced in each of the 3 months?

   Answer.   Month 1: 158   Month 2: 166   Month 3: 174

2.5. In problem 2.3, how much will be produced in each of the 3 months?

2.6. A production line is to run at 1000 units per month. Sales are forecast as shown in the following. Calculate the expected period-end inventory. The opening inventory is 600 units. All periods have the same number of working days.

Period	1	2	3	4	5	6
Forecast	750	700	1050	1600	1000	850
Planned Production	1000	1000	1000	1000	1000	1000
Planned Inventory	600					

Answer. For period 1, the ending inventory is 850 units.

2.7. A company wants to develop a level production plan for a family of products. The opening inventory is 100 units, and an increase to 150 units is expected by the end of the plan. The demand for each period is given in what follows. How much should the company produce each period? What will be the ending inventories in each period? All periods have the same number of working days.

Period	1	2	3	4	5	6	Total
Forecast Demand	100	120	125	130	115	110	
Planned Production							
Planned Inventory	100						

Answer. Total production = 750 units.

Period production = 125 units.

The ending inventory for period 1 is 125; for period 5, 135.

2.8. A company wants to develop a level production plan for a family of products. The opening inventory is 450 units, and a decrease to 200 units is expected by the end of the plan. The demand for each of the periods is given in what follows. All periods have the same number of working days. How much should the company produce each period? What will be the ending inventories in each period? Do you see any problems with the plan?

Period	1	2	3	4	5	6	Total
Forecast Demand	1300	1200	800	600	800	900	
Planned Production							
Planned Inventory	500						

2.9. A company wants to develop a level production plan. The beginning inventory is zero. Demand for the next four periods is given in what follows.

   a. What production rate per period will give a zero inventory at the end of period 4?

   b. When and in what quantities will back orders occur?

   c. What level production rate per period will avoid back orders? What will be the ending inventory in period 4?

Period		1	2	3	4	Total
Forecast Demand		9	5	9	9	
Planned Production						
Planned Inventory	0					

   Answer.   a. 8 units
       b. period 1, minus 1
       c. 9 units; 4 units

2.10. If the cost of carrying inventory is $50 per unit per period and stockout cost $500 per unit, what will be the cost of the plan developed in problem 2.9a? What will be the cost of the plan developed in 2.9c?

   Answer.   Total cost for plan in question 2.9a = $650

       Total cost for plan in question 2.9c = $600

2.11. A company wants to develop a level production plan for a family of products. The opening inventory is 100 units, and an increase to 130 units is expected by the end of the plan. The demand for each month is given in what follows. Calculate the total production, daily production, and production and ending inventory for each month.

Month		May	Jun	Jul	Aug	Total
Working Days		21	19	20	10	
Forecast Demand		115	125	140	150	
Planned Production						
Planned Inventory	100					

   Answer.   Total monthly production for May = 168 units

       The ending inventory for May = 153 units

2.12. A company wants to develop a level production plan for a family of products. The opening inventory is 500 units, and a decrease to 100 units is expected by the end of the plan. The demand for each of the months is given in what follows. How much should the company produce each month? What will be the ending inventory in each month? Do you see any problems with the plan?

Month	Jan	Feb	Mar	Apr	May	Jun	Total
Working Days	20	22	20	20	18	19	
Forecast Demand	1200	1300	800	700	700	900	
Planned Production							
Planned Inventory	500						

2.13. Because of its labor contract, a company must hire enough labor for 100 units of production per week on one shift or 200 units per week on two shifts. It cannot hire, lay off, or assign overtime. During the fourth week, workers will be available from another department to work part or all of an extra shift (up to 100 units). There is a planned shutdown for maintenance in the second week, which will cut production to half. Develop a production plan. The opening inventory is 200 units, and the desired ending inventory is 300 units.

Week	1	2	3	4	5	6	Total
Forecast Demand	120	160	240	240	160	160	
Planned Production							
Planned Inventory							

2.14. If the opening backlog is 500 units, forecast demand is 700 units, and production is 800 units, what will be the ending backlog?

Answer. 400 units

2.15. The opening backlog is 800 units. Forecast demand is shown in the following. Calculate the weekly production for level production if the backlog is to be reduced to 100 units.

Week	1	2	3	4	5	6	Total
Forecast Demand	750	700	550	700	600	500	
Planned Production							
Projected Backlog	800						

Answer. Total production = 4500 units
Weekly production = 750 units
Backlog at end of week 1 = 800 units

2.16. The opening backlog is 1100 units. Forecast demand is shown in the following. Calculate the weekly production for level production if the backlog is to be increased to 1200 units.

Week	1	2	3	4	5	6	Total
Forecast Demand	1200	1100	1200	1200	1100	1000	
Planned Production							
Projected Backlog	1100						

2.17. For the following data, calculate the number of workers required for level production and the resulting month-end inventories. Each worker can produce 15 units per day, and the desired ending inventory is 9000 units.

Month		1	2	3	4	Total
Working Days		20	24	12	19	
Forecast Demand		28,000	27,500	28,500	28,500	
Planned Production						
Planned Inventory	11,250					

Answer. Workers needed = 98 workers

First month's ending inventory = 12,650 units

2.18. For the following data, calculate the number of workers required for level production and the resulting month-end inventories. Each worker can produce 9 units per day, and the desired ending inventory is 800 units. Why is it not possible to reach the exact ending inventory target?

Month		1	2	3	4	5	6	Total
Working Days		20	24	12	22	20	19	
Forecast Demand		2800	3000	2700	3300	2900	3200	
Planned Production								
Planned Inventory	1000							

MERIDIAN WATER PUMPS

John Lopez, president of Meridian Water Pumps (a small water pump producer), was holding a meeting with his department managers. They were in the process of planning production of medium-sized pumps for the next 6 months. Mr. Lopez tolerated some of the arguing before he felt it necessary to stop the discussion as it was going so that he could direct it toward a solution. A summary of some of the arguments follows:

Mary Welch, Marketing and Sales Manager—"My sales people are very good, but get very frustrated at times. Several times last year the sales people spent lots of their time trying to calm down frustrated customers. As they are supposed to do, the sales people sold as many of these pumps as they could, yet at times the production could not keep up with the orders. Production knows that we have some cyclicality in the demand, but we have plenty of machine capacity. They should be able to hire people so that we can meet the demand that we sell. Why can't they get their area to work correctly?"

Frank Jackson, Production Manager—"Come on, Mary, we know the sales are cyclical, but we never know exactly when the cycles happen. Even if we did, the Human Resource (HR) people always take too long to get us the people we need. By the time we get the new people hired and trained, the sales seem to drop again. What am I supposed to do? If we keep them and allow them to keep producing pumps, our inventory climbs and the finance people start yelling. I can't just let those new people sit around doing nothing. The only other alternative is to lay them off, but then the HR people get really angry."

Elizabeth Conrad, Human Resource Manager—"You bet we get angry. The production people will occasionally start pushing us to hurry and hire more people, yet get very impatient. It takes time to go through the interview process and get people hired and oriented to our business. Then we no sooner get them on site and working when production asks us to lay them off. That is a real problem for two reasons. First, there are costs involved. It takes an average of $100 to get a person hired, and another $100 to lay them off. Secondly, those people that we hire and then quickly lay off tend to not return. I can't blame them, since from their perspective it looks like we have no idea how to run our business. In addition, as those people complain to other people about our treatment of them, our reputation is getting to look bad, and that makes it increasingly difficult to find good people to hire."

Joseph Western, Finance Manager—"Frank is correct that I get upset when the inventory climbs. It costs us about $5 to keep one of these pumps in our inventory for a month. That cost comes right out of our profit. Since my job is to maximize profitability, I can't sit by and let those inventory dollars shrink that profitability. The same goes for all that hiring and layoffs. That money also hurts profitability. Can't we do better?"

At this point Mr. Lopez stopped the discussion and said "Enough of trying to blame each other. It is our job as managers to manage this process more effectively. Marketing has just completed a 6-month forecast of anticipated demand for this family of pumps, and we know from past history that their forecasts are pretty good. We should be able to come up with an approach that we all can live with and focus our efforts to meet. Let's get to work on it."

ASSIGNMENT: Assume you have been given the job to develop an effective approach to the problem. First, here is the forecast developed by Marketing:

Month	1	2	3	4	5	6
Forecasted Demand	600	750	1000	850	750	700

The production manager said there were currently 50 units in inventory, and they would like to end the 6 months with only 25 in inventory. He also said that currently each worker produces an average of 25 pumps in any given month. There are currently 20 workers in the medium-size pump area.

1. Using the data, develop a level production plan. How much extra cost (inventory and HR costs) are involved in this plan? What additional costs (both financial and nonfinancial) might be involved with such a plan?

2. Using the data, develop a chase production plan. How much extra cost (inventory and HR costs) are involved in this plan? What additional costs (both financial and nonfinancial) might be involved with such a plan?

3. Try to develop a possible hybrid plan that would accomplish the task with smaller total costs than either level or chase.

4. Based on your work, what would you recommend and why? What are some of the pros and cons of the solution you recommend?

MASTER SCHEDULING

INTRODUCTION

After production planning, the next step in the manufacturing planning and control process is to prepare a **master production schedule** (MPS). This chapter examines some basic considerations in making and managing an MPS. It is an extremely important planning tool and forms the basis for communication between sales and manufacturing. The MPS is a vital link in the production planning system.

- It forms the link between production planning and what manufacturing will actually build.
- It forms the basis for calculating the capacity and resources needed.
- It drives the material requirements plan. As a schedule of items to be built, the MPS and bills of material determine what components are needed from manufacturing and purchasing.
- It keeps priorities valid. The MPS is a priority plan for manufacturing.

Whereas the production plan deals in families of products, the MPS works with end items. It breaks down the production plan into the requirements for individual end items, in each family, by date and quantity. The production plan limits the MPS. Therefore the total of the items in the MPS should not be different from the total shown on the production plan. For example, if the production plan shows a planned production of 1000 tricycles in a particular week, the total of the individual models planned for by the MPS should be 1000. Within this limit, its objective is to balance the demand (priorities) set by the marketplace with the availability of materials, labor, and equipment (capacity) of manufacturing.

The end items made by the company are assembled from component and subcomponent parts. These must be available in the right quantities at the right time to support the master production schedule. The material requirements planning system plans the schedule for these components based on the needs of the MPS. Thus the MPS drives the material requirements plan.

The MPS is a plan for manufacturing. It reflects the needs of the marketplace and the capacity of manufacturing and forms a priority plan for manufacturing to follow.

The MPS forms a vital link between sales and production:

- It makes possible valid order promises. The MPS is a plan of what is to be produced and when. As such, it tells sales and manufacturing when goods will be available for delivery.
- It is a contract between marketing and manufacturing. It is an agreed-upon plan.

The MPS forms a basis for sales and production to determine what is to be manufactured. It is not meant to be rigid. It is a device for communication and a basis to make changes that are consistent with the demands of the marketplace and the capacity of manufacturing.

The information needed to develop an MPS is provided by

- The production plan.
- Forecasts for individual end items.

- Actual orders received from customers and for stock replenishment.
- Inventory levels for individual end items.
- Capacity restraints.

RELATIONSHIP TO PRODUCTION PLAN

Suppose the following production plan is developed for a family of three items:

Week	1	2	3	4	5	6
Aggregate Forecast (units)	160	160	160	160	215	250
Production Plan	205	205	205	205	205	205
Aggregate Inventory (units)	545	590	635	680	670	625

Opening inventories (units) are

Product A	350
Product B	100
Product C	50
Total	500

The next step is to forecast demand for each item in the product family.

Week	1	2	3	4	5	6
Product A	70	70	70	70	70	80
Product B	40	40	40	40	95	120
Product C	50	50	50	50	50	50
Total	160	160	160	160	215	250

With these data, the master scheduler must now devise a plan to fit the constraints. The following illustrates a possible solution.

Master Schedule

Week	1	2	3	4	5	6
Product A						205
Product B	205	205	205			
Product C				205	205	
Total Planned	205	205	205	205	205	205

Inventory

Week	1	2	3	4	5	6
Product A	280	210	140	70	0	125
Product B	265	430	595	555	460	340
Product C	0	−50	−100	55	210	160
Total Planned	545	640	735	680	670	625

This schedule is satisfactory for the following reasons:

- It tells the plant when to start and stop production of individual items.
- Capacity is consistent with the production plan.

It is unsatisfactory for the following reasons:

- It has a poor inventory balance compared to total inventory.
- It results in a stockout for product C in periods 2 and 3.

The term *master production schedule* refers to the last line of the matrix. The term *master scheduling* refers to the *process* of arriving at that line. Thus, the total matrix is called a master schedule.

Example Problem

The Hotshot Lightning Rod Company makes a family of two lightning rods, Models H and I. It bases its production planning on weeks. For the present month, production is leveled at 1000 units. Opening inventory is 500 units, and the plan is to reduce that to 300 units by the end of the month. The MPS is made using weekly periods. There are 4 weeks in this month, and production is to be leveled at 250 units per week. The forecast and projected available for the two lightning rods follows. Calculate an MPS for each item.

ANSWER

Production Plan

Week		1	2	3	4	Total
Forecast		300	350	300	250	1200
Projected Available	500	450	350	300	300	
Production Plan		250	250	250	250	1000

Master Schedule: Model H

Week		1	2	3	4	Total
Forecast		200	300	100	100	700
Projected Available	200	250	200	100	100	
MPS		250	250		100	

Master Schedule: Model I

Week		1	2	3	4	Total
Forecast		100	50	200	150	500
Projected Available	300	200	150	200	200	
MPS				250	150	

DEVELOPING A MASTER PRODUCTION SCHEDULE

The objectives in developing an MPS are as follows:

- To maintain the desired level of customer service by maintaining finished-goods inventory levels or by scheduling to meet customer delivery requirements.
- To make the best use of material, labor, and equipment.
- To maintain inventory investment at the required levels.

To reach these objectives, the plan must satisfy customer demand, be within the capacity of manufacturing, and be within the guidelines of the production plan.

There are three steps in preparing an MPS:

1. Develop a preliminary MPS.
2. Check the preliminary MPS against available capacity.
3. Resolve differences between the preliminary MPS and capacity availability.

Preliminary Master Production Schedule

To show the process of developing an MPS, an example is used that assumes that the product is made to stock, an inventory is kept, and the product is made in lots.

A particular item is made in lots of 100, and the expected opening inventory is 80 units. Figure 3.1 shows the forecast of demand, the projected available on hand, and the preliminary MPS.

Period 1 begins with an inventory of 80 units. After the forecast demand for 60 units is satisfied, the projected available is 20 units. A further forecast demand of 60 in period 2 is not satisfied, and it is necessary to schedule an MPS receipt of 100 for week 2. This produces a projected available of 60 units ($20 + 100 - 60 = 60$) at the end of period 2. In period 3, the forecast demand for 60 is satisfied by the projected 60 on hand, leaving a projected available of 0. In period 4, a further 100 must be received, and when the forecast demand of 60 units is satisfied, 40 units remain in inventory.

On hand = 80 units
Lot size = 100 units

Period		1	2	3	4	5	6
Forecast		60	60	60	60	60	60
Projected Available	80	20	60	0	40	80	20
MPS			100		100	100	

FIGURE 3.1 MPS example.

This process of building an MPS occurs for each item in the family. If the total planned production of all the items in the family and the total ending inventory do not agree with the production plan, some adjustment to the individual plans must be made so the total production is the same.

Once the preliminary master production schedules are made, they must be checked against the available capacity. This process is called rough-cut capacity planning.

Example Problem

Amalgamated Nut Crackers, Inc., makes a family of nut crackers. The most popular model is the walnut, and the sales department has prepared a 6-week forecast. The opening inventory is 50 dozen (dozen is the unit used for planning). As master planner, you must prepare an MPS. The nutcrackers are made in lots of 100 dozen.

ANSWER

Week		1	2	3	4	5	6
Forecast Sales		75	50	30	40	70	20
Projected Available	50	75	25	95	55	85	65
MPS		100		100		100	

Rough-Cut Capacity Planning

Rough-cut capacity planning checks whether critical resources are available to support the preliminary master production schedules. Critical resources include "bottleneck" operations, labor, and critical materials (perhaps material that is scarce or has a long lead time).

The process is similar to resource requirements planning used in the production planning process. The difference is that now we are working with a product and not a family of products. The resource bill, used in resource requirements planning, assumes a typical product in the family. Here the resource bill is for a single product. As before, the only interest is in bottleneck work centers and critical resources.

One reason this method is described as "rough" is not only because it focuses primarily on critical resources but also because there are several other variables that can impact specific details of capacity usage. These include existing inventory, existing work orders that are partially complete, and lead times. Inclusion of those and other capacity variables are discussed in more detail in Chapter 5.

Suppose a firm manufactures four models of desktop computers assembled in a work center that is a bottleneck operation. The company wants to schedule to the capacity of this work center and not beyond. Figure 3.2 shows a resource bill for that work center showing the time required to assemble one computer.

Resource Bill	
Desktop Computer Assembly	
Computer	Assembly Time (standard hours)
Model D24	0.203
Model D25	0.300
Model D26	0.350
Model D27	0.425

FIGURE 3.2 Resource bill.

Suppose that in a particular week the master production schedules show that the following computers are to be built:

Model D24	200 units
Model D25	250 units
Model D26	400 units
Model D27	100 units

The capacity required on this critical resource is

$$\text{Model D24 } 200 \times 0.203 = 40.6 \text{ standard hours}$$

$$\text{Model D25 } 250 \times 0.300 = 75.0 \text{ standard hours}$$

$$\text{Model D26 } 400 \times 0.350 = 140.0 \text{ standard hours}$$

$$\text{Model D27 } 100 \times 0.425 = 42.5 \text{ standard hours}$$

$$\text{Total time required} = 298.1 \text{ standard hours}$$

Example Problem

The Acme Tweezers Company makes tweezers in two models, medium and fine. The bottleneck operation is in work center 20. Following is the resource bill (in hours per dozen) for work center 20.

	Hours per Dozen	
Work Center	Medium	Fine
20	0.5	1.2

The master production schedule for the next 4 weeks is

Week	1	2	3	4	Total
Medium	40	25	40	15	120
Fine	20	10	30	20	80

Using the resource bill and the master production schedule, calculate the number of hours required in work center 20 for each of the 4 weeks. Use the following table to record the required capacity on the work center.

ANSWER

Week	1	2	3	4	Total
Medium	20	12.5	20	7.5	60
Fine	24	12	36	24	96
Total Hours	44	24.5	56	31.5	156

Resolution of Differences

The next step is to compare the total time required to the available capacity of the work center. If available capacity is greater than the required capacity, the MPS is workable. If not, methods of increasing capacity have to be investigated. Is it possible to adjust the available capacity with overtime, extra workers, routing through other work centers, or subcontracting? If not, it will be necessary to revise the master production schedule.

Finally, the master production schedule must be judged by three criteria:

1. **Resource use.** Is the MPS within capacity restraints in each period of the plan? Does it make the best use of resources?

2. **Customer service.** Will due dates be met and will delivery performance be acceptable?

3. **Cost.** Is the plan economical, or will excess costs be incurred for overtime, subcontracting, expediting, or transportation?

Master Schedule Decisions

The MPS should represent as efficiently as possible what manufacturing will make. If too many items are included, it will lead to difficulties in forecasting and managing the MPS. In each of the manufacturing environments—make to stock, make to order, and assemble to order—master scheduling should take place where the smallest number of product options exists. Figure 3.3 shows the level at which items should be master scheduled.

Make-to-stock products In this environment, a limited number of standard items are assembled from many components. Televisions and other consumer products are examples. The MPS is usually a schedule of finished-goods items.

Make-to-order products In this environment, many different end items are made from a small number of components. Custom-tailored clothes are an example. The MPS is usually a schedule of the actual customer orders.

Assemble-to-order products In this environment, many end items can be made from combinations of basic components and subassemblies. For example, suppose a company manufactures paint from a base color and adds tints to arrive at the final color. Suppose there are 10 tints and a final color is made by mixing any three of them with the base. There are 720 possible colors ($10 \times 9 \times 8 = 720$). Forecasting and planning production for 720 items is a difficult task. It is much easier if production is planned at the level of the base color and the 10 tints. There are then only 10 items with which to deal: the base color and each of the 10 tints. Once a customer's order is received, the base color and the required tints can be combined (assembled) according to the order.

Final assembly schedule (FAS) This step, assembly to customer order, is generally planned using a final assembly schedule. This is a schedule of what will be assembled. It is used when there are many options and it is difficult to forecast which combination the

FIGURE 3.3 Different MPS environments.

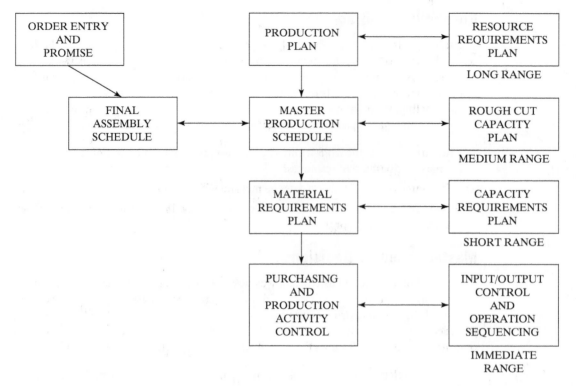

FIGURE 3.4 MPS, FAS, and other planning activities.

customers will want. Master production scheduling is done at the component level, for example, the base color and tint level. The final assembly takes place only when a customer order is received.

The FAS schedules customer orders as they are received and is based on the components planned in the MPS. It is responsible for scheduling from the MPS through final assembly and shipment to the customer.

Engineer to order This is a form of make-to-order (MTO) products. In this environment, the product is designed before manufacturing, based on the customer's very special needs. A bridge is an example.

Figure 3.4 shows the relationship of the MPS, the FAS, and other planning activities.

Planning Horizon

The planning horizon is the time span for which plans are made. It must cover a period at least equal to the time required to accomplish the plan. For master production scheduling, the minimum planning horizon is the longest cumulative or end-to-end lead time (LT). For example, in Figure 3.5, the longest cumulative lead time path is A to D to F to G. The cumulative lead time is $1 + 2 + 3 + 6 = 12$ weeks. The minimum planning horizon must be 12 weeks; otherwise, raw material G would not be ordered in time to meet delivery.

The planning horizon is usually longer for several reasons. The longer the horizon, the greater the "visibility" and the better management's ability to avoid future problems or to take advantage of special circumstances. For example, firms might take advantage of economical purchase plans, avoid future capacity problems, or manufacture in more economical lot sizes.

As a minimum, the planning horizon for a final assembly schedule must include time to assemble a customer's order. It does not need to include the time necessary to manufacture the components. That time will be included in the planning horizon of the MPS.

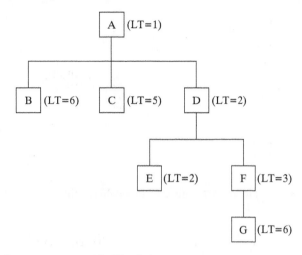

FIGURE 3.5 Product structure: critical lead time.

PRODUCTION PLANNING, MASTER SCHEDULING, AND SALES

The production plan reconciles total forecast demand with available resources. It takes information from the strategic business plan and market forecasts to produce an overall plan of what production intends to make to meet forecast. It is dependent on the forecast and, within capacity limits, must plan to satisfy the forecast demand. It is not concerned with the detail of what will actually be made. It is intended to provide a framework in which detailed plans can be made in the MPS.

The MPS is built from forecasts and actual demands for individual end items. It reconciles demand with the production plan and with available resources to produce a plan that manufacturing can fulfill. The MPS is concerned with what items will actually be built, in what quantities, and when, to meet expected demand.

The production plan and the MPS uncouple the sales forecast from manufacturing by establishing a manufacturing plan. Together, they attempt to balance available resources of plant, equipment, labor, and material with forecast demand. However, they are not a sales forecast, nor are they necessarily what is desired. The MPS is a plan for what production *can and will do.*

Figure 3.6 shows the relationship among the sales forecast, production plan, and MPS.

The MPS must be realistic about what manufacturing can and will do. If it is not, it will result in overloaded capacity plans, past-due schedules, unreliable delivery promises, surges in shipments, and lack of accountability.

The MPS is a plan for specific end items or "buildable" components that manufacturing expects to make over some time in the future. It is the point at which manufacturing

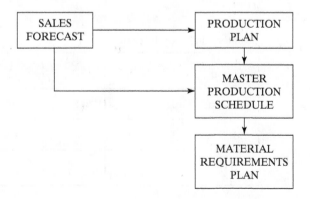

FIGURE 3.6 Sales forecast, production plan, and master production schedule.

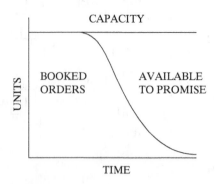

FIGURE 3.7 The MPS and delivery time.

and marketing must agree what end items are going to be produced. Manufacturing is committed to making the goods, and marketing to selling the goods. However, the MPS is not meant to be rigid. Demand changes, problems occur in production, and, sometimes, components are scarce. These events may make it necessary to alter the MPS. Changes must be made with the full understanding and agreement of sales and production. The MPS provides the basis for making changes and a plan on which all can agree.

The MPS and Delivery Promises

In a make-to-stock environment, customer orders are satisfied from inventory. However, in make-to-order or assemble-to-order environments, demand is satisfied from production capacity. In either case, sales and distribution need to know what is available to satisfy customer demand. Since demand can be satisfied either from inventory or from scheduled receipts, the MPS provides a plan for doing either. Figure 3.7 illustrates the concept. As orders are received, they "consume" the available inventory or capacity. Any part of the plan that is not consumed by actual customer orders is available to promise to customers. In this way, the MPS provides a realistic basis for making delivery promises.

Using the MPS, sales and distribution can determine the **available to promise** (ATP). Available to promise is that portion of a firm's inventory and planned production that is not already committed and is available to the customer. This allows delivery promises to be made and customer orders and deliveries to be scheduled accurately.

The ATP is calculated by adding **scheduled receipts** to the beginning inventory and then subtracting actual orders scheduled before the next scheduled receipt. A scheduled receipt is an order that has been issued either to manufacturing or to a supplier. Figure 3.8 illustrates a calculation of an ATP:

$$\text{ATP for period 1} = \text{on hand} - \text{customer orders due before next MPS}$$
$$= 100 - 80$$
$$= 20 \text{ units}$$

Inventory on hand: 100 units

Period	1	2	3	4	5
Customer Orders	80	10	10		30
MPS		100		100	
ATP	20	80		70	

FIGURE 3.8 Available-to-promise calculation.

$$\text{ATP for period 2} = \text{MPS scheduled receipt} - \text{customer orders due before next MPS}$$

$$= 100 - (10 + 10)$$

$$= 80 \text{ units}$$

$$\text{ATP for period 4} = 100 - 30 = 70 \text{ units}$$

This method assumes that the ATP will be sold before the next scheduled receipt arrives. It is there to be sold, and the assumption is that it will be sold. If it is not sold, whatever is left forms an on-hand balance available for the next period.

Continuing with the example problem on page 45, Amalgamated Nut Crackers, Inc., has now received customer orders. Following is the schedule of orders received and the resulting available-to-promise calculation (recall that there are 50 units in inventory):

Inventory on hand = 50 units

Week	1	2	3	4	5	6
Customer Orders	80	45	40	50	50	5
MPS	100		100		100	
ATP	25		10		45	

Sometimes, customer orders are greater than the scheduled receipts. In this case, the *previous* ATP is reduced by the amount needed. In this example can the master planner accept an order for another 20 for delivery in week 3? Ten of the units are available from week 3, and 10 can be taken from the ATP in week 1, so the order can be accepted as shown in the following.

Inventory on hand = 50 units

Week	1	2	3	4	5	6
Customer Orders	80	45	60	50	50	5
MPS	100		100		100	
ATP	15		0		45	

Example Problem

Calculate the available to promise for the following example. Can an order for 30 more be accepted for delivery in week 5? What will be the ATP if the order is accepted?

Week	1	2	3	4	5
Customer Orders	50	20	30	30	15
MPS	100		100		
ATP	30		25		

ANSWER

Week	1	2	3	4	5
Customer Orders	50	20	30	30	45
MPS	100		100		
ATP	25		0		

Projected Available Balance

Our calculations so far have based the projected available balance on the forecast demand. Now there are also customer orders to consider. Customer orders will sometimes be greater than forecast and sometimes less. Projected available balance is now calculated based on whichever is greater. For example, if the beginning projected available balance is 100 units, the forecast is 40 units, and customer orders are 50 units, the ending projected available balance is 50 units, not 60. The **projected available balance** (PAB) is calculated in one of two ways, depending on whether the period is before or after the **demand time fence**. The demand time fence is the number of periods, beginning with period 1, in which changes are not accepted due to excessive cost caused by schedule disruption.

For periods before the demand time fence, PAB is calculated as

$$PAB = \text{prior period PAB or on-hand balance} + \text{MPS} - \text{customer orders}$$

This process ignores the forecast and assumes that the only effect will be from the customer orders. Any new orders will have to be approved by senior management. For periods after the demand time fence, forecast will influence the PAB so it is calculated using either the forecast or customer orders, whichever is greater. Thus the PAB becomes

$$PAB = \text{prior period PAB} + \text{MPS} - \text{greater of customer orders or forecast}$$

Example Problem

Given the following data, calculate the projected available balance. The demand time fence is the end of week 3, the order quantity is 100, and 40 are available at the beginning of the period.

Week	1	2	3	4	5
Forecast	40	40	40	40	40
Customer Orders	39	42	39	33	23

ANSWER

Week		1	2	3	4	5
Projected Available Balance	40	1	59	20	80	40
MPS			100		100	

So far we have considered how to calculate projected available balance and available to promise. Using the Amalgamated Nut Cracker, Inc., example, we now combine the two calculations into one record. The demand time fence is at the end of 3 weeks.

Week		1	2	3	4	5	6
Forecast Demand		75	50	30	40	70	20
Customer Orders		80	45	40	50	50	5
Projected Available Balance	50	70	25	85	35	65	45
ATP		25		10		45	
MPS		100		100		100	

Time Fences

Consider the product structure shown in Figure 3.9. Item A is a master-scheduled item and is assembled from B, C, and D. Item D, in turn, is made from raw material E. The lead times to make or to buy the parts are shown in parentheses. The lead time to assemble A is 2 weeks. To purchase B and C, the respective lead times are 6 and 5 weeks. To make D takes 8 weeks, and the purchase lead time for raw material E is 16 weeks. The longest cumulative lead time is thus 26 weeks (A + D + E = 2 + 8 + 16 = 26 weeks).

Since the cumulative lead time is 26 weeks, the MPS must have a planning horizon of at least 26 weeks.

Suppose that E is a long-lead-time electronic component and is used in the assembly of other boards as well as D. When E is received 16 weeks after ordering, a decision must be made to commit E to be made into a D or to use it in another board. In 8 weeks, a decision must be made to commit D to the final assembly of A. The company would not have to commit the E to making D until 10 weeks before delivery of the A. At each of these stages, the company commits itself to more cost and fewer alternatives. Therefore, the cost of making a change increases and the company's flexibility decreases as production gets closer to the delivery time.

Changes to the master production schedule will occur. For example,

- Customers cancel or change orders.
- Machines break down or new machines are added, changing capacity.
- Suppliers have problems and miss delivery dates.
- Processes create more scrap than expected.

A company wants to minimize the cost of manufacture and also be flexible enough to adapt to changing needs. Changes to production schedules can result in the following:

- Increased costs. Cost increases due to rerouting, rescheduling, extra setups, expediting, and buildup of work-in-process inventory.

FIGURE 3.9 Product structure.

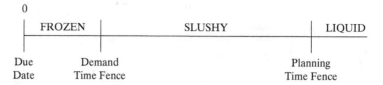

FIGURE 3.10 MPS and time fences.

- Decreased customer service. A change in quantity of delivery can disrupt the schedule of other orders.
- Reduced credibility. Loss of credibility for the MPS and the planning process.

Changes that are far off on the planning horizon can be made with little or no cost or disruption to manufacturing, but the nearer to delivery date, the more disruptive and costly changes will be. To help in the decision-making process, companies establish zones divided by time fences. Figure 3.10 shows how this concept might be applied to product A. The zones and time fences are as follows:

- Frozen zone. Capacity and materials are committed to specific orders. Since changes would result in excessive costs, reduced manufacturing efficiency, and poor customer service, senior management's approval is usually required to make changes. The extent of the frozen zone is defined by the **demand time fence**. Within the demand time fence, demand is usually based on customer orders, not forecast.
- Slushy zone. Capacity and material are committed to a less extent. This is an area for trade-offs that must be negotiated between marketing and manufacturing. In this zone, materials have been ordered and capacity established; these are difficult to change. However, changes in priorities are easier to change. The extent of the slushy zone is defined by the **planning time fence**. Within this time fence, the computer will generally not allow the computer to automatically reschedule MPS orders. Often, the planning time fence is determined by the cumulative lead time of the product.
- Liquid zone. Any change can be made to the MPS as long as it is within the limits set by the production plan. Changes are routine and are often made by the computer program without the need for input from the planner.

Changes to the MPS will occur. They must be managed and decisions made with full knowledge of the costs involved.

Error Management

Errors in customer orders occur all the time and require constant attention. Three general types of errors occur:

1. Wrong product or specification.
2. Wrong amount (too little or too much).
3. Wrong shipping date (too early or too late).

They require different responses, reengineering, or alteration, negotiation of partial shipment, or expediting of shipment.

SUMMARY

The master production schedule is a plan for the production of individual end items. It must match demand for the product in total, but it is not a forecast of demand. The MPS must be realistic. It must be achievable and reflect a balance between required and available capacity.

The MPS is the meeting ground for sales and production. It provides a plan from which realistic delivery promises can be made to customers. If adjustments have to be made in deliveries or the booking of orders, they are done through the MPS.

Master production scheduling's major functions are as follows:

- To form the link between production planning and what manufacturing builds.
- To plan capacity requirements. The master production schedule determines the capacity required.
- To plan material requirements. The MPS drives the material requirements plan.
- To keep priorities valid. The MPS is a priority plan for manufacturing.
- To aid in making order promises. The MPS is a plan for what is to be produced and when. As such, it tells sales and manufacturing when goods will be available for delivery.
- To be a contract between marketing and manufacturing. It is an agreed-upon plan.

The MPS must be realistic and based on what production can and will do. If it is not, the results will be as follows:

- Overload or underload of plant resources.
- Unreliable schedules resulting in poor delivery performance.
- High levels of work-in-process (WIP) inventory.
- Poor customer service.
- Loss of credibility in the planning system.

KEY TERMS

Available to promise 50	Planning time fence 54
Demand time fence 52	Projected available balance (PAB) 52
Frozen zone 54	Scheduled receipt 50
Liquid zone 54	Slushy zone 54
Master production schedule 41	

QUESTIONS

1. What four functions does the master production schedule (MPS) perform in the production planning system?
2. What functions does the MPS perform between sales and production?
3. Does the MPS work with families of products or with individual items?
4. Where does the information come from to develop an MPS?
5. What are the three steps in making an MPS?
6. What is the purpose of a rough-cut capacity plan?
7. Where is the resource bill used?
8. At what level should master production scheduling take place?
   a. In a make-to-stock environment?
   b. In a make-to-order environment?
   c. In an assemble-to-order environment?
9. What is a final assembly schedule (FAS)? What is its purpose?
10. What is a planning horizon? What decides its minimum time? Why would it be longer?
11. How do the production plan and the MPS relate to sales and to the sales forecast?
12. What is the ATP (available to promise)? How is it calculated?
13. What is the purpose of time fences? Name and describe the three main divisions.
14. What would happen if the planning horizon for the master schedule were too short? Why?
15. What potential problem might arise if time fences are not used? Why?
16. What types of production environments might use both the FAS and the MPS? Why?

PROBLEMS

3.1. The Wicked Witch Whisk Company manufactures a line of broomsticks. The most popular is the 36-inch model, and the sales department has prepared a forecast for 6 weeks. The opening inventory is 30. As master scheduler, you must prepare an MPS. The brooms are manufactured in lots of 100.

Week		1	2	3	4	5	6
Forecast Sales		10	50	25	50	10	15
Projected Available Balance	30						
MPS							

Answer. There should be scheduled receipts in weeks 2 and 4.

3.2. The Shades Sunglass Company assembles sunglasses from frames, which it makes, and lenses, which it purchases from an outside supplier. The sales department has prepared the following 6-week forecast for Ebony, a popular model. The sunglasses are assembled in lots of 200, and the opening inventory is 300 pairs. Complete the projected available balance and the master production schedule.

Week		1	2	3	4	5	6
Forecast Sales		200	300	300	200	150	150
Projected Available Balance	300						
MPS							

3.3. The Amalgamated Mailbox Company manufactures a family of two mailboxes. The production plan and the MPS are developed on a quarterly basis. The forecast for the product group follows. The opening inventory is 270 units, and the company wants to reduce this to 150 units at the end of the year. Develop a level production plan.

Production Plan

Quarter		1	2	3	4	Total
Forecast Sales		220	300	200	200	
Projected Available Balance	270					
Production Plan						

Answer. Quarterly production = 200 units

The forecast sales for each of the mailboxes in the family also follow. Develop an MPS for each item, bearing in mind that production is to be leveled as in the production plan. For each mailbox, the lot size is 200.

Mailbox A. Lot size: 200

Quarter		1	2	3	4	Total
Forecast Sales		120	180	100	120	
Projected Available Balance	120					
MPS						

Answer.   Scheduled receipts in quarters 2 and 3

Mailbox B. Lot size: 200

Quarter		1	2	3	4	Total
Forecast Sales		100	120	100	80	
Projected Available Balance	150					
MPS						

Answer.   Scheduled receipts in quarters 1 and 4

3.4. Worldwide Can-Openers, Inc., makes a family of two hand-operated can openers. The production plan is based on months. There are 4 weeks in this month. Opening inventory is 2000 dozen, and it is planned to increase that to 4000 dozen by the end of the month. The MPS is made using weekly periods. The forecast and projected available balance for the two models follow. The lot size for both models is 1000 dozen. Calculate the production plan and the MPS for each item.

Production Plan

Week		1	2	3	4	Total
Forecast		3000	3500	3500	4000	
Projected Available Balance	2000					
Production Plan						

Model A

Week		1	2	3	4	Total
Forecast		2000	2000	2500	2000	
Projected Available Balance	1500					
MPS						

Model B

Week		1	2	3	4	Total
Forecast		1000	1500	1000	2000	
Projected Available Balance	500					
MPS						

3.5. In the example given on page 42, the MPS was unsatisfactory because there were poor inventory balances compared to the production plan. There was also a stockout for product C in periods 2 and 3. Revise the production plans for the three products to cut out or reduce these problems.

3.6. The Acme Widget Company makes widgets in two models, and the bottleneck operation is in work center 10. Following is the resource bill (in hours per part).

	Hours per Part	
Work Center	Model A	Model B
10	2.4	3.5

The master production schedule for the next 5 weeks is

Week	1	2	3	4	5
Model A	70	50	50	60	48
Model B	20	40	55	30	45

a. Using the resource bill and the master production schedule, calculate the number of hours required in work center 10 for each of the 5 weeks. Use the following table to record the required capacity on the work center.

Week	1	2	3	4	5
Model A					
Model B					
Total Hours					

Answer. The total hours required are as follows: week 1, 238; week 2, 260; week 3, 313; week 4, 249; and week 5, 273.

b. If the available capacity at work station 10 is 260 hours per week, suggest possible ways of meeting the demand in week 3.

3.7. Calculate the available to promise using the following data. There are 100 units on hand.

Week	1	2	3	4	5	6
Customer Orders	70	70	20	40	10	
MPS		100		100		100
ATP						

Answer.   ATP in week 1, 30; week 2, 10; week 4, 50; and week 6, 100.

3.8. Given the following data, calculate how many units are available to promise. There are zero units on hand.

Week	1	2	3	4	5	6
Customer Orders	21		17	8		3
MPS	30		30	30		
ATP						

3.9. Using the scheduled receipts, calculate the ATP. There are zero units on hand.

Week	1	2	3	4	5	6	7	8	9	10
Customer Orders	10		10		60	16			10	
MPS	50				50				50	
ATP										

3.10. Using the scheduled receipts, calculate the ATP. There are 45 units on hand.

Week	1	2	3	4	5	6	7	8
Customer Orders	45	50	35	40	30	40	20	18
MPS		100		100		100		100
ATP								

3.11. Calculate the available to promise using the following data. There are 60 units on hand.

Week	1	2	3	4	5	6
Customer Orders	20	50	30	30	50	30
MPS		100			100	
ATP						

3.12. Given the following data, can an order for 20 for delivery in week 4 be accepted? Calculate the ATP using the following table. On hand = 50 units.

Week	1	2	3	4	5	6	7	8
Customer Orders	50	50	30	40	50	40	30	15
MPS		100		100		100		100
ATP								

Answer. Yes. Ten can come from the ATP for week 4 and 10 from the ATP for week 2.

3.13. Given the following data, can an order for 30 more units for delivery in week 5 be accepted? If not, what do you suggest can be done? There are zero units on hand.

Week	1	2	3	4	5	6	7	8
Customer Orders	70	10	50	40	10	15	20	15
MPS	100		100			100		
ATP								

3.14. Given the following data, calculate the projected available balance and the planned MPS receipts. The lot size is 200. The demand time fence is 2 weeks.

Week		1	2	3	4
Forecast		80	80	80	70
Customer Orders		100	90	50	40
Projected Available Balance	140				
MPS					

Answer. There is a planned MPS receipt in week 2.

3.15. Given the following data, calculate the projected available balance and the planned MPS receipts. The lot size is 100. The demand time fence is 2 weeks.

Week		1	2	3	4
Forecast		50	50	50	50
Customer Orders		60	30	65	25
Projected Available Balance	60				
MPS					

3.16. Complete the following problem. The lead time is 1 week and the demand time fence is the end of week 3. There are 20 on hand. The lot size is 60.

Period		1	2	3	4	5	6
Forecast		20	21	22	20	28	25
Customer Orders		19	18	20	18	30	22
Projected Available Balance	20						
MPS							
ATP							

ACME WATER PUMPS

The Acme Water Pump company has a problem. The pumps are fairly expensive to make and store, so the company tends to keep the inventory low. At the same time, it is important to respond to demand quickly, since a customer who wants a water pump is very likely to get one from a competitor if Acme doesn't have one available immediately. Acme's current policy to produce pumps is to produce 100 per week, which is the average demand. Even this is a problem, as the production manager has pointed out, since the equipment is also used for other products and the lot size of 300 would be much more efficient. He said he is currently set up for water pump production for the next week and states that he has capacity available to produce 300 at a time next week.

The following lists the forecasts and actual customer orders for the next 12 weeks:

Week	1	2	3	4	5	6	7	8	9	10	11	12
Forecast	90	120	110	80	85	95	100	110	90	90	100	110
Customer Orders	105	97	93	72	98	72	53	21	17	6	2	5

The president of Acme has said that he wants to consider using a formal MPS with ATP logic to try to meet demand more effectively without a large impact on inventory. Acme has decided to use a demand time fence at the end of week 3 and has also found out that its current inventory is 25 units. Assume Acme will use the MPS lot size of 300 and that it will produce the first of those lots in week 1.

Discussion Questions

1. Develop a master schedule using the information above.
2. A customer has just requested a major order of 45 pumps for delivery in week 5. What would you tell the customer about having such an order? Why? What, if anything, would such an order do to the operation?

MATERIAL REQUIREMENTS PLANNING

INTRODUCTION

Chapter 3 described the role of the master production schedule (MPS) in showing the end items, or major components, that manufacturing intends to build. These items are made or assembled from components that must be available in the right quantities and at the right time to meet the MPS requirements. If any component is missing, the product cannot be built and shipped on time. Material requirements planning (MRP) is the system used to avoid missing parts. It establishes a schedule (priority plan) showing the components required at each level of the assembly and, based on lead times, calculates the time when these components will be needed.

This chapter will describe bills of material (the major building block of material requirements planning), detail the MRP process, and explain how the material requirements plan is used. But first, some details about the environment in which MRP operates.

Nature of Demand

There are two types of demand: independent and dependent. Independent demand is not related to the demand for any other product. For example, if a company makes wooden tables, the demand for the tables is independent. Master production schedule items are independent demand items. The demand for the sides, ends, legs, and tops depends on the demand for the tables, and these are dependent demand items.

Figure 4.1 depicts a product tree that shows the relationship between independent and dependent demand items. The figures in parentheses show the required quantities of each component.

Since independent demand is not related to the demand for any other assemblies or products, it must be forecast. However, since dependent demand is directly related to the demand for higher-level assemblies or products, it can be calculated. Material requirements planning is designed to do this calculation.

An item can have both a dependent and an independent demand. A service or replacement part has both. A manufacturer of vacuum cleaners uses flexible hose in the assembly of the units. In the assembly of the vacuums, the hose is a dependent demand item. However, the hose has a nasty habit of breaking, and the manufacturer must have replacement hoses available. Demand for replacement hoses is independent since demand for them does not depend directly upon the number of vacuums manufactured.

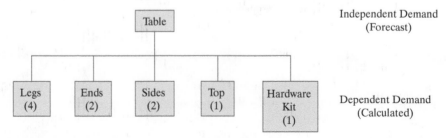

FIGURE 4.1 Product tree.

Dependency can be horizontal or vertical. The dependency of a component on its parent is vertical. However, components also depend on each other (horizontal dependency). If one component is going to be a week late, then the final assembly is a week late. The other components are not needed until later. This is also a dependency and is called horizontal dependency. Planners are concerned with horizontal dependency when a part is delayed or there is a shortage, for then other parts will have to be rescheduled.

Objectives of MRP

Material requirements planning has two major objectives: determine requirements and keep priorities current.

Determine requirements   The main objective of any manufacturing planning and control system is to have the right materials in the right quantities available at the right time to meet the demand for the firm's products. The material requirements plan's objective is to determine what components are needed to meet the master production schedule and, based on lead time, to calculate the periods when the components must be available. It must determine the following:

- What to order.
- How much to order.
- When to order.
- When to schedule delivery.

Keep priorities current   The demand for, and supply of, components changes daily. Customers enter or change orders. Components get used up, suppliers are late with delivery, scrap occurs, orders are completed, and machines break down. In this ever-changing world, a material requirements plan must be able to reorganize priorities to keep plans current. It must be able to add and delete, expedite, delay, and change orders.

Linkages to Other Manufacturing Planning and Control Functions

The master production schedule drives the material requirements plan. The MRP is a priority plan for the components needed to make the products in the MPS. The plan is valid only if capacity is available when needed to make the components, and the plan must be checked against available capacity. The process of doing so is called capacity requirements planning and is discussed in Chapter 5.

Material requirements planning drives, or is input to, production activity control (PAC) and purchasing. MRP plans the release and receipt dates for orders. PAC and purchasing must plan and control the performance of the orders to meet the due dates.

Figure 4.2 shows a diagram of the production planning and control system with its inputs and outputs.

The Computer

If a company makes a few simple products, it might be possible to perform material requirements planning manually. However, most companies need to keep track of thousands of components in a world of changing demand, supply, and capacity.

In the days before computers, it was necessary to maintain extensive manual systems and to have large inventories and long lead times. These were needed as a cushion due to the lack of accurate, up-to-date information and the inability to perform the necessary calculations quickly. Somehow, someone in the organization figured out what was required sooner or, very often, later than needed. "Get it early and get lots of it" was a good rule then.

Computers are incredibly fast, accurate, and ideally suited for the job at hand. With their ability to store and manipulate data and produce information rapidly, manufacturing now has a tool to use modern manufacturing planning and control systems properly. There are many application programs available that will perform the calculations needed in MRP systems. The computer software program that organizes and maintains the bills of material structures and their linkages is called a **bill of material processor.**

INPUT

OUTPUT

Business Plan
Financial Plan
Marketing Plan
Capacity

PRODUCTION
PLAN

Aggregate Plan
• By-Product Groups
• Inventory Levels

Production Plan
Forecasts
Customer Orders
Inventory
Capacity

MASTER
PRODUCTION
SCHEDULE

Detailed Plan
• By Week
• By End Item

MPS
Bill of Materials
Inventory
Capacity

MATERIAL
REQUIREMENTS
PLAN

Time-Phased
Manufacturing and
Purchase Orders
• For Raw Material
• For Components

PURCHASING

PRODUCTION
ACTIVITY
CONTROL

FIGURE 4.2 Production planning and control system.

Inputs to the Material Requirements Planning System

There are three inputs to MRP systems:

1. Master production schedule.
2. Inventory records.
3. Bills of material.

> **Master production schedule.** The **master production schedule** is a statement of which end items are to be produced, the quantity of each, and the dates they are to be completed. It drives the MRP system by providing the initial input for the items needed.
>
> **Inventory records.** A major input to the MRP system is inventory. When a calculation is made to find out how many are needed, the quantities available must be considered.
>
> There are two kinds of information needed. The first is called **planning factors** and includes information such as order quantities, lead times, safety stock, and scrap. This information does not change often; however, it is needed to plan what quantities to order and when to order for timely deliveries.
>
> The second kind of information necessary is on the status of each item. The MRP system needs to know how much is available, how much is allocated, and how much is available for future demand. This type of information is dynamic and changes with every transaction that takes place.
>
> These data are maintained in an **inventory record file**, also called a part master file or item master file. Each item has a record, and all the records together form the file.
>
> **Bills of material.** The bill of material is one of the most important documents in a manufacturing company. It is discussed next.

BILLS OF MATERIAL

Before we can make something, we must know what components are needed to make it. To bake a cake, we need a recipe. To mix chemicals together, we need a formula. To assemble a wheelbarrow, we need a parts list. Even though the names are different, recipes, formulas, and parts lists tell us what is needed to make the end product. All of these are bills of material.

The Association for Operations Management (APICS) defines a bill of material as "a listing of all the subassemblies, intermediates, parts, and raw materials that go into making

| Description: TABLE | | |
| Part Number: 100 | | |

Part Number	Description	Quantity Required
203	Wooden Leg	4
411	Wooden Ends	2
622	Wooden Sides	2
023	Table Top	1
722	Hardware Kit	1

FIGURE 4.3 Simplified bill of material.

the parent assembly showing the quantities of each required to make an assembly." Figure 4.3 shows a simplified bill of material. There are three important points:

1. The bill of material shows all the parts required to make *one* of the item.

2. Each part or item has only one part number. A specific number is unique to one part and is not assigned to any other part. Thus, if a particular number appears on two different bills of material, the part so identified is the same.

3. A part is defined by its form, fit, or function. If any of these change, then it is not the same part and it must have a different part number. For example, a part when painted becomes a different part and must have a different number. If the part could be painted in three different colors, then each must be identified with its unique number.

The bill of material shows the components that go into making the parent. It does not show the steps or process used to make the parent or the components. That information is recorded in a routing file. This file is discussed in Chapters 5 and 6.

Bills of Material Structure

Bills of material structure refer to the overall design for the arrangement of bills of material files. Different departments in a company use bills of material for a variety of purposes. Although each user has individual preferences for the way the bill should be structured, there must be only one structure, and it should be designed to satisfy most needs. However, there can be several formats, or ways, to present the bill. Following are some important formats for bills.

Product tree   Figure 4.4 shows a product tree for the bill of material shown in Figure 4.3. The **product tree** is a convenient way to think about bills of material, but it is seldom used except for teaching and testing. In this text, it is used for that purpose.

Parent–component relationship   The product tree and the bill of material shown in Figures 4.1 and 4.3 are called single-level structures. An assembly is considered a **parent**, and the items that comprise it are called its **component items**. Figure 4.4 shows the parent–component relationship of the table (P/N 100). Unique part numbers have also been assigned to each part. This makes identification of the part absolute.

Multilevel bill   Figure 4.5 shows the same product as the single-level bill shown in Figures 4.3 and 4.4. However, the single-level components have been expanded into their components.

FIGURE 4.4 Product tree.

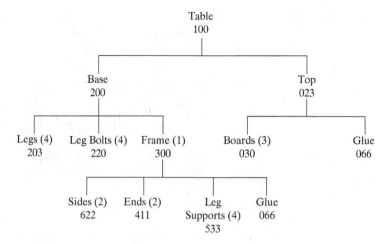

FIGURE 4.5 Multilevel bill.

Multilevel bills are formed as logical groupings of parts into subassemblies based on the way the product is assembled. For example, a frame, chassis, doors, windows, and engine are required to construct an automobile. Each of these forms a logical group of components and parts and, in turn, has its own bill of material.

It is the responsibility of manufacturing engineering to decide how the product is to be made: the operations to be performed, their sequence, and their grouping. The subassemblies created are the result of this. Manufacturing has decided to assemble the sides, ends, and leg supports (part of the hardware kit) of the table (P/N 100) in Figure 4.4 into a frame (P/N 300). The legs, leg bolts, and frame subassembly are to be assembled into the base (P/N 200). The top (P/N 023) is to be made from three boards glued together. Note that the original parts are all there, but they have been grouped into subassemblies and each subassembly has its own part number.

One convention used with multilevel bills of material is that the last items on the tree (legs, leg bolts, ends, sides, glue, and boards) are all purchased items. Generally, a bill of material is not complete until all branches of the product structure tree end in a purchased part.

Each level in the bill of material is assigned a number starting from the top and working down. The top level, or end product level, is level zero, and its components are at level one.

Multiple bill   A **multiple bill** is used when companies usually make more than one product, and the same components are often used in several products. This is particularly true with families of products. Using our example of a table, the company makes two models. They are similar except the tops are different. Figure 4.6 shows the two bills of material. Because the boards used in the top are different, each top has a different part number. The balance of the components are common to both tables.

Single-level bill   A **single-level bill** of material contains only the parent and its immediate components, which is why it is called a single-level bill. The tables shown in Figure 4.6 have six single-level bills, and these are shown in Figure 4.7. Note that many components are common to both tables.

The computer stores information describing the product structure as a single-level bill. A series of single-level bills is needed to completely define a product. For example, the table needs four single-level bills, one each for the table, base, top, and frame. These can be chained together to form a multilevel, or indented, bill. Using this method, the information has to be stored only once. For example, the frame (P/N 300) might be used on other tables with different legs or tops.

There are several advantages to using single-level bills, including the following:

- Duplication of records is avoided. For instance, base 200 is used in both table 100 and table 150. Rather than have two records of base 200—one in the bill for table 100 and one in the bill for table 150—only one record need be kept.

- The number of records and the file size are reduced by avoiding duplication of records.

- Maintaining bills of material is simplified. For example, if there is a change in base 200, the change need be made in only one place.

FIGURE 4.6 Multiple bills.

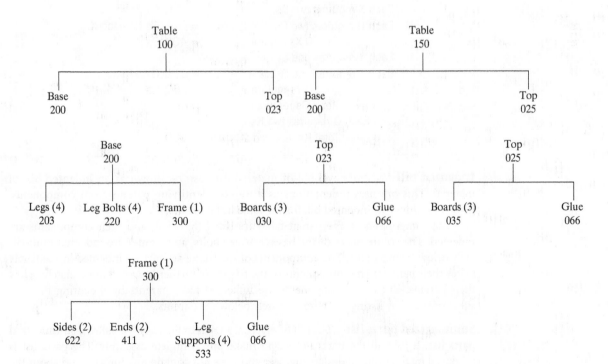

FIGURE 4.7 Single-level bills.

Example Problem

Using the following product tree, construct the appropriate single-level trees. How many Ks are needed to make 100 Xs and 50 Ys?

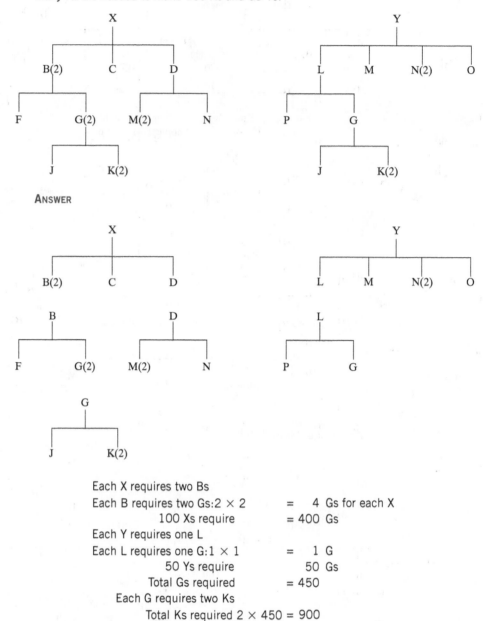

ANSWER

Each X requires two Bs
Each B requires two Gs:2 × 2   =   4 Gs for each X
            100 Xs require   = 400 Gs
Each Y requires one L
Each L requires one G:1 × 1   =   1 G
            50 Ys require   50 Gs
        Total Gs required   = 450
Each G requires two Ks
    Total Ks required 2 × 450 = 900

Indented bill   A multilevel bill of material can also be shown as an **indented bill** of material. This bill uses indentations as a way of identifying parents from components. Figure 4.8 shows an indented bill for the table in Figure 4.5.

The components of the parent table are listed flush left, and their components are indented. The components of the base (legs, leg bolts, and frame) are indented immediately below their parents. The components of the frame are further indented immediately below their parents. The components of the frame are further indented immediately below their parents. Thus, the components are linked to their parents by indenting them as subentries and by listing them immediately below the parents.

Summarized parts list   The bill of material shown in Figure 4.3 is called a **summarized parts list**. It lists all the parts needed to make one complete assembly. The parts list is produced by the product design engineer and does not contain any information about the way the product is made or assembled.

MANUFACTURING BILL OF MATERIAL
TABLE P/N 100

Part Number	Description	Quantity Required
200	Base	1
203	Legs	4
220	Leg Bolts	4
300	Frame	1
622	Sides	2
411	Ends	2
533	Leg Supports	4
066	Glue	
023	Top	1
030	Boards	3
066	Glue	

FIGURE 4.8 Indented bill of material.

Planning bill   A major use of bills of material is to plan production. **Planning bills** are an artificial grouping of components for planning purposes. They are used to simplify forecasting, master production scheduling, and material requirements planning. They do not represent *buildable* products but an *average* product. Using the table example, suppose the company manufactured tables with three different leg styles, three different sides and ends, and three different tops. In total, they are making $3 \times 3 \times 3 = 27$ different tables, each with its own bill of material. For planning purposes, the 27 bills can be simplified by showing the percentage split for each type of component on one bill. Figure 4.9 shows how the product structure would look. The percentage usage of components is obtained from a forecast or past usage. Note that the percentage for each category of component adds up to 100%.

Where-Used and Pegging Reports

Where-used report   Where-used reports give the same information as bills of material, but the where-used report gives the parents for a component whereas the bill gives the components for a parent. A component may be used in making several parents. Wheels on an automobile, for example, might be used on several models of cars. A listing of all the parents in which a component is used is called a **where-used report**. This has several uses, such as in implementing an engineering change, or when materials are scarce, or in costing a product.

Pegging report   A **pegging report** is similar to a where-used report. However, the pegging report shows only those parents for which there is an existing requirement, whereas the where-used report shows all parents for a component. The pegging report shows the parents creating the demand for the components, the quantities needed, and when they are needed. Pegging keeps track of the origin of the demand. Figure 4.10 shows an example of a product tree in which part C is used twice and a pegging report.

FIGURE 4.9 Planning bill.

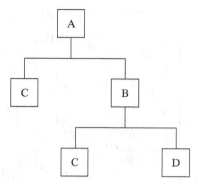

Pegged Requirements

Item Number	Week				
	1	2	3	4	5
C	50	125	25	50	150

Source of Requirements

A	50	25	25	50	50
B		100			100

FIGURE 4.10 Pegged requirements.

Uses for Bills of Material

The bill of material is one of the most widely used documents in a manufacturing company. Some major uses are as follows:

- **Product definition.** The bill specifies the components needed to make the product.
- **Engineering change control.** Product design engineers sometimes change the design of a product and the components used. These changes must be recorded and controlled. The bill provides the method for doing so.
- **Service parts.** Replacement parts needed to repair a broken component are determined from the bill of material.
- **Planning.** Bills of material define what materials have to be scheduled to make the end product. They define what components have to be purchased or made to satisfy the master production schedule.
- **Order entry.** When a product has a very large number of options (e.g., cars), the order-entry system very often configures the end product bill of materials. The bill can also be used to price the product.
- **Manufacturing.** The bill provides a list of the parts needed to make or assemble a product.
- **Costing.** Product cost is usually broken down into direct material, direct labor, and overhead. The bill provides not only a method of determining direct material but also a structure for recording direct labor and distributing overhead.

This list is not complete, but it shows the extensive use made of the bill of material in manufacturing. There is scarcely a department of a company that will not use the bill at some time. Maintaining bills of material and their accuracy is extremely important. Again, the computer is an excellent tool for centrally maintaining bills and for updating them.

MATERIAL REQUIREMENTS PLANNING PROCESS

Each component shown on the bill of material is planned for by the material requirements planning system. For convenience, it is assumed that each component will go into inventory and be accounted for. Whether the components actually go into a physical inventory or not is unimportant. However, it is important to realize that planning and control take place for each component on the bill. Raw material may go through several operations before it is processed and ready for assembly, or there may be several assembly operations between components and parent. These operations are planned and controlled by production activity control, not material requirements planning.

The purpose of material requirements planning is to determine the components needed, quantities, and due dates so items in the master production schedule are made on time. This section presents the basic MRP techniques for doing so. These techniques are discussed under the following headings:

- Exploding and offsetting
- Gross and net requirements

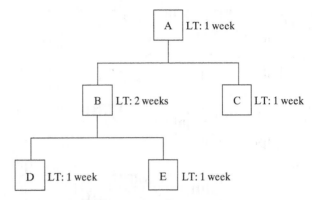

FIGURE 4.11 Product tree with lead time.

- Releasing orders
- Capacity requirements planning
- Low-level coding and netting
- Multiple bills of material

Exploding and Offsetting

Consider the product tree shown in Figure 4.11. It is similar to the ones used before but contains another necessary piece of information: lead time (LT).

Lead time   Lead time is the span of time needed to perform a process. In manufacturing it includes time for order preparation, queuing, processing, moving, receiving and inspecting, and any expected delays. From the product tree shown in Figure 4.11, if B and C are available, it will take 1 week to assemble A. Thus, the lead time for A is 1 week. Similarly, if D and E are available, the time required to manufacture B is 2 weeks. The purchase lead times for D, E, and C are all 1 week.

In this particular product tree, the usage quantities—the quantity of components needed to make one of a parent—are all one. To make an A requires one B and one C, and to make a B requires one D and one E.

Exploding the requirements   **Exploding** is the process of multiplying the requirements by the usage quantity and recording the appropriate requirements throughout the product tree.

Offsetting   **Offsetting** is the process of placing the exploded requirements in their proper periods based on lead time. For example, if 50 units of A are required in week 5, the order to assemble the As must be released in week 4, and 50 Bs and 50 Cs must be available in week 4.

Planned orders   If it is planned to receive 50 of part A in week 5 and the lead time to assemble an A is 1 week, the order will have to be released and production started no later than week 4.

Thus, there should be a **planned order receipt** for 50 in week 5 and a **planned order release** for that number in week 4. If an order for 50 As is to be released in week 4, 50 Bs and 50 Cs must be available in that week. Thus, there must be planned order receipts for those components in week 4. Since the lead time to assemble a B is 2 weeks, there must be a planned order release for the Bs in week 2. Since the lead time to make a C is 1 week, there must be a planned order release for 50 in week 3. The planned order receipts and planned order releases for the Ds and Es are determined in the same manner. Figure 4.12 shows when orders must be released and received so the delivery date can be met.

Example Problem

Using the product tree and lead times shown in Figure 4.11, complete the following table to determine the planned order receipts and releases. There are 50 As required in week 5 and 100 in week 6.

Part Number		Week					
		1	2	3	4	5	6
A	Planned Order Receipt					50	100
	Planned Order Release						
B	Planned Order Receipt						
	Planned Order Release						
C	Planned Order Receipt						
	Planned Order Release						
D	Planned Order Receipt						
	Planned Order Release						
E	Planned Order Receipt						
	Planned Order Release						

ANSWER

Part Number		Week					
		1	2	3	4	5	6
A	Planned Order Receipt					50	100
	Planned Order Release				50	100	
B	Planned Order Receipt				50	100	
	Planned Order Release		50	100			
C	Planned Order Receipt				50	100	
	Planned Order Release			50	100		
D	Planned Order Receipt		50	100			
	Planned Order Release	50	100				
E	Planned Order Receipt		50	100			
	Planned Order Release	50	100				

Gross and Net Requirements

The previous section assumed that no inventory was available for the As or any of the components. Often inventory is available and must be included when calculating quantities to be produced. If for example, in the preceding problem, there are 20 As in stock, at the beginning of period 5, only 30 need to be made. The requirements for component parts would be reduced accordingly. The calculation is as follows:

Gross requirement = 50

Inventory available = 20

Net requirements = gross requirements − available inventory

Net requirements = 50 − 20 = 30 units

Since only 30 As need to be made, the gross requirement for Bs and Cs is only 30.

The planned order release of the parent becomes the gross requirement of the component.

The time-phased inventory record shown in Figure 4.12 can now be modified to consider any inventory available. For example, suppose there are 10 Bs available as well as the 20 As. The requirements for the components D and E would change. Figure 4.13 shows the change in the MRP record.

Part Number		Week 1	Week 2	Week 3	Week 4	Week 5
A	Planned Order Receipt					50
	Planned Order Release				50	
B	Planned Order Receipt				50	
	Planned Order Release		50			
C	Planned Order Receipt				50	
	Planned Order Release			50		
D	Planned Order Receipt		50			
	Planned Order Release	50				
E	Planned Order Receipt		50			
	Planned Order Release	50				

FIGURE 4.12 Exploding and offsetting.

Part Number		Week 1	Week 2	Week 3	Week 4	Week 5
A	Gross Requirements					50
	Projected Available 20	20	20	20	20	0
	Net Requirements					30
	Planned Order Receipt					30
	Planned Order Release				30	
B	Gross Requirements				30	
	Projected Available 10	10	10	10	0	
	Net Requirements				20	
	Planned Order Receipt				20	
	Planned Order Release		20			
C	Gross Requirements				30	
	Projected Available		0		0	
	Net Requirements				30	
	Planned Order Receipt				30	
	Planned Order Release			30		
D	Gross Requirements		20			
	Projected Available	0	0			
	Net Requirements		20			
	Planned Order Receipt		20			
	Planned Order Release	20				
E	Gross Requirements		20			
	Projected Available	0	0			
	Net Requirements		20			
	Planned Order Receipt		20			
	Planned Order Release	20				

FIGURE 4.13 Gross and net requirements.

Example Problem

Complete the following table. Lead time for the part is 2 weeks. The order quantity (lot size) is 100 units.

Week	1	2	3	4
Gross Requirements		50	45	20
Projected Available 75				
Net Requirements				
Planned Order Receipt				
Planned Order Release				

ANSWER

Week	1	2	3	4
Gross Requirements		50	45	20
Projected Available 75	75	25	80	60
Net Requirements			20	
Planned Order Receipt			100	
Planned Order Release	100			

Releasing Orders

So far we have looked at the process of planning when orders should be released so work is done in time to meet gross requirements. In many cases, requirements change daily. A computer-based material requirements planning system automatically recalculates the requirements for subassemblies and components and re-creates planned order releases to meet the shifts in demand.

Planned order releases are just planned; they have not been released. It is the responsibility of the material planner to release planned orders, not the computer.

Since the objective of the MRP is to have material available when it is needed and not before, orders for material should not be released until the planned order release date arrives. Thus, an order is not normally released until the planned order is in the current week (week 1).

Releasing an order means that authorization is given to purchasing to buy the necessary material or to manufacturing to make the component.

Before a manufacturing order is released, component availability must be checked. The computer program checks the component inventory records to be sure that enough material is available and, if so, to allocate the necessary quantity to that work order. If the material is not available, the computer program will advise the planner of the shortage.

When the authorization to purchase or manufacture is released, the planned order receipt is canceled, and a scheduled receipt is created in its place. For the example shown in Figure 4.13, parts D and E have planned order releases of 20 scheduled for week 1. These orders will be released by the planner, and then the MRP records for parts D and E will appear as shown in Figure 4.14. Notice that scheduled receipts have been created, replacing the planned order releases.

When a manufacturing order is released the computer will **allocate** the required quantities of a parent's components to that order. This does not mean the components are withdrawn from inventory but that the projected *available* quantity is reduced. The allocated quantity of components is still in inventory, but they are not available for other orders. They will stay in inventory until withdrawn for use.

Scheduled receipts   **Scheduled receipts** are orders placed on manufacturing or on a vendor and represent a commitment to make or buy. For an order in a factory, necessary materials are committed, and work-center capacity is allocated to that order. For purchased

Part Number		Week				
		1	2	3	4	5
D	Gross Requirements		20			
	Scheduled Receipts		20			
	Projected Available	0	0			
	Net Requirements		0			
	Planned Order Receipt					
	Planned Order Release					
E	Gross Requirements		20			
	Scheduled Receipts		20			
	Projected Available	0	0			
	Net Requirements		0			
	Planned Order Receipt					
	Planned Order Release					

FIGURE 4.14 Scheduled receipts.

parts, similar commitments are made to the vendor. The scheduled receipts row shows the quantities ordered and when they are expected to be completed and available.

Open orders   Scheduled receipts on the MRP record are **open orders** on the factory or a vendor and are the responsibility of purchasing and of production activity control. When the goods are received into inventory and available for use, the order is closed out, and the scheduled receipt disappears to become part of the on-hand inventory.

Net requirements   The calculation for **net requirements** can now be modified to include scheduled receipts.

Net requirements = gross requirements − scheduled receipts − available inventory

Example Problem

Complete the following table. Lead time for the item is 2 weeks, and the order quantity is 200. What action should be taken?

Week	1	2	3	4
Gross Requirements	50	250	100	50
Scheduled Receipts		200		
Projected Available 150				
Net Requirements				
Planned Order Receipt				
Planned Order Release				

ANSWER

Week	1	2	3	4
Gross Requirements	50	250	100	50
Scheduled Receipts		200		
Projected Available 150	100	50	150	100
Net Requirements			50	
Planned Order Receipt			200	
Planned Order Release	200			

The order for 200 units should be released.

Part Number		Week				
		1	2	3	4	5
	Gross Requirements					35
	Scheduled Receipts				20	
	Projected Available 10	10	10	10	30	
	Net Requirements					5
	Planned Order Receipt					5
	Planned Order Release				5	

FIGURE 4.15 Basic MRP record.

Basic MRP Record

Figure 4.15 shows a basic MRP record. There are several points that are important:

1. The current time is the beginning of the first period.
2. The top row shows periods, called **time buckets**. These are often a week but can be any length of time convenient to the company. Some companies are moving to daily time buckets.
3. The number of periods in the record is called the **planning horizon**, which shows the number of future periods for which plans are being made. It should be at least as long as the cumulative product lead time. Otherwise, the MRP system would not be able to release planned orders of items at the lower level at the correct time.
4. An item is considered available at the beginning of the time bucket in which it is required.
5. The quantity shown in the projected available row is the projected on-hand balance at the *end* of the period.
6. The immediate or most current period is called the **action bucket**. A quantity in the action bucket means that some action is needed now to avoid a future problem.
7. A **bucketless system** shows only the time buckets which have MRP activity omitting the time periods with no activity.

Capacity Requirements Planning

As in the previous planning levels discussed, the MRP priority plan must be checked against available capacity. At the MRP planning level, the process is called capacity requirements planning (CRP). Chapter 5 examines this problem in some detail. If the capacity is available, the plan can proceed. If not, either capacity has to be made available or the priority plans must be changed.

Low-Level Coding and Netting

A component may reside on more than one level in a bill of material. If this is the case, it is necessary to make sure that all gross requirements for that component have been recorded before netting takes place. Consider the product shown in Figure 4.16. Component C occurs twice in the product tree and at different levels. It would be a mistake to net the requirements for the Cs before calculating the gross requirements for those required for parent B.

The process of collecting the gross requirements and netting can be simplified by using low-level codes. The **low-level code** is the lowest level on which a part resides in all bills of material. Every part has only one low-level code. The low-level codes for the parts in the product tree shown in Figure 4.16 are

Part	Low-Level Code
A	0
B	1
C	2
D	2

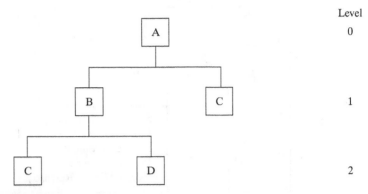

FIGURE 4.16 Multilevel product tree.

Low-level codes are determined by starting at the lowest level of a bill of material and, working up, recording the level against the part. If a part occurs again on a higher level, it is not assigned a code because its existence on the lower level has already been recorded.

Once the low-level codes are obtained, the net requirements for each part can be calculated using the following procedure. For the purpose of this exercise, there is a gross requirement for part A of 50 in week 5, all lead times are 1 week, and the following amounts are in inventory: A, 20 units; B, 10 units; and C, 10 units.

Procedure

1. Starting at level zero of the tree, determine if any of the parts on that level have a low-level code of zero. If so, those parts occur at no lower level, and all the gross requirements have been recorded. These parts can, therefore, be netted and exploded down to the next level, that is, into their components. If the low-level code is greater than zero, there are more gross requirements, and the part is not netted. In this example, A has a low-level code of zero so there is no further requirement for As; it can be netted and exploded into its components. Figure 4.17 shows the results.

Low-Level Code	Part Number		Week				
			1	2	3	4	5
0	A	Gross Requirements					50
		Scheduled Receipts					
		Projected Available 20	20	20	20	20	0
		Net Requirements					30
		Planned Order Receipt					30
		Planned Order Release				30	
1	B	Gross Requirements				30	
		Scheduled Receipts					
		Projected Available 10					
		Net Requirements					
		Planned Order Receipt					
		Planned Order Release					
2	C	Gross Requirements				30	
		Scheduled Receipts					
		Projected Available 10					
		Net Requirements					
		Planned Order Receipt					
		Planned Order Release					

FIGURE 4.17 Netting and exploding zero-level parts.

Low-Level Code	Part Number		Week				
			1	2	3	4	5
1	B	Gross Requirements Scheduled Receipts Projected Available 10 Net Requirements Planned Order Receipt Planned Order Release	10	10	10 20	30 0 20 20	
2	C	Gross Requirements Scheduled Receipts Projected Available 10 Net Requirements Planned Order Receipt Planned Order Release			20	30	
2	D	Gross Requirements Scheduled Receipts Projected Available Net Requirements Planned Order Receipt Planned Order Release			20		

FIGURE 4.18 Netting and exploding first-level parts.

2. The next step is to move down to level 1 on the product tree and to repeat the routine followed in step 1. Since B has a low-level code of 1, all requirements for B are recorded, and it can be netted and exploded. The bill of material for B shows that it is made from a C and a D. Figure 4.18 shows the result of netting and exploding the Bs. Part C has a low-level code of 2, which tells us there are further requirements for Cs and at this stage they are not netted.

3. Moving down to level 2 on the product tree, we find that part C has a low-level code of 2. This tells us that all gross requirements for Cs are accounted for and that we can proceed and determine its net requirements. Notice there is a requirement for 30 Cs in week 4 to be used on the As and a requirement of 20 Cs in week 3 to be used on the Bs. Looking at its bill of material, we see that it is a purchased part and no explosion is needed.

Figure 4.19 shows the completed material requirements plan. The process of level-by-level netting is now completed using the low-level codes of each part. The low-level codes are used to determine when a part is eligible for netting and exploding. In this way, each part is netted and exploded only once. There is no time-consuming re-netting and re-exploding each time a new requirement is met.

Multiple Bills of Material

Most companies make more than one product and often use the same components in many of their products. The material requirements planning system gathers the planned order releases from all the parents and creates a schedule of gross requirements for the components. Figure 4.20 illustrates what happens. Part F is a component of both C and B.

The same procedure used for a single bill of material can be used when multiple products are being manufactured. All bills must be netted and exploded level by level as was done for a single bill.

Low-Level Code	Part Number		Week				
			1	2	3	4	5
0	A	Gross Requirements					50
		Scheduled Receipts					
		Projected Available 20	20	20	20	20	0
		Net Requirements					30
		Planned Order Receipt					30
		Planned Order Release				30	
1	B	Gross Requirements				30	
		Scheduled Receipts					
		Projected Available 10	10	10	10	0	
		Net Requirements				20	
		Planned Order Receipt				20	
		Planned Order Release			20		
2	C	Gross Requirements			2 0	30	
		Scheduled Receipts					
		Projected Available 10	10	10	0	0	
		Net Requirements			10	30	
		Planned Order Receipt			10	30	
		Planned Order Release		10	30		
2	D	Gross Requirements			20		
		Scheduled Receipts					
		Projected Available	0	0	0		
		Net Requirements			20		
		Planned Order Receipt			20		
		Planned Order Release		20			

FIGURE 4.19 Completed material requirements plan.

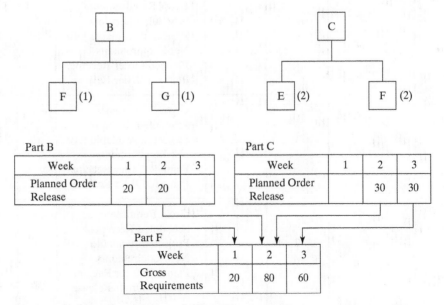

FIGURE 4.20 Multiproduct MRP explosion.

FIGURE 4.21 Multiproduct tree.

Figure 4.21 shows the product trees for two products. Both are made from several components, but, for simplicity, only those components containing an F are shown in the product tree. Note that both have F as a component but at different levels in their product tree. All lead times are 1 week. The quantities required are shown in parentheses; that is, two Cs are required to make an A, one F is required to make a B, and two Fs are needed to make a C. Figure 4.22 shows the completed material requirements plan that would result if 50 As were required in week 5 and 30 Bs in week 3.

Scrap is inherent in some processes due to errors or as a result of the process. As an example the loss due to bones, juice and evaporation when cooking a turkey is estimated at 50%. Industries that mix and pour liquids usually lose some product in the system. Due to scrap as shown in these examples extra production must be scheduled to produce the desired end amount. To accommodate scrap MRP increases the planned order release from the amount needed for the planned order receipt. For example, a process may

Low-Level Code	Part Number		Week				
			1	2	3	4	5
0	A	Gross Requirements					50
		Scheduled Receipts					
		Projected Available 20	20	20	20	20	0
		Net Requirements					30
		Planned Order Receipt					30
		Planned Order Release				30	
0	B	Gross Requirements			30		
		Scheduled Receipts					
		Projected Available 10	10	10	0		
		Net Requirements			20		
		Planned Order Receipt			20		
		Planned Order Release		20			
1	C	Gross Requirements				60	
		Scheduled Receipts					
		Projected Available 10	10	10	10	0	
		Net Requirements				50	
		Planned Order Receipt				50	
		Planned Order Release			50		
2	F	Gross Requirements		40	50		
		Scheduled Receipts					
		Projected Available		0	0		
		Net Requirements		40	50		
		Planned Order Receipt		40	50		
		Planned Order Release	40	50			

FIGURE 4.22 Partial material requirements plan.

generate 15% scrap. If the planned order receipt for an item is for 400 units, then the planned order release for that item would be: $400/(1 - .15) = 471$ units.

Planned order release = Planned order receipt $(1 - \text{scrap factor})$

USING THE MATERIAL REQUIREMENTS PLAN

The people who manage the material requirements planning system are planners. They are responsible for making detailed decisions that keep the flow of material moving into, through, and out of the factory. In many companies where there are thousands of parts to manage, planners are usually organized into logical groupings based on the similarity of parts or supply.

The basic responsibilities of a planner are to

1. Launch (release) orders to purchasing or manufacturing.
2. Reschedule due dates of open (existing) orders as required.
3. Reconcile errors and try to find their cause.
4. Solve critical material shortages by expediting or replanning.
5. Coordinate with other planners, master production schedulers, production activity control, and purchasing to resolve problems.

The material planner works with three types of orders: planned, released, and firm.

Planned orders. **Planned orders** are automatically scheduled and controlled by the computer. As gross requirements, projected available inventory, and scheduled receipts change, the computer recalculates the timing and quantities of planned order releases. The MRP program recommends to the planner the release of an order when the order enters the action bucket but does not release the order.

Released orders. Releasing, or launching, a planned order is the responsibility of the planner. When released, the order becomes an open order to the factory or to purchasing and appears on the MRP record as a scheduled receipt. It is then under the control of the planner, who may expedite, delay, or even cancel the order.

Firm planned orders. The computer-based MRP system automatically recalculates planned orders as the gross requirements change. At times, the planner may prefer to hold a planned order firm against changes in quantity and time despite what the computer calculates. This might be necessary because of future availability of material or capacity or special demands on the system. The planner can tell the computer that the order is not to be changed unless the planner advises the computer to do so. The order is "firmed" or frozen against the logic of the computer.

The MRP software nets, offsets, and explodes requirements and creates planned order releases. It keeps priorities current for all planned orders according to changes in gross requirements for the part. But it does not issue purchase or manufacturing orders or reschedule open orders. However, it does print action or exception messages, suggesting that the planner should act and what kind of action might be appropriate.

Exception messages If the manufacturing process is under control and the material requirements planning system is working properly, the system will work according to plan. However, sometimes there are problems that need the attention of the planner. A good MRP system generates **exception messages** to advise the planner when some event needs attention. Following are some examples of situations that will generate exception messages.

- Components for which planned orders are in the action bucket and which should be considered for release.
- Open orders for which the timing or quantity of scheduled receipts does not satisfy the plan. Perhaps a scheduled receipt is timed to arrive too early or late, and its due date should be revised.
- Situations in which the standard lead times will result in late delivery of a zero-level part. This situation might call for expediting to reduce the standard lead times.

Transaction messages   **Transaction messages** mean that the planner must tell the MRP software of all actions taken that will influence the MRP records. For example, when the planner releases an order, or a scheduled receipt is received, or when any change to the data occurs, the MRP program must be told. Otherwise, the records will be inaccurate, and the plan will become unworkable.

Material requirements planners must manage the parts for which they are responsible. This means not only releasing orders to purchasing and the factory, rescheduling due dates of open orders, and reconciling differences and inconsistencies but also finding ways to improve the system and removing the causes of potential error. If the right components are to be in the right place at the right time, the planner must manage the process.

Managing the Material Requirements Plan

The planner receives feedback from many sources such as

- Suppliers' actions through purchasing.
- Changes to open orders in the factory such as early or late completions or differing quantities.
- Management action such as changing the master production schedule.

The planner must evaluate this feedback and take corrective action if necessary. The planner must consider three important factors in managing the material requirements plan.

Priority   Priority refers to maintaining the correct due dates by constantly evaluating the true due-date need for released orders and, if necessary, expediting or de-expediting.

Consider the following MRP record. The order quantity is 300 units and the lead time is 3 weeks.

Week	1	2	3	4	5
Gross Requirements	100	50	100	150	200
Scheduled Receipts			300		
Projected Available 150	50	0	200	50	150
Net Requirements					150
Planned Order Receipt					300
Planned Order Release		300			

What will happen if the gross requirements in week 2 are changed from 50 units to 150? The MRP record will look like the following.

Week	1	2	3	4	5
Gross Requirements	100	150	100	150	200
Scheduled Receipts			300		
Projected Available 150	50	−100	100	250	50
Net Requirements				50	
Planned Order Receipt				300	
Planned Order Release	300				

Note that there is a shortage of 100 units in week 2 and that the planned order release originally in week 2 is now in week 1. What can the planner do? One solution is to expedite the scheduled receipt of 300 units from week 3 to week 2. If this is not possible, the extra 100 units wanted in week 2 must be rescheduled into week 3. Also, there is now a planned order release in week 1, and this order should be released.

Bottom-up replanning   Action to correct for changed conditions should occur as low in the product structure as possible. Suppose the part in the previous example is a component of another part. The first alternative is to expedite the scheduled receipt of 300 into week 2. If this can be done, there is no need to make any changes to the parent. If the 300 units cannot be expedited, the planned order release and net requirement of the parent must be changed.

Reducing system nervousness   Sometimes requirements change rapidly and by small amounts, causing the material requirements plan to change back and forth. The planner must judge whether the changes are important enough to react to and whether an order should be released. One method of **reducing system nervousness** is firm planned orders.

Example Problem

As the MRP planner, you arrive at work Monday morning and look at the MRP record for part 2876 as shown below.

Order quantity = 30 units
Lead time = 2 weeks

Week		1	2	3	4	5	6
Gross Requirements		35	10	15	30	15	20
Scheduled Receipts		30					
Projected Available	20	15	5	20	20	5	15
Net Requirements				10	10		15
Planned Order Receipt				30	30		30
Planned Order Release		30	30		30		

The computer draws attention to the need to release the planned order for 30 in week 1. Either you release this order, or there will be a shortage in week 3. During the first week, the following transactions take place:

a. Only 25 units of the scheduled receipt are received into inventory. The balance is scrapped.

b. The gross requirement for week 3 is changed to 10.

c. The gross requirement for week 4 is increased to 50.

d. The requirement for week 7 is 15.

e. An inventory count reveals there are 10 more in inventory than the record shows.

f. The 35 gross requirement for week 1 is issued from inventory.

g. The planned order release for 30 in week 1 is released and becomes a scheduled receipt in week 3.

   As these transactions occur during the first week, you must enter these changes in the computer record. At the beginning of the next week, the MRP record appears as follows:

Order quantity = 30 units
Lead time = 2 weeks

Week		2	3	4	5	6	7
Gross Requirements		10	10	50	15	20	15
Scheduled Receipts			30				
Projected Available	20	10	30	10	25	5	20
Net Requirements				20	5		10
Planned Order Receipt				30	30		30
Planned Order Release		30	30		30		

The opening on-hand balance for week 2 is 20 (20 + 25 + 10 − 35 = 20). The planned order release originally set in week 4 has shifted to week 3. Another planned order has been created for release in week 5. More importantly, the scheduled receipt in week 3 will not be needed until week 4. You should reschedule this to week 4. The planned order in week 2 should be released and become a scheduled receipt in week 4.

SUMMARY

The job of the MRP is to produce the right components at the right time so that the MPS can be maintained. The MRP depends on accurate bills of material and on accurate inventory records. Bills of material can be created in many ways, but one department (or individual) must be responsible for them. Inventory records are indispensable to the MRP, and the MRP is only as good as the inventory records.

The MRP exploding and offsetting processes outlined in this text are largely done by the computer. The logic used is repetitive and, while error prone when done by individuals, can be accomplished well by computer. Good MRP practice is achieved by planners being able to work with the system.

The MRP process uses the bill of materials that lists components used to make a product, the lead time to make or obtain those components, and the existing inventory of those components to calculate a series of planned order releases to obtain or make components to meet future product needs.

KEY TERMS

Action bucket 76	Parent 66
Allocate 74	Pegging report 70
Bill of material processor 64	Planned orders 81
Bottom-up replanning 83	Planned order receipt 72
Component items 66	Planned order release 72
Exception messages 81	Planning bills 69
Exploding 71	Planning factors 64
Firm planned orders 81	Planning horizon 76
Indented bill 69	Product tree 65
Inventory record file 64	Reducing system nervousness 83
Lead time 71	Releasing an order 74
Low-level code 76	Scheduled receipts 74
Master production schedule 64	Single-level bill 66
Multilevel bills 66	Summarized parts list 69
Multiple bill 66	Time buckets 76
Net requirements 75	Transaction messages 82
Offsetting 71	Where-used report 70
Open orders 75	

QUESTIONS

1. What is a material requirements plan?
2. What is the difference between dependent and independent demand?
3. Should an MRP be used with dependent or independent demand items?
4. What are the objectives of the MRP?

5. What is the relationship between the MPS and the MRP?

6. Why is a computer necessary in an MRP system?

7. What are the major inputs to the MRP system?

8. What data are found in a part master file or an item master file?

9. What is a bill of material? What are two important points about bills of material?

10. To what does *bill of material structure* refer? Why is it important?

11. Describe the parent–component relationship.

12. Describe the following types of bills of material:
    a. Product tree.
    b. Multilevel bill.
    c. Single-level bill.
    d. Indented bill.
    e. Summarized parts list.
    f. Planning bill.

13. Why do MRP computer programs store single-level bills?

14. Describe each of the seven uses of a bill of material described in the text.

15. What are where-used and pegging reports? Give some of their uses.

16. Describe the processes of offsetting and exploding.

17. What is a planned order? How is it created?

18. From where does the gross requirement of a component come?

19. Who is responsible for releasing an order? Describe what happens to the inventory records and to PAC and purchasing.

20. What is a scheduled receipt? From where does it originate?

21. What is an open order? How does it get closed?

22. What is the meaning of the term *low-level code?* How is the low-level code of an MPS part represented?

23. What are the responsibilities of a material requirements planner?

24. Give two examples of processes with inherent scrap. Hint, the use of natural products often involves some scrap.

25. What would make the planned order release for an item different from the planned order receipt?

26. Describe the differences among planned orders, released orders, and firm planned orders. Who controls each?

27. What are exception messages? What is their purpose?

28. What is a transaction message? Why is it important?

29. What are the three important factors in managing the material requirements plan? Why is each important?

30. Describe the problems that might come from using an incorrect bill of material in MRP.

31. Describe how MRP might be used to plan for a change in design for a product.

PROBLEMS

4.1. Using the following product tree, construct the appropriate single-level trees. How many Cs are needed to make 50 Xs and 100 Ys?

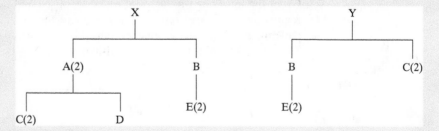

Answer.   400 Cs

4.2. Given the following parents and components, construct a product tree. Figures in parentheses show the quantities per item. How many Gs are needed to make one A?

Parent	A	B	C	E
Component	B(2)	E(2)	G(3)	G(4)
	C(4)	F(1)		F(3)
	D(4)			H(2)

4.3. Using the following product tree, determine the planned order receipts and planned order releases if 200 As are to be produced in week 5. All lead times are 1 week except for component E, which has a lead time of 2 weeks.

	Week	1	2	3	4	5
Part A Lead Time: 1 week	Planned Order Receipt Planned Order Release					
Part B Lead Time: 1 week	Planned Order Receipt Planned Order Release					
Part C Lead Time: 1 week	Planned Order Receipt Planned Order Release					
Part D Lead Time: 1 week	Planned Order Receipt Planned Order Release					
Part E Lead Time: 2 weeks	Planned Order Receipt Planned Order Release					

4.4. Complete the following table. Lead time for the part is 2 weeks, and the order quantity is 40. What action should be taken?

Week	1	2	3	4
Gross Requirements	20	15	15	20
Projected Available 40				
Net Requirements				
Planned Order Receipt				
Planned Order Release				

Answer. An order for 40 should be released in week 1.

4.5. Given the following product tree, explode, offset, and determine the gross and net requirements. All lead times are 1 week, and the quantities required are shown in parentheses. The master production schedule calls for 100 As to be available in week 5. There are 20 Bs available. All other on-hand balances = 0.

	Week	1	2	3	4	5
Part A Lead Time: 1 week	Gross Requirements Scheduled Receipts Projected Available Net Requirements Planned Order Receipt Planned Order Release					
Part B Lead Time: 1 week	Gross Requirements Scheduled Receipts Projected Available Net Requirements Planned Order Receipt Planned Order Release					
Part C Lead Time: 1 week	Gross Requirements Scheduled Receipts Projected Available Net Requirements Planned Order Receipt Planned Order Release					
Part D Lead Time: 1 week	Gross Requirements Scheduled Receipts Projected Available Net Requirements Planned Order Receipt Planned Order Release					
Part E Lead Time: 1 week	Gross Requirements Scheduled Receipts Projected Available Net Requirements Planned Order Receipt Planned Order Release					
Part F Lead Time: 1 week	Gross Requirements Scheduled Receipts Projected Available Net Requirements Planned Order Receipt Planned Order Release					

Answer. Planned order releases are

Part A: 100 in week 4

Part B: 180 in week 3

Part C: 100 in week 3

Part D: 380 in week 2

Part E: 180 in week 2

Part F: 100 in week 2

4.6. Complete the following table. Lead time for the part is 2 weeks. The lot size is 100. What is the projected available at the end of week 3? When is it planned to release an order?

Week	1	2	3	4
Gross Requirements	20	65	35	25
Scheduled Receipts		100		
Projected Available 30				
Net Requirements				
Planned Order Receipt				
Planned Order Release				

Answer. Projected available at the end of week 3 is 10.
An order release is planned for the beginning of week 2.

4.7. Complete the following table. Lead time for the part is 2 weeks. The lot size is 50. What is the projected available at the end of week 3? When is it planned to release an order?

Week	1	2	3	4
Gross Requirements	30	25	10	10
Scheduled Receipts	50			
Projected Available 10				
Net Requirements				
Planned Order Receipt				
Planned Order Release				

4.8. Given the following partial product tree, explode, offset, and determine the gross and net requirements for components H, I, J, and K. There are other components, but they are not connected to this problem. The quantities required are shown in parentheses. The master production schedule calls for the completion of 50 Hs in week 3 and 70 in week 5. There is a scheduled receipt of 100 Is in week 2. There are 400 Js and 400 Ks available.

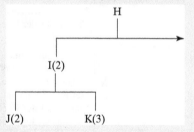

	Week	1	2	3	4	5
Part H Lead Time: 1 week	Gross Requirements Scheduled Receipts Projected Available Net Requirements Planned Order Receipt Planned Order Release					
Part I Lead Time: 2 weeks	Gross Requirements Scheduled Receipts Projected Available Net Requirements Planned Order Receipt Planned Order Release					
Part J Lead Time: 1 week	Gross Requirements Scheduled Receipts Projected Available 400 Net Requirements Planned Order Receipt Planned Order Release					
Part K Lead Time: 1 week	Gross Requirements Scheduled Receipts Projected Available 400 Net Requirements Planned Order Receipt Planned Order Release					

Answer.   There is a planned order release for part K of 20 in week 1.

4.9. MPS parent X has planned order releases of 30 in weeks 2 and 4. Given the following product tree, complete the MRP records for parts Y and Z. Quantities required are shown in brackets.

Part Y Lead Time: 2 weeks Lot Size: 50	Week			
	1	2	3	4
Gross Requirements Scheduled Receipts Projected Available 30 Net Requirements Planned Order Receipt Planned Order Release				

Part Z Lead Time: 1 week Lot Size: 100	Week			
	1	2	3	4
Gross Requirements Scheduled Receipts Projected Available 20 Net Requirements Planned Order Receipt Planned Order Release				

4.10. Given the following product tree, explode, offset, and determine the gross and net requirements. The quantities required are shown in parentheses. The master production schedule calls for the completion of 100 As in week 5. There is a scheduled receipt of 100 Bs in week 1. There are 200 Fs available. All order quantities are lot-for-lot.

	Week	1	2	3	4	5
Part A Lead Time: 1 week	Gross Requirements Scheduled Receipts Projected Available Net Requirements Planned Order Receipt Planned Order Release					
Part B Lead Time: 1 week	Gross Requirements Scheduled Receipts Projected Available Net Requirements Planned Order Receipt Planned Order Release					
Part C Lead Time: 1 week	Gross Requirements Scheduled Receipts Projected Available Net Requirements Planned Order Receipt Planned Order Release					
Part D Lead Time: 1 week	Gross Requirements Scheduled Receipts Projected Available Net Requirements Planned Order Receipt Planned Order Release					
Part E Lead Time: 1 week	Gross Requirements Scheduled Receipts Projected Available Net Requirements Planned Order Receipt Planned Order Release					
Part F Lead Time: 1 week	Gross Requirements Scheduled Receipts Projected Available Net Requirements Planned Order Receipt Planned Order Release					

4.11. Given the following product tree, complete the MRP records for parts X, Y, and Z. Note that parts X and Y have specified order quantities.

	Week	1	2	3	4	5
Part X	Gross Requirements	15	10	15	10	15
	Scheduled Receipts	20				
Lead Time: 1 week	Projected Available 10					
	Net Requirements					
	Planned Order Receipt					
	Planned Order Release					
Part Y	Gross Requirements					
	Scheduled Receipts		50			
Lead Time: 2 weeks	Projected Available 30					
	Net Requirements					
Lot Size: 50	Planned Order Receipt					
	Planned Order Release					
Part Z	Gross Requirements					
Lead Time: 1 week	Scheduled Receipts		90			
	Projected Available					
	Net Requirements					
Lot Size: lot-for-lot	Planned Order Receipt					
	Planned Order Release					
Part W	Gross Requirements					
	Scheduled Receipts					
Lead Time: 1 week	Projected Available					
	Net Requirements					
Lot Size: 400	Planned Order Receipt					
	Planned Order Release					

4.12. Given the following product tree, determine the low-level codes for all the components.

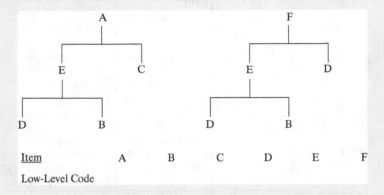

4.13. Given the following product tree, determine the low-level codes for all the components.

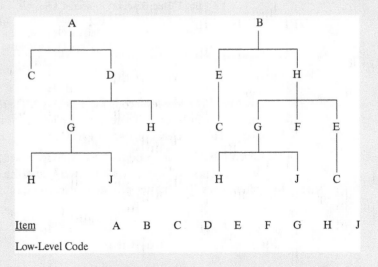

4.14. Given the following product tree, develop a material requirements plan for the components. Quantities per are shown in parentheses. The following worksheet shows the present active orders, the available balances, and the lead times.

Low-Level Code		Week	1	2	3	4	5
0	Part A Lead Time: 1 week Lot-for-lot	Gross Requirements Scheduled Receipts Projected Available Net Requirements Planned Order Receipt Planned Order Release			60		70
0	Part F Lead Time: 1 week Lot-for-lot	Gross Requirements Scheduled Receipts Projected Available Net Requirements Planned Order Receipt Planned Order Release				100	
	Part B Lead Time: 2 weeks Lot Size: 300	Gross Requirements Scheduled Receipts Projected Available 200 Net Requirements Planned Order Receipt Planned Order Release					
	Part C Lead Time: 2 weeks Lot Size: Lot-for-lot	Gross Requirements Scheduled Receipts Projected Available Net Requirements Planned Order Receipt Planned Order Release		120			
	Part D Lead Time: 2 weeks Lot Size: 300	Gross Requirements Scheduled Receipts Projected Available Net Requirements Planned Order Receipt Planned Order Release	300				
	Part E Lead Time: 3 weeks Lot Size: 500	Gross Requirements Scheduled Receipts Projected Available 400 Net Requirements Planned Order Receipt Planned Order Release					

Answer: The low-level code for part D is 2. There is a planned order release of 300 for part D in week 1. There are no planned order releases for part E. There is a planned order release of 100 for Part C in week 1 and 140 in week 2.

4.15. Given the following product tree, explode, offset, and determine the gross and net requirements. All lead times are 1 week, and the quantities required are shown in parentheses. The master production schedule calls for the completion of 100 As in week 4 and 50 in week 5. There are 300 Bs scheduled to be received in week 1 and 200 Ds in week 3. There are also 20 As available.

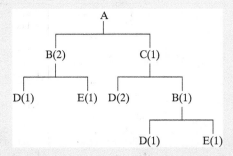

Low-Level Code		Week	1	2	3	4	5
	Part A Lead Time: 1 week Lot Size: lot-for-lot	Gross Requirements Scheduled Receipts Projected Available 20 Net Requirements Planned Order Receipt Planned Order Release					
	Part B Lead Time: 1 week Lot Size: lot-for-lot	Gross Requirements Scheduled Receipts Projected Available Net Requirements Planned Order Receipt Planned Order Release					
	Part C Lead Time: 1 week Lot Size: lot-for-lot	Gross Requirements Scheduled Receipts Projected Available Net Requirements Planned Order Receipt Planned Order Release					
	Part D Lead Time: 1 week Lot Size: lot-for-lot	Gross Requirements Scheduled Receipts Projected Available Net Requirements Planned Order Receipt Planned Order Release					
	Part E Lead Time: 1 week Lot Size: lot-for-lot	Gross Requirements Scheduled Receipts Projected Available Net Requirements Planned Order Receipt Planned Order Release					

4.16. Given the following product tree, determine the low-level codes and the gross and net quantities for each part. There is a requirement for 100 As in week 4 and 50 Bs in week 5. There is a scheduled receipt of 100 Cs in week 2. Quantities required of each are also shown.

Low-Level Code		Week	1	2	3	4	5
	Part A Lead Time: 1 week Lot Size: lot-for-lot	Gross Requirements Scheduled Receipts Projected Available Net Requirements Planned Order Receipt Planned Order Release					
	Part B Lead Time: 1 week Lot Size: lot-for-lot	Gross Requirements Scheduled Receipts Projected Available Net Requirements Planned Order Receipt Planned Order Release					
	Part C Lead Time: 1 week Lot Size: lot-for-lot	Gross Requirements Scheduled Receipts Projected Available Net Requirements Planned Order Receipt Planned Order Release					
	Part D Lead Time: 1 week Lot Size: lot-for-lot	Gross Requirements Scheduled Receipts Projected Available Net Requirements Planned Order Receipt Planned Order Release					
	Part E Lead Time: 1 week Lot Size: 500	Gross Requirements Scheduled Receipts Projected Available Net Requirements Planned Order Receipt Planned Order Release					
	Part F Lead Time: 1 week Lot Size: lot-for-lot	Gross Requirements Scheduled Receipts Projected Available Net Requirements Planned Order Receipt Planned Order Release					

4.17. Complete the following MRP record. The lead time is 4 weeks, and the lot size is 200. What will happen if the gross requirements in week 3 are increased to 150 units? As a planner, what actions can you take?

Initial MRP

Week	1	2	3	4	5
Gross Requirements	50	125	100	60	40
Scheduled Receipts		200		200	
Projected Available 100					
Net Requirements					
Planned Order Receipt					
Planned Order Release					

Revised MRP

Week	1	2	3	4	5
Gross Requirements					
Scheduled Receipts					
Projected Available 100					
Net Requirements					
Planned Order Receipt					
Planned Order Release					

4.18. It is Monday morning, and you have just arrived at work. Complete the following MRP record as it would appear Monday morning. Lead time is 2 weeks, and the lot size is 100.

Initial MRP

Week	1	2	3	4	5
Gross Requirements	70	40	80	50	40
Scheduled Receipts	100				
Projected Available 50					
Net Requirements					
Planned Order Receipt					
Planned Order Release					

During the week, the following events occur. Enter them in the MRP record.

a. The planned order for 100 in week 1 is released.

b. Thirty of the scheduled receipts for week 1 are scrapped.

c. An order for 20 is received for delivery in week 3.

d. An order for 40 is received for delivery in week 6.

e. The gross requirements of 70 in week 1 are issued.

MRP record at the end of week 1

Week	2	3	4	5	6
Gross Requirements					
Scheduled Receipts					
Projected Available					
Net Requirements					
Planned Order Receipt					
Planned Order Release					

CASE STYDY 4.1

Apix Polybob Company

Ken Mack, plant manager for the Apix Polybob Company, was having a heated discussion with Jim Gould, the production and inventory control manager. Ken was getting tired of frantic calls from Ellen Uphouse, the marketing manager, concerning late orders for their Polybob customers and was once again after Jim to solve the problem. Some of the discussion points follow:

JIM: Look, Ken, I'm not sure what more we can do. I've reexamined the EOQ (economic order quantity lot size) values and all the reorder points for all our inventory for all our Polybob models, including all component levels and purchased items. I've implemented strict inventory control procedures to ensure our accuracy levels to at least 80%, and I've worked with the production people to make sure we are maximizing both labor efficiency and utilization of our equipment. The real problem is with those salespeople. We no sooner have a production run nicely going, and they change the order or add a new one. If they'd only leave us alone for a while and let us catch up with our current late order bank, we'd be okay. As it is, everyone is getting tired of order changes, expediting, and making everything into a crisis. Even our suppliers are losing patience with us. They tend to disbelieve any order we give them until we call them up for a crisis shipment.

KEN: I find it hard to believe that you really have the EOQ and reorder point values right. If they were, we shouldn't have all these part shortages all the time while our overall inventory is going up in value. I also don't see any way we can shut off the orders coming in. I can imagine the explosion from Ellen if I even suggested such a thing. She'll certainly remind me that our mission statement clearly points out that our number-one priority is customer service, and refusing orders and order changes certainly doesn't fit as good customer service.

JIM: Then maybe the approach is to deal with Frank Adams (the chief financial officer). He's the one who is always screaming that we have too much inventory, too much expediting cost, too much premium freight costs from suppliers, and poor efficiency. I've tried to have him authorize more overtime to relieve some of the late order conditions, but all he'll say is that we must be making the wrong models. He continually points to the fact that the production hours we are paying for currently are more than enough to make our orders shipped at standard, and that condition has held for over a year. He just won't budge on that point. Maybe you can convince him.

KEN: I'm not sure that's the answer either. I think he has a point, and he certainly has the numbers to back him up. I'd have a real rough time explaining what we were doing to Ron Marrison [the CEO]. There's got to be a better answer. I've heard about a systems approach called material requirements planning or something like that. Why don't you look into that. Take a representative model and see if that approach could help us deal with what appears to be an impossible situation. I'm sure something would work. I know other factories have similar production conditions yet don't seem to have all our problems.

Following is the information about Polybob model A that Ken suggested as a representative model to use for the analysis:

Component	Lot Size	Inventory	Lead Time	Scheduled Receipts	Reorder point
B	80	10	1	None	5
C	150	40	1	None	15
D	200	180	2	None	50
E	400	300	2	None	70
F	500	50	2	500, week 1	80

The following are the master schedule production lots for Model A:

Complete 50 units, week 3

Complete 50 units, week 5

Complete 60 units, week 7

Complete 60 units, week 9

Complete 50 units, week 11

Upon seeing this information, Jim stated, "Look at how regular our production schedule is for this model. The reorder points will more than cover requirements, and none have lead times that make it tough to respond. This analysis should show that all the work I did on EOQ and reorder points was right, and the real problem lies with those sales and finance people who don't understand our production needs."

Discussion Questions

1. What are the key issues brought about in the conversation? What are the key symptoms, and what are the underlying problems? Be specific in your answers.
2. Use the product information to develop an MRP approach to the problems. Would MRP solve the problems? If so, show specifically how MRP would avoid the problems discussed by Ken and Jim.
3. Do any conditions bother you about the ability of MRP to deal with the problems? What specifically are those conditions?
4. Suppose it was discovered that only 250 of component E were in stock instead of the 300 listed on the inventory record. What problems would this cause (if any), and what are some of the ways that these problems could be addressed? How would (if at all) MRP help you when other methods might not?
5. Suppose that the design engineer advises that he has a new design for component F. It won't be ready until sometime after week 2, but he wants you to give a date for the first supplier shipment to come in, and you should be ready to tell the supplier how many to ship. Since the change is transparent to the customer, the design engineer advises you to go ahead and use up any existing material of the model. How will MRP help you to deal with this issue?
6. Can you think of any other "what if" questions that might be more easily addressed by a systematic approach such as MRP?

CAPACITY MANAGEMENT

INTRODUCTION

So far we have been concerned with planning priority, that is, determining what is to be produced and when. The system is hierarchical, moving from long planning horizons and few details (production plan) through medium time spans (master production schedule) to a high level of detail and short time spans (material requirements plan). At each level, manufacturing develops priority plans to satisfy demand. However, without the resources to achieve the priority plan, the plan will be unworkable. Capacity management is concerned with supplying the necessary resources. This chapter looks more closely at the question of capacity: what it is, how much is available, how much is required, and how to balance priority and capacity.

DEFINITION OF CAPACITY

Capacity is the amount of work that can be done in a specified time period. In the twelfth edition of the *APICS Dictionary*, capacity is defined as "the capability of a worker, machine, work center, plant, or organization to produce output per time period." Capacity is a *rate* of doing work, not the *quantity* of work done.

Two kinds of capacity are important: capacity available and capacity required. Capacity available is the capacity of a system or resource to produce a quantity of output in a given time period. **Capacity required** is the capacity of a system or resource needed to produce a desired output in a given time period. A term closely related to capacity required is **load**. This is the amount of released and planned work assigned to a facility for a particular time period. It is the sum of all the required capacities.

These three terms—capacity required, load, and capacity available—are important in capacity management and will be discussed in subsequent sections of this chapter. Capacity is often pictured as a funnel, as shown in Figure 5.1. Capacity available is the rate at which work can be withdrawn from the system. Load is the amount of work in the system.

Capacity management is responsible for determining the capacity needed to achieve the priority plans as well as providing, monitoring, and controlling that capacity so the

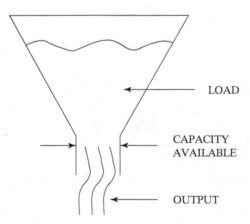

LOAD

CAPACITY
AVAILABLE

OUTPUT

FIGURE 5.1 Capacity versus load.

priority plan can be met. The twelfth edition of the *APICS Dictionary* defines capacity management as "the function of establishing, measuring, monitoring, and adjusting limits or levels of capacity in order to execute all manufacturing schedules." As with all management processes, it consists of planning and control functions.

Capacity planning is the process of determining the resources required to meet the priority plan and the methods needed to make that capacity available. It takes place at each level of the priority planning process. Production planning, master production scheduling, and material requirements planning determine priorities: what is wanted and when. These priority plans cannot be implemented, however, unless the firm has sufficient capacity to fulfill the demand. Capacity planning, thus, links the various production priority schedules to manufacturing resources.

Capacity control is the process of monitoring production output, comparing it with capacity plans, and taking corrective action when needed. Capacity control will be examined in Chapter 6.

CAPACITY PLANNING

Capacity planning involves calculating the capacity needed to achieve the priority plan and finding ways of making that capacity available. If the capacity requirement cannot be met, the priority plans have to be changed.

Priority plans are usually stated in units of product or some standard unit of output. Capacity can sometimes be stated in the same units, for example, tons of steel or yards of cloth. If there is no common unit, capacity must be stated as the hours available. The priority plan must then be translated into hours of work required and compared to the hours available. The process of capacity planning is as follows:

1. Determine the capacity available at each work center in each time period.
2. Determine the load at each work center in each time period.
   - Translate the priority plan into the hours of work required at each work center in each time period.
   - Sum up the capacities required for each item on each work center to determine the load on each work center in each time period.
3. Resolve differences between available capacity and required capacity. If possible, adjust available capacity to match the load. Otherwise, the priority plans must be changed to match the available capacity.

This process occurs at each level in the priority planning process, varying only in the level of detail and time spans involved.

Planning Levels

Resource planning involves long-range capacity resource requirements and is directly linked to production planning. Typically, it involves translating monthly, quarterly, or annual product priorities from the production plan into some total measure of capacity, such as gross labor hours. Resource planning involves changes in staffing, capital equipment, product design, or other facilities that take a long time to acquire and eliminate. If a resource plan cannot be devised to meet the production plan, the production plan has to be changed. The two plans set the limits and levels for production. If they are realistic, the master production schedule (MPS) should work. (See Chapter 2, Resource Planning.)

Rough-cut capacity planning takes capacity planning to the next level of detail. The master production schedule is the primary information source. The purpose of rough-cut capacity planning is to check the feasibility of the MPS, provide warnings of any bottlenecks, ensure utilization of work centers, and advise vendors of capacity requirements. (See Chapter 3, Rough-Cut Capacity Planning.)

Capacity requirements planning is directly linked to the material requirements plan. Since this type of planning focuses on component parts, greater detail is involved than in

Priority   Capacity

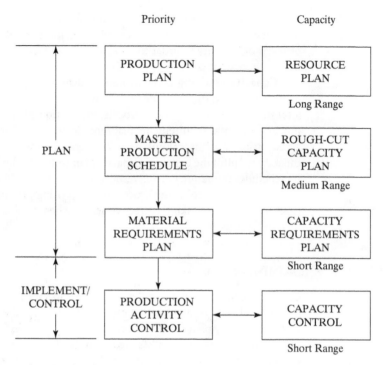

FIGURE 5.2 Planning levels.

rough-cut capacity planning. It is concerned with individual orders at individual work centers and calculates work center loads and labor requirements for each time period at each work center.

Figure 5.2 shows the relationship between the different levels of priority planning and capacity planning. Notice that, although the upper levels of priority planning are input to lower levels, the various capacity plans relate only to their level in the priority plan, not to subsequent capacity planning levels. Resource planning relates to production planning but is not an input to rough-cut capacity planning.

After the plans are completed, production activity control and purchasing must be authorized to process, or implement, shop orders and purchase orders. Capacity must still be considered. Work center capacity control will be covered in Chapter 6.

CAPACITY REQUIREMENTS PLANNING

The capacity requirements plan (CRP) occurs at the level of the material requirements plan (MRP). It is the process of determining in detail the amount of labor and machine resources needed to achieve the required production. Planned orders from the MRP and open shop orders (scheduled receipts) are converted into demand for time in each work center in each time period. This process takes into consideration the lead times for operations and offsets the operations at work centers accordingly. In considering open shop orders, it accounts for work already done on a shop order. Capacity requirements planning is the most detailed, complete, and accurate of the capacity planning techniques. This accuracy is most important in the immediate time periods. Because of the detail, a great amount of data and computation are required.

Inputs

The inputs needed for a CRP are open shop orders, planned order releases, routings, time standards, lead times, and work center capacities. This information can be obtained from the following:

- Open order file.
- Material requirements plan.

- Routing file.
- Work center file.

Open order file   An open shop order appears as a scheduled receipt on the material requirements plan. It is a released order for a quantity of a part to be manufactured and completed on a specific date. It shows all relevant information, such as quantities, due dates, and operations. The **open order file** is a record of all the active shop orders. It can be maintained manually or as a computer file.

Planned order releases   Planned orders are determined by the computer's MRP logic based upon the gross requirements for a particular part. They are inputs to the CRP process in assessing the total capacity required in future time periods.

Routing file   A routing is the path that work follows from work center to work center as it is completed. Routing is specified on a route sheet or, in a computer-based system, in a route file. A routing file should exist for every component manufactured and contain the following information:

- Operations to be performed.
- Sequence of operations.
- Work centers to be used.
- Possible alternate work centers.
- Tooling needed at each operation.
- Standard times: setup times and run times per piece.

Figure 5.3 shows an example of a routing file.

Work center file   A work center is composed of a number of machines or workers capable of doing the same work. The machinery will normally be similar so there are no differences in the kind of work the machines can do or the capacity of each. Several sewing machines of similar capacity could be considered a work center. A **work center file** contains information on the capacity and move, wait, and queue times associated with the center.

The **move time** is the time normally taken to move material from one workstation to another. The **wait time** is the time a job is at a work center after completion and before being moved. The **queue time** is the time a job waits at a work center before being handled. **Lead time** is the sum of queue, setup, run, wait, and move times.

Shop calendar   Another piece of information needed is the number of working days available. The Gregorian calendar (which is the one we use every day) has some serious drawbacks for manufacturing planning and control. The months do not have the same number of days, holidays are spread unevenly throughout the year, and the calendar does not work on a decimal base. Suppose that the lead time for an item is 35 working days and

Part Name: Gear shaft   Part Number: SG 123
Drawing Number: D123X

Operation No.	Work Center	S/U Time (standard hours)	Run Time/piece (standard hours)	Operation
10	12	1.50	0.20	Turn shaft
20	14	0.50	0.25	Mill slot
30	17	0.30	0.05	Drill 2 holes
40	03	0.45	0.10	Grind
50	Stores			Inventory

FIGURE 5.3 Routing file.

MONTH	WEEK	MON.	TUES.	WED.	THURS.	FRI.	SAT.	SUN.
JULY	27	2 / 123	3 / 124	④	5 / 125	6 / 126	⑦	⑧
	28	9 / 127	10 / 128	11 / 129	12 / 130	13 / 131	⑭	⑮
	29	16 / 132	17 / 133	18 / 134	19 / 135	20 / 136	㉑	㉒
	30	23 / 137	24 / 138	25 / 139	26 / 140	27 / 141	㉘	㉙
	31	30 / 142	31 / 143	1 / 144	2 / 145	3 / 146	④	⑤

JULY 2 ⟶ �ढ 2 / 123 ⟵ WORK DAY — 123   ◯ DEFINES NON-WORK DAYS

FIGURE 5.4 Planning calendar. (*Source: The American Production and Inventory Control Society, Inc.*, Material Requirements Planning Training Aid, 5-21. Reprinted with permission.)

on December 13 we are asked if we can deliver by January 22. This is about six weeks away, but with the Gregorian calendar, some calculations have to be made to decide if there is enough time to make the delivery. Holidays occur in that period, and the plant will be shut down for inventory the first week in January. How many working days do we really have?

Because of these problems, it is desirable to develop a **shop calendar**. This can be set up in different ways, but the example shown in Figure 5.4 is typical.

CAPACITY AVAILABLE

Capacity available is the capacity of a system or resource to produce a quantity of output in a given time period. It is affected by the following:

- **Product specifications.** If the product specifications change, the work content (work required to make the product) will change, thus affecting the number of units that can be produced.
- **Product mix.** Each product has its own work content measured in the time it takes to make the product. If the mix of products being produced changes, the total work content (time) for the mix will change.
- **Plant and equipment.** This relates to the methods used to make the product. If the method is changed—for example, a faster machine is used—the output will change. Similarly, if more machines are added to the work center, the capacity will change.
- **Work effort.** This relates to the speed or pace at which the work is done. If the workforce changes pace, perhaps producing more in a given time, the capacity will be altered.

Product specification and product mix depend on the design of the product and the mix of products made. If these vary considerably, it is difficult to use units of product to measure capacity. So what units should be used to measure capacity?

Measuring Capacity

Units of output If the variety of products produced at a work center or in a plant is not large, it is often possible to use a unit common to all products. Paper mills measure capacity in tons of paper, breweries in barrels of beer, and automobile manufacturers in numbers of cars. However, if a variety of products is made, a good common unit may not exist. In this case, the unit common to all products is time.

Standard time   The work content of a product is expressed as the time required to make the product using a given method of manufacture. Using time-study techniques, the **standard time** for a job can be determined—that is, the time it would take a qualified operator working at a normal pace to do the job. It provides a yardstick for measuring work content and a unit for stating capacity. It is also used in loading and scheduling.

Levels of Capacity

Capacity needs to be measured on at least three levels:

- Machine or individual worker.
- Work center.
- Plant, which can be considered as a group of different work centers.

Determining Capacity Available

There are two ways of determining the capacity available: measurement and calculation. **Demonstrated (measured) capacity** is figured from historical data. **Calculated or rated capacity** is based on available time, utilization, and efficiency.

Rated capacity   Rated, or calculated, capacity is the product of available time, utilization, and efficiency.

Available time   The **available time** is the number of hours a work center can be used. For example, a work center working one 8-hour shift for 5 days a week is available 40 hours a week. The available time depends on the number of machines, the number of workers, and the hours of operation.

Example Problem

A work center has 3 machines and is operated for 8 hours a day 5 days a week. What is the available time?

ANSWER

$$\text{Available time} = 3 \times 8 \times 5 = 120 \text{ hours per week}$$

Utilization   The available time is the maximum hours we can expect from the work center. However, it is unlikely this will be attained all the time. Downtime can occur due to machine breakdown, absenteeism, lack of material, and all those problems that cause unavoidable delays. The percentage of time that the work center is active compared to the available time is called work center **utilization**:

$$\text{Utilization} = \frac{\text{hours actually worked}}{\text{available hours}} \times 100\%$$

Example Problem

A work center is available 120 hours but actually produced goods for 100 hours. What is the utilization of the work center?

ANSWER

$$\text{Utilization} = \frac{100}{120} \times 100\% = 83.3\%$$

Utilization can be determined from historical records or by a work sampling study.

Efficiency   It is possible for a work center to utilize 100 hours a week but not produce 100 standard hours of work. The workers might be working at a faster or slower pace than the standard working pace, causing the **efficiency** of the work center to be more or less than 100%:

$$\text{Efficiency} = \frac{\text{standard hours produced}}{\text{hours actually worked}} \times 100\%$$

Example problem

A work center produces 120 standard hours of work in 100 hours. What is the efficiency?

$$\text{Efficiency} = \frac{120}{100} \times 100\% = 120\%$$

Rated capacity   Rated capacity is calculated by taking into account the work center utilization and efficiency:

$$\text{Rated capacity} = \text{available time} \times \text{utilization} \times \text{efficiency}$$

Example Problem

A work center consists of 4 machines and is operated 8 hours per day for 5 days a week. Historically, the utilization has been 85% and the efficiency 110%. What is the rated capacity?

ANSWER

$$\text{Available time} = 4 \times 8 \times 5 = 160 \text{ hours per week}$$
$$\text{Rated capacity} = 160 \times 0.85 \times 1.10 = 149.6 \text{ standard hours}$$

We can expect to get 149.6 standard hours of work from that work center in an average week.

Demonstrated Capacity

One way to find out the capacity of a work center is to examine the previous production records and to use that information as the available capacity of the work center.

Example Problem

Over the previous 4 weeks, a work center produced 120, 130, 150, and 140 standard hours of work. What is the demonstrated capacity of the work center?

ANSWER

$$\text{Demonstrated capacity} = \frac{120 + 130 + 150 + 140}{4} = 135 \text{ standard hours}$$

Notice that demonstrated capacity is average, not maximum, output. It also depends on the utilization and efficiency of the work center, although these are not included in the calculation.

Efficiency and utilization can be obtained from historical data if a record is maintained of the hours available, hours actually worked, and the standard hours produced by a work center.

Example Problem

Over a 4-week period, a work center produced 540 standard hours of work, was available for work 640 hours, and actually worked 480 hours. Calculate the utilization and the efficiency of the work center.

ANSWER

$$\text{Utilization} = \frac{\text{hours actually worked}}{\text{available hours}} \times 100 = \frac{480}{640} \times 100\% = 75\%$$

CAPACITY REQUIRED (LOAD)

Capacity requirements are generated by the priority planning system and involve translating priorities, given in units of product or some common unit, into hours of work required at each work center in each time period. This translation takes place at each of the priority planning levels, from production planning to master production scheduling to material requirements planning. Figure 5.2 illustrates this relationship.

The level of detail, the planning horizon, and the techniques used vary with each planning level. In this text, we will study the material requirements planning/capacity requirements planning level.

Determining the capacity required is a two-step process. First, determine the time needed for each order at each work center; then, sum up the capacity required for individual orders to obtain the load.

Time Needed for Each Order

The time needed for each order is the sum of the setup time and the run time. The run time is equal to the run time per piece multiplied by the number of pieces in the order.

Example Problem

A work center is to process 150 units of gear shaft SG 123 on work order 333. The setup time is 1.5 hours, and the run time is 0.2 hours per piece. What is the standard time needed to run the order?

ANSWER

$$\text{Total standard time} = \text{setup time} + \text{run time}$$
$$= 1.5 + (150 \times 0.2)$$
$$= 31.5 \text{ standard hours}$$

Example Problem

In the previous problem, how much actual time will be needed to run the order if the work center has an efficiency of 120% and a utilization of 80%?

$$\text{Capacity required} = (\text{actual time})(\text{efficiency})(\text{utilization})$$
$$\text{Actual time} = \frac{\text{capacity required}}{(\text{efficiency})(\text{utilization})}$$
$$= \frac{31.5}{(1.2)(0.8)}$$
$$= 32.8 \text{ hours}$$

Load

The load on a work center is the sum of the required times for all the planned and actual orders to be run on the work center in a specified period. The steps in calculating load are as follows:

1. Determine the standard hours of operation time for each planned and released order for each work center by time period.

2. Add all the standard hours together for each work center in each period. The result is the total required capacity (load) on that work center for each time period of the plan.

Example Problems

A work center has the following open orders and planned orders for week 20. Calculate the total standard time required (load) on this work center in week 20. Order 222 is already in progress, and there are 100 remaining to run.

	Order Quantity	Setup Time (hours)	Run Time (hours/piece)	Total Time (hours)
Released Orders				
222	100	0	0.2	
333	150	1.5	0.2	
Planned Orders				
444	200	3	0.25	
555	300	2.5	0.15	
Total Time				

ANSWER

Released Orders	222	Total time = 0 + (100 × 0.2)	=	20.0 standard hours
	333	Total time = 1.5 + (150 × 0.2)	=	31.5 standard hours
Planned Orders	444	Total time = 3 + (200 × 0.25)	=	53.0 standard hours
	555	Total time = 2.5 + (300 × 0.15)	=	47.5 standard hours
Total Time			=	152.0 standard hours

In week 20, there is a load (requirement) for 152 standard hours.

The load must now be compared to the available capacity. One way of doing this is with a work center load report.

Work Center Load Report

The work center load report shows future capacity requirements based on released and planned orders for each time period of the plan.

The load of 152 hours calculated in the previous example is for week 20. Similarly, loads for other weeks can be calculated and recorded on a load report such as the one shown in Figure 5.5. Figure 5.6 shows the same data in graphical form. Note that the report shows released and planned load, total load, rated capacity, and (over)/under capacity. The term *overcapacity* means that the work center is overloaded and the term *undercapacity*

Week	20	21	22	23	24	Total
Released Load	51.5	45	30	30	25	181.5
Planned Load	100.5	120	100	90	100	510.5
Total Load	152	165	130	120	125	692
Rated Capacity	140	140	140	140	140	700
(Over)/Under capacity	(12)	(25)	10	20	15	8

FIGURE 5.5 Work center load report.

FIGURE 5.6 Graph of a load profile.

means the work center is underloaded. This type of display gives information used to adjust available capacity or to adjust the load by changing the priority plan. In this example, weeks 20 and 21 are overloaded, the rest are underloaded, and the cumulative load is less than the available. For the planner, this shows there is enough total capacity over the planning horizon, and available capacity or priority can be juggled to meet the plan.

SCHEDULING ORDERS

So far we have assumed that we know when an order should be run on one work center. Most orders are processed across a number of work centers, and it is necessary to calculate when orders must be started and completed on each work center so the final due date can be met. This process is called **scheduling**. In the twelfth edition of the *APICS Dictionary*, a *schedule* is defined as "a timetable for planned occurrences."

Back scheduling The usual process is to start with the due date and, using the lead times, to work back to find the start date for each operation. This process is called **back scheduling**. To schedule, we need to know for each order:

- Quantity and due date.
- Sequence of operations and work centers needed.
- Setup and run times for each operation.
- Queue, wait, and move times.
- Work center capacity available (rated or demonstrated).

The information needed is obtained from the following:

- **Order file.** Quantities and due dates.
- **Route file.** Sequence of operations, work centers needed, setup time, and run time.
- **Work center file.** Queue, move, and wait times and work center capacity.

The process is as follows:

1. For each work order, calculate the capacity required (time) at each work center.
2. Starting with the due date, schedule back to get the completion and start dates for each operation.

Example Problem

Suppose there is an order for 150 of gear shaft SG 123. The due date is day 135. The route sheet, shown in Figure 5.3, gives information about the operations to be performed and the setup and run times. The work center file, shown in Figure 5.7, gives lead time data for each work center. Calculate the start and finish dates for each operation. Use the following scheduling rules.

a. Operation times are rounded up to the nearest 8 hours and expressed as days on a one-shift basis. That is, if an operation takes 6.5 standard hours, round it up to 8 hours, which represents one day.

b. Assume an order starts at the beginning of the day and finishes at the end of a day. For example, if an order starts on day 1 and is finished on day 5, it has taken 5 days to complete. If move time is 1 day, the order will be available to the next workstation at the start of day 7.

ANSWER

The calculations for the operation time at each work center are as follows:

$$\text{Setup time} + \text{run time} = \text{total time (standard hours)}$$

Operation 10: Work center 12: $1.5 + 0.20 \times 150 = 31.5$ standard hours
$$= 4 \text{ days}$$

Operation 20: Work center 14: $0.50 + 0.25 \times 150 = 38.0$ standard hours
$$= 5 \text{ days}$$

Operation 30: Work center 17: 0.30 + 0.05 × 150 = 7.8 standard hours
= 1 day

Operation 40: Work center 03: 0.45 + 0.10 × 150 = 15.45 standard hours
= 2 days

The next step is to schedule back from the due date (day 135) to get the completion and start dates for each operation. To do so, we need to know not only the operation times just calculated but also the queue, wait, and move times. These are in the work center file. Suppose that the information shown in Figure 5.7 is obtained from these files.

The process starts with the last operation. The goods are to be in the stores on day 135. It takes 1 day to move them, so the order must be completed on operation 40 on day 133. Subtracting the wait, queue, and operation times (11 days), the order must be started on day 123. With a move time of 1 day, it must be completed on operation 30 on day 121. Using this process, the start and completion dates can be calculated for all operations. Figure 5.8 shows the resulting schedule and Figure 5.9 shows the same thing graphically.

Work Center	Queue Time (days)	Wait Time (days)	Move Time (days)
12	4	1	1
14	3	1	1
17	5	1	1
03	8	1	1

FIGURE 5.7 Lead time data from work center file.

Operation Number	Work Center	Arrival Date	Queue (days)	Operation (days)	Wait (days)	Finish Date
10	12	95	4	4	1	103
20	14	105	3	5	1	113
30	17	115	5	1	1	121
40	03	123	8	2	1	133
50	Stores	135				

FIGURE 5.8 Work schedule.

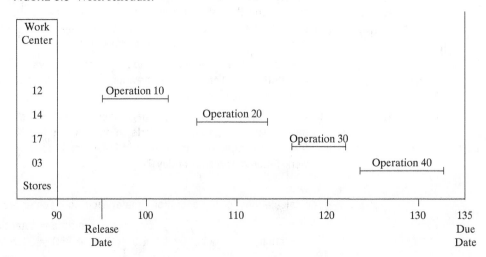

FIGURE 5.9 Graphical work schedule.

MAKING THE PLAN

So far we have discussed the data needed for a capacity requirements plan, where the data come from, and the scheduling and loading of shop orders through the various work centers. The next step is to compare the load to available capacity to see if there are imbalances and if so, to find possible solutions.

There are two ways of balancing capacity available and load: alter the load, or change the capacity available. Altering the load means shifting orders ahead or back so the load is leveled. If orders are processed on other work stations, the schedule and load on the other work stations have to be changed as well. It may also mean that other components should be rescheduled and the master production schedule changed.

Consider the bill of material shown in Figure 5.10. If component B is to be rescheduled to a later date, then the priority for component C is changed, as is the master production schedule for A. For these reasons, changing the load may not be the preferred course of action. In the short run, capacity can be adjusted. Some ways that this may be done are as follows:

- Schedule overtime or undertime. This will provide temporary and quick relief for cases where the load/capacity imbalance is not too large.
- Adjust the level of the workforce by hiring or laying off workers. The ability to do so will depend on the availability of the skills required and the training needed. The higher the skill level and the longer the training needed, the more difficult it becomes to change quickly the level of the workforce.
- Shift workforce from underloaded to overloaded work centers. This requires a flexible cross-trained workforce.
- Use alternate routings to shift some load to another work center. Often the other work center is not as efficient as the original. Nevertheless, the important thing is to meet the schedule, and this is a valid way of doing so.
- Subcontract work when more capacity is needed or bring in previously subcontracted work to increase required capacity. It may be more costly to subcontract rather than make the item in-house, but again it is important to maintain the schedule.

The result of capacity requirements planning should be a detailed workable plan that meets the priority objectives and provides the capacity to do so. Ideally, it will satisfy the material requirements plan and allow for adequate utilization of the workforce, machinery, and equipment.

FIGURE 5.10 Simple bill of material.

SUMMARY

Capacity management occurs at all levels of the planning process. It is directly related to the priority plan, and the level of detail and time spans will be similar to the related priority plan.

Capacity planning is concerned with translating the priority plan into the hours of capacity required in manufacturing to make the items in the priority plan and with methods of making that capacity available. Capacity available depends upon the number of workers and machines, their utilization, and efficiency.

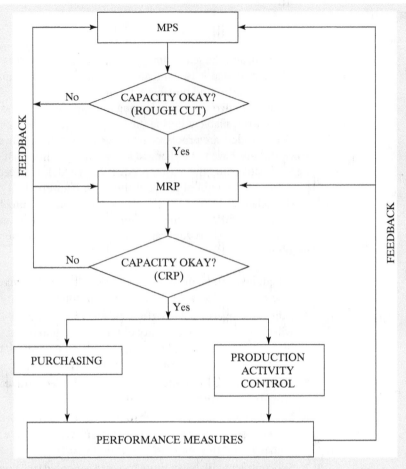

FIGURE 5.11 MRP and CRP closed-loop system.

Capacity requirements planning occurs at the material requirements planning level. It takes planned orders from the MRP and open shop orders from the open order file and converts them to a load on each work center. It considers lead times and actual order quantities. It is the most detailed of the capacity planning techniques.

Material requirements planning and capacity requirements planning should form part of a closed-loop system that not only includes planning and control functions but also provides feedback so planning can always be current. Figure 5.11 illustrates the concept.

KEY TERMS

Available time 103	Load 98
Back scheduling 107	Move time 101
Calculated or rated capacity 103	Open order file 101
Capacity available 102	Queue time 101
Capacity control 99	Resource planning 99
Capacity management 98	Rough-cut capacity planning 99
Capacity planning 99	Scheduling 107
Capacity required 98	Shop calendar 101
Capacity requirements planning 99	Standard time 103
Demonstrated (measured) capacity 103	Utilization 103
Efficiency 104	Wait time 101
Lead time 101	Work center file 101

QUESTIONS

1. What are the responsibilities of capacity management?
2. What is capacity planning?
3. Describe the three steps of capacity planning.
4. Relate the three levels of priority planning to capacity planning. Describe each level in terms of the detail and the time horizons used.
5. What is capacity requirements planning? At what level of the priority planning process does it occur?
6. What are the inputs to the CRP process? Where is this information obtained?
7. Describe each of the following and the information they contain.
    a. Open order file.
    b. Route file.
    c. Work center file.
8. What is a shop calendar? Why is it needed?
9. In which file would you find the following information?
    a. A scheduled receipt.
    b. A planned receipt.
    c. Efficiency and utilization.
    d. Sequence of operations on a part.
10. Define *capacity available*. What are the four factors that affect it?
11. Why is standard time usually used to measure capacity?
12. What are rated capacity, utilization, and efficiency? How are they related?
13. What is measured or demonstrated capacity? How is it different from rated capacity?
14. What is load?
15. What is a work center load report? What information does it contain?
16. What is a schedule?
17. Describe the process of back scheduling.
18. What are the two ways of balancing capacity available and load? Which is preferred? Why?
19. What are some of the ways capacity available can be altered in the short run?
20. Why is feedback necessary in a control system?
21. What might be some of the problems in scheduling rated capacity too closely to the load?

PROBLEMS

5.1. A work center consists of 4 machines each working a 16-hour day for 5 days a week. What is the weekly available time?

Answer.   320 hours per week

5.2. The work center in problem 5.1 is utilized 75% of the time. What are the hours per week actually worked?

5.3. If the efficiency of the work center in problem 5.1 is 120%, what is the rated capacity of the work center?

Answer.   288 standard hours per week

5.4. A work center consisting of 7 machines is operated 16 hours a day for a 5-day week. Utilization is 80%, and efficiency is 110%. What is the rated weekly capacity in standard hours?

Answer.   492.8 standard hours per week

5.5. A work center consists of 3 machines working 8 hours a day for a 5-day week. If the utilization is 75% and the efficiency is 120%, what is the rated capacity of the work center?

5.6. Over a period of 4 weeks, a work center produced 50, 45, 40, and 55 standard hours of work. What is the demonstrated capacity of the work center?

Answer.   47.5 standard hours of work per week

5.7. In an 11-week period, a work center produces 1050 standard hours of work. What is the measured capacity of the work center?

5.8. In 1 week, a work center produces 85 standard hours of work. The hours scheduled are 80, and 75 hours are actually worked. Calculate the utilization and efficiency of the work center.

Answer.   Utilization is 93.75%; efficiency is 113.33%

5.9. A work center consisting of 3 machines operates 40 hours a week. In a 4-week period, it actually worked 355 hours and produced 475 standard hours of work. Calculate the utilization and efficiency of the work center. What is the demonstrated weekly capacity of the work center?

5.10. A firm wishes to determine the efficiency and utilization of a work center composed of 3 machines each working 16 hours per day for 5 days a week. A study undertaken by the materials management department found that over the past year the work center was available for work 12,000 hours, work was actually being done for 10,000 hours, and work was performed 11,480 standard hours. Calculate the utilization, efficiency, and demonstrated weekly capacity. Assume a 50-week year.

5.11. How many standard hours are needed to run an order of 200 pieces if the setup time is 1.3 hours and the run time 0.3 hours per piece? How many actual hours are needed at the work center if the efficiency is 130% and the utilization is 70%?

Answer.   61.3 standard hours; 67.4 actual hours

5.12. How many standard hours are needed to run an order of 500 pieces if the setup time is 3.0 hours and the run time 0.2 hours per piece? How many actual hours are needed at the work center if the efficiency is 125% and the utilization is 85%?

5.13. A work center has the following open and planned orders for week 4. Calculate the total standard time required (load).

		Order Quantity	Setup time (hours)	Run time (hours/piece)	Total time (hours)
Released Orders	120	300	1.00	0.10	
	340	200	2.50	0.30	
Planned Orders	560	300	3.00	0.25	
	780	500	2.00	0.15	
Total Time (standard hours)					

Answer.   Total time = 248.5 standard hours

5.14. A work center has the following open and planned orders for week 4. Calculate the total standard time required (load).

		Order Quantity	Setup time (hours)	Run time (hours/piece)	Total time (hours)
Released Orders	125	200	0.25	0.12	
	345	70	0.70	0.05	
Planned Orders	565	80	1.00	0.25	
	785	35	1.50	0.15	
Total Time (standard hours)					

5.15. Using the information in the following route file, open order file, and MRP planned orders, calculate the load on the work center.

Routing: Part 123:   Setup time   = 2 standard hours
                         Run time per piece = 3 standard hours per piece
            Part 456:   Setup time   = 3 standard hours
                         Run time per piece = 1 standard hour per piece

Open Orders for parts

Week	1	2	3
123	12	8	5
456	15	5	5

Planned Orders for parts

	1	2	3
	0	5	10
	0	10	15

Load report

Week	1	2	3
Released Load 123			
456			
Planned Load 123			
456			
Total Load			

5.16. Complete the following load report and suggest possible courses of action.

Week	18	19	20	21	Total
Released Load	150	155	100	70	475
Planned Load	0	0	80	80	160
Total Load					
Rated Capacity	150	150	150	150	600
(Over)/Under					

5.17. Back schedule the following shop order. All times are given in days. Move time between operations is 1 day, and wait time is 1 day. Due date is day 150. Assume orders start at the beginning of a day and finish at the end of a day.

Operation Number	Work Center	Operation Time (days)	Queue Time (days)	Arrival Date	Finish Date
10	111	2	4		
20	130	4	5		
30	155	1	2		
	Stores			150	

Answer.   The order must arrive at work center 111 on day 126.

5.18. Back schedule the following shop order. All times are given in days. Move time between operations is 1 day, and wait time is 1 day. Due date is day 200. Assume orders start at the beginning of a day and finish at the end of a day.

Operation Number	Work Center	Operation Time (days)	Queue Time (days)	Arrival Date	Finish Date
10	110	4	3		
20	120	2	4		
30	130	3	2		
	Stores			200	

CASE STUDY 5.1

Wescott Products

Whenever Jason Roberts thought about going to work on Friday morning, he started to get a little knot in his stomach. Jason had recently accepted the job as operations manager for a small manufacturing company that specialized in a line of assemble-to-order products. When he accepted the job he was a recent graduate of a business program where he specialized in operations. He had done fairly well in his classes and had emerged as a confident, self-assured person who was sure he could handle such a job in a small company.

The company, Wescott Products, had recently experienced rapid growth from the original start in a two-car garage just five years earlier. In fact, Jason was the first person ever named as operations manager. Prior to that, the only production "manager" reporting to the owner (Judy Wescott) was Frank Adams, the production supervisor. While Frank was an experienced supervisor, he had been promoted to supervisor directly from his old job as a machine operator and had no formal training in planning and control. He soon found that planning was too complex and difficult for him to handle, especially since he also had full responsibility for all the Wescott workers and equipment. Randy Stockard, the sales and marketing manager, had requested and finally applauded Judy Wescott's decision to hire Jason, since he felt production was having a much more difficult time in promising and delivering customer orders. Randy was starting to spend more and more time on the phone with angry customers when they didn't get their orders at the time they expected them. The time away from developing new sales and the danger of losing established customers started to make him highly concerned about sustaining sales growth, to say nothing about his potential bonus check tied to new sales!

Once Jason was placed in the position, however, the "honeymoon" was short, and soon Jason started doubting how much he really did know. The company was still having trouble with promising customer orders and having the capacity to meet those orders. At first he thought it was the forecasting method he used, but a recent analysis told him the total actual orders were generally within 10% of what the forecast projected. In addition, production never seemed to have any significant shortages in either subassemblies or components. In fact, many felt they had far too much material, and in the last couple of staff meetings Jake Marris (the company controller) was grumbling that he thought the inventory turn ratio of just less than 3.5 was unreasonable and costing the company a lot of money. It must be something else, and he had to discover it quickly.

The first idea he thought about was to request the assembly areas to work overtime, but he soon found out that was a sensitive topic that was to be used as a last resort. The workers in that area were highly skilled and would be difficult, if not impossible, to replace in any reasonable time. Adding more would also be difficult for the same reason. A year earlier they were being worked a lot of overtime but had finally had enough. Even though Wescott had no union, the workers got together and demanded better overtime control or they would all quit to move to other jobs that were plentiful for skilled workers in this area. The agreement was that they were to be asked for no more than four hours of overtime per worker per week unless it was truly an emergency situation. They were well paid and all had families, and the time with their families was worth more to them than additional overtime pay. At least the high skill level had one advantage: Each of the workers in the assembly area could skillfully assemble any of the models, and the equipment each had was flexible enough to handle all the models.

Friday mornings were when Jason made his master schedule for the next week (since the standard lead time for all assemblies was quoted as one week, the company had felt no need to schedule farther into the future when very few orders existed there), and no matter how hard he tried he never seemed to be able to get it right. He was sure that he had to start the process by loading the jobs that were missed in the current week into the Monday and Tuesday time blocks and then hope that production could catch up with those in addition to the new jobs that were already promised. The promises came when Randy would inform him of a customer request and ask for a promise date—which was often "as soon as possible." Jason would look at the order to see if the material to make it was in stock and if the equipment to make it was running. He would then typically promise to have it available when requested. Now that a lot of promises were not being met, however, Randy was starting to demand that Jason "get control" of the operation. Jason tried to respond by scheduling a lot of each model to be run every week, but he often found he had to break into the run of a lot to respond to expediting from sales. He knew this made matters worse by using extra time to set up the equipment, but what else could he do? Even Judy Wescott was asking him what she needed to do to help him improve the performance. His normal high level of self-confidence was being shaken.

Jason started poring over his old operations book looking for something he could use. He finally realized that what he needed was a more effective system to develop master schedules from which he could promise orders, order components, and plan capacity. Unfortunately, he also recalled that when that material was covered in his class he had taken off early for spring break! Even though he knew enough to recognize the nature of the problem, he didn't know enough to set up such a schedule. Humbly, he called his former instructor to ask for advice. Once she was briefed on the problem, she told him to gather some information that he could use to develop a sample master schedule and rough-cut capacity plan. Once he had the information, she would help show him how to use it.

The following describes what she asked him to collect:

1. Pick a work center or piece of equipment that has caused some capacity problem in the recent past. List all the product models that use that work center.

2. For each of the models, list the amount of run time they use the work center per item. Also list the setup time, if any. These times can be gathered from standards or, if the standard data are suspect in their accuracy or do not exist, use the actual average time from recent production.

3. For each of the models, list the usual lot size. This should be the same lot size used for the master schedule.

4. For each of the models, list the current inventory, the current forecast, and the current firm customer order quantities.

5. List the current capacity (hours) available for the equipment.

The following tables summarize the data Jason collected:

WORK CENTER 12

Model	Run Time (per item, in minutes)	Setup Time (per lot)	Lot Size (minimum qty.)	On-hand*
A	3.7	90 minutes	150	10
B	5.1	40 minutes	100	0
C	4.3	60 minutes	120	0
D	8.4	200 minutes	350	22
E	11.2	120 minutes	400	153

*Most of the on-hand was really forced when the lot size exceeded orders for the week for that model. They would then assemble the rest of the lot as "plain vanilla," such that they could easily add any subassembly options once the actual customer orders came in.

Two workers are currently assigned to the work center, and only to the first shift. Even though assembly workers are very flexible, Jason cannot take workers from another assembly area, as those work centers are also behind and therefore appear to be equally overloaded.

The following is the forecast and customer orders for each of the five models assembled in work center 12:

Model	Weeks	1	2	3	4	5	6	7	8	9	10
A	Forecast	45	45	45	45	45	45	45	45	45	45
	Customer Orders	53	41	22	15	4	7	2	0	0	0
B	Forecast	35	35	35	35	35	35	35	35	35	35
	Customer Orders	66	40	31	30	17	6	2	0	0	0
C	Forecast	50	50	50	50	50	50	50	50	50	50
	Customer Orders	52	43	33	21	14	4	7	1	0	0
D	Forecast	180	180	180	180	180	180	180	180	180	180
	Customer Orders	277	190	178	132	94	51	12	7	9	2
E	Forecast	200	200	200	200	200	200	200	200	200	200
	Customer Orders	223	174	185	109	74	36	12	2	0	0

Once Jason had gathered all the data, he immediately called his instructor, only to find out that by an ironic twist of fate she would be gone for more than a week on spring break!

Assignment

This leaves you to help Jason. Specifically, you need to do the following:

1. Discuss the nature and probable sources of the problem.

2. Examine the rough-cut capacity situation using the data Jason gathered. Discuss the results and how they are linked to the problems identified in question 1.

3. Use the information and your knowledge of the situation to develop a complete plan for Jason to use in the future. Part of this plan should be to build and demonstrate the approach to master scheduling for the data given in the case.

PRODUCTION ACTIVITY CONTROL

INTRODUCTION

The time comes when plans must be put into action. Production activity control (PAC) is responsible for executing the master production schedule and the material requirements plan (MRP). At the same time, it must make good use of labor and machines, minimize work-in-process inventory, and maintain customer service.

The material requirements plan authorizes PAC:

- To release work orders to the shop for manufacturing.
- To take control of work orders and make sure they are completed on time.
- To be responsible for the immediate detailed planning of the flow of orders through manufacturing, carrying out the plan, and controlling the work as it progresses to completion.
- To manage day-to-day activity and provide the necessary support.

Figure 6.1 shows the relationship between the planning system and PAC.

The activities of the PAC system can be classified into planning, implementation, and control functions.

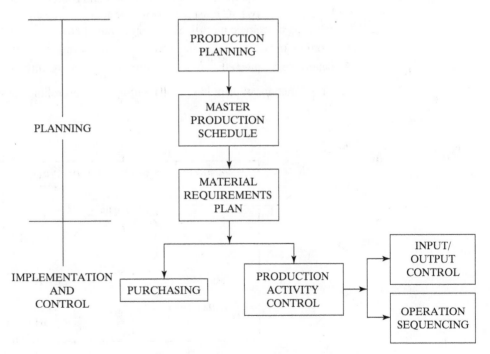

FIGURE 6.1 Priority planning and production activity control.

Planning

The flow of work through each of the work centers must be planned to meet delivery dates, which means production activity control must do the following:

- Ensure that the required materials, tooling, personnel, and information are available to manufacture the components when needed.
- Schedule start and completion dates for each shop order at each work center so the scheduled completion date of the order can be met. This will involve the planner in developing a load profile for the work centers.

Implementation

Once the plans are made, production activity control must put them into action by advising the shop floor what must be done. Usually instructions are given by issuing a shop order. Production activity control will:

- Gather the information needed by the shop floor to make the product.
- Release orders to the shop floor as authorized by the material requirements plan. This is called dispatching.

Control

Once plans are made and shop orders released, the process must be monitored to learn what is actually happening. The results are compared to the plan to decide whether corrective action is necessary. Production activity control will do the following:

- Rank the shop orders in desired priority sequence by work center and establish a dispatch list based on this information.
- Track the actual performance of work orders and compare it to planned schedules. Where necessary, PAC must take corrective action by replanning, rescheduling, or adjusting capacity to meet final delivery requirements.
- Monitor and control work-in-process, lead times, and work center queues.
- Report work center efficiency, operation times, order quantities, and scrap.

The functions of planning, implementing, and controlling are shown schematically in Figure 6.2.

FIGURE 6.2 Schematic of a production control system.

Manufacturing Systems

The particular type of production control system used varies from company to company, but all should perform the functions just mentioned. However, the relative importance of these functions will depend on the type of manufacturing process. Manufacturing processes can be conveniently organized into three categories:

1. Flow manufacturing.
2. Intermittent manufacturing.
3. Project manufacturing.

Flow manufacturing   **Flow manufacturing** is concerned with the production of high-volume standard products. If the units are discrete (e.g., cars and appliances), the process is usually called **repetitive manufacturing**, and if the goods are made in a continuous flow (e.g., gasoline), the process is called **continuous manufacturing**. There are four major characteristics to flow manufacturing:

1. Routings are fixed, and work centers are arranged according to the routing. The time taken to perform work at one work center is almost the same as at any other work center in the line.
2. Work centers are dedicated to producing a limited range of similar products. Machinery and tooling are especially designed to make the specific products.
3. Material flows from one workstation to another using some form of mechanical transfer. There is little buildup in work-in-process inventory, and throughput times are low.
4. Capacity is fixed by the line.

Production activity control concentrates on planning the flow of work and making sure that the right material is fed to the line as stated in the planned schedule. Since work flows from one workstation to another automatically, implementation and control are relatively simple.

Intermittent manufacturing   **Intermittent manufacturing** is characterized by many variations in product design, process requirements, and order quantities. This kind of manufacturing is characterized by the following:

1. Flow of work through the shop is varied and depends on the design of a particular product. As orders are processed, they will take more time at one workstation than at another. Thus, the work flow is not balanced.
2. Machinery and workers must be flexible enough to do the variety of work involved in intermittent manufacturing. Machinery and work centers are usually grouped according to the function they perform (e.g., all lathes in one department).
3. Throughput times are generally long. Scheduling work to arrive just when needed is difficult, the time taken by an order at each work center varies, and work queues before work centers, causing long delays in processing. Work-in-process inventory is often large.
4. The capacity required depends on the particular mix of products being built and is difficult to predict.

Production activity control in intermittent manufacturing is complex. Because of the number of products made, the variety of routings, and scheduling problems, PAC is a major activity in this type of manufacturing. Planning and control are typically exercised using shop orders for each batch being produced. Our discussion of PAC assumes this kind of environment.

Project manufacturing   **Project manufacturing** usually involves the creation of one unit or a small number of units. Complex shipbuilding is an example. Because the design of a product is often carried out or modified as the project develops, there is close coordination between manufacturing, marketing, purchasing, and engineering.

DATA REQUIREMENTS

To plan the processing of materials through manufacturing, PAC must have the following information:

- What and how much to produce.
- When parts are needed so the completion date can be met.
- What operations are required to make the product and how long the operations will take.
- What the available capacities of the various work centers are.

Production activity control must have a data or information system from which to work. Usually the data needed to answer these questions are organized into databases. The files contained in the databases are of two types: planning and control.

Planning Files

Four planning files are needed: item master file, product structure file, routing file, and work center master file.

Item master file   There is one record in the **item master file** for each part number. The file contains, in one place, all of the pertinent data related to the part. For PAC, this includes the following:

- Part number, a unique number assigned to a component.
- Part description.
- Manufacturing lead time, the normal time needed to make this part.
- Quantity on hand.
- Quantity available.
- Allocated quantity, quantities assigned to specific work orders but not yet withdrawn from inventory.
- On-order quantities, the balance due on all outstanding orders.
- Lot-size quantity, the quantity normally ordered at one time.

Product structure file (bill of material file)   The **product structure file (bill of material file)** contains a list of the single-level components and quantities needed to assemble a parent. It forms a basis for a "pick list" to be used by storeroom personnel to collect the parts required to make the assembly. According to the Association for Operations Management (APICS), there are a variety of ways of displaying a bill of material, "including the single level bill of material, an indented bill of material, transient bill of material, matrix bill of material and costed bill of material. . . . The BOM may also be called the formula, recipe, or ingredients list in certain process industries."

Routing file   The **routing file** contains a record for each part manufactured. The routing consists of a series of operations required to make the item. For each product, this file contains a step-by-step set of instructions describing how the product is made. It gives details of the following:

- The operations required to make the product and the sequence in which those operations are performed.
- A brief description of each operation.
- Equipment, tools, and accessories needed for each operation.

- Setup times, the standard time required for setting up the equipment for each operation.
- Run times, the standard time required to process one unit through each operation.
- Lead times for each operation.

Work center master file　The **work center master file** collects all of the relevant data on a work center. For each work center, it gives details on the following:

- Work center number.
- Capacity.
- Number of shifts worked per week.
- Number of machine hours per shift.
- Number of labor hours per shift.
- Efficiency.
- Utilization.
- Queue time, the average time that a job waits at the work center before work is begun.
- Alternate work centers, work centers that may be used as alternatives.

Control Files

Control in intermittent manufacturing is exercised through shop orders and control files that contain data on these orders. There are generally two kinds of files: the shop order master file and the shop order detail file.

Shop order master file　Each active manufacturing order has a record in the **shop order master file**. The purpose is to provide summarized data on each shop order, such as the following information:

- Shop order number, a unique number identifying the shop order.
- Order quantity.
- Quantity completed.
- Quantity scrapped.
- Quantity of material issued to the order.
- Due date, the date the order is expected to be finished.
- Priority, a value used to rank the order in relation to others.
- Balance due, the quantity not yet completed.
- Cost information.

Shop order detail file　Each shop order has a **shop order detail file**, which contains a record for each operation needed to make the item. Each record contains the following information:

- Operation number.
- Setup hours, planned and actual.
- Run hours, planned and actual.
- Quantity reported complete at that operation.
- Quantity reported scrapped at that operation.
- Due date or lead time remaining.

ORDER PREPARATION

Once authorization to process an order has been received, production activity control is responsible for planning and preparing its release to the shop floor. The order should be reviewed to be sure that the necessary tooling, material, and capacity are available. If they are not, the order cannot be completed and should not be released.

Tooling is not generally considered in the material requirements planning program, so at this stage, material availability must be checked. If MRP software is used, it will have checked the availability of material and allocated it to a shop order so no further checking is necessary. If MRP software is not used, production activity control must manually check material availability.

If a capacity requirements planning system has been used, necessary capacity should be available. However, at this stage, there may be some differences between planned capacity and what is actually available. When capacity requirements planning is not used, it is necessary to determine if capacity is available.

Checking capacity availability is a two-step process. First, the order must be scheduled to see when the capacity is needed, and second, the load on work centers must be checked in that period. Scheduling and loading are discussed in the next two sections.

SCHEDULING

The objective of scheduling is to meet delivery dates and to make the best use of manufacturing resources. It involves establishing start and finish dates for each operation required to complete an item. To develop a reliable schedule, the planner must have information on routing, required and available capacity, competing jobs, and manufacturing lead times (MLTs) at each work center involved.

Manufacturing Lead Time

Manufacturing lead time is the time normally required to produce an item in a typical lot quantity. Typically, MLT consists of five elements:

1. *Queue time*, amount of time the job is waiting at a work center before operation begins.
2. *Setup time*, time required to prepare the work center for operation.
3. *Run time*, time needed to run the order through the operation.
4. *Wait time*, amount of time the job is at the work center before being moved to the next work center.
5. *Move time*, transit time between work centers.

The total manufacturing lead time will be the sum of order preparation and release plus the MLTs for each operation. Figure 6.3 shows the elements making up manufacturing lead time. Setup time and run time are straightforward, and determining them is the responsibility of the industrial engineering department. Queue, wait, and move times are under the control of manufacturing and PAC.

The largest of the five elements is queue time. Typically, in an intermittent manufacturing operation, it accounts for 85%–95% of the total lead time. Production activity control is

FIGURE 6.3 Manufacturing lead time.

responsible for managing the queue by regulating the flow of work into and out of work centers. If the number of orders waiting to be worked on (load) is reduced, so is the queue time, the lead time, and work-in-process. Increasing capacity also reduces queue. Production activity control must manage both the input of orders to the production process and the available capacity to control queue and work-in-process.

A term that is closely related to manufacturing lead time is *cycle time*. The twelfth edition of the *APICS Dictionary* defines **cycle time** as "the length of time from when material enters a production facility until it exits." A synonym is **throughput time**.

Example Problem

An order for 100 of a product is processed on work centers A and B. The setup time on A is 30 minutes, and run time is 10 minutes per piece. The setup time on B is 50 minutes, and the run time is 5 minutes per piece. Wait time between the two operations is 4 hours. The move time between A and B is 10 minutes. Wait time after operation B is 4 hours, and the move time into stores is 15 minutes. There is no queue at either workstation. Calculate the total manufacturing lead time for the order.

ANSWER

```
Work center A operation time = 30 + (100 × 10) = 1030 minutes
Wait time                                    =  240 minutes
Move time from A to B                        =   10 minutes
Work center B operation time = 50 + (100 × 5) =  550 minutes
Wait time                                    =  240 minutes
Move time from B to stores                   =   15 minutes
Total manufacturing lead time                = 2085 minutes
                                             =   34 hours, 45 minutes
```

Scheduling Techniques

There are many techniques to schedule shop orders through a plant, but all of them require an understanding of forward and backward scheduling as well as finite and infinite loading.

Forward scheduling assumes that material procurement and operation scheduling for a component start when the order is received, whatever the due date, and that operations are scheduled forward from this date. The first line in Figure 6.4 illustrates this method. The result is completion before the due date, which usually results in a buildup of inventory. This method is used to decide the earliest delivery date for a product.

Forward scheduling is used to calculate how long it will take to complete a task. The technique is used for purposes such as developing promise dates for customers or figuring out whether an order behind schedule can be caught up.

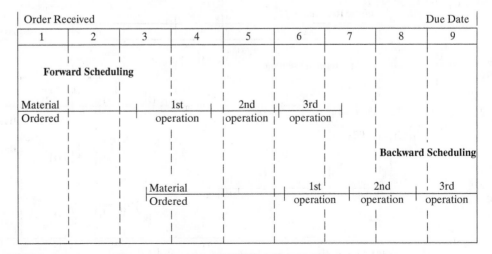

FIGURE 6.4 Forward and backward scheduling: infinite loading.

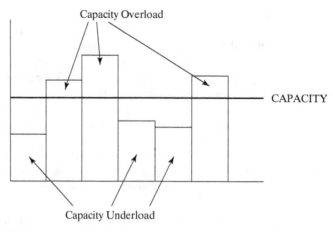

FIGURE 6.5 Infinite load profile.

Backward scheduling is illustrated by the second line in Figure 6.4. The last operation on the routing is scheduled first and is scheduled for completion at the due date. Previous operations are scheduled back from the last operation. This schedules items to be available as needed and uses the same logic as the MRP system. Work-in-process inventory is reduced, but because there is little slack time in the system, customer service may suffer.

Backward scheduling is used to determine when an order must be started. Backward scheduling is common in industry because it reduces inventory.

Infinite loading is also illustrated in Figure 6.4. The assumption is made that the workstations on which operations 1, 2, and 3 are done have capacity available when required. It does not consider the existence of other shop orders competing for capacity at these work centers. It assumes infinite capacity will be available. Figure 6.5 shows a load profile for infinite capacity. Notice the over- and underload.

Finite loading assumes there is a defined limit to available capacity at any workstation. If there is not enough capacity available at a workstation because of other shop orders, the order has to be scheduled in a different time period. Figure 6.6 illustrates the condition.

In the forward-scheduling example shown in Figure 6.6, the first and second operations cannot be performed at their respective workstations when they should be because the required capacity is not available at the time required. These operations must be rescheduled to a later time period. Similarly, in the example of scheduling back, the second and first operations cannot be performed when they should be and must be rescheduled to an earlier time period. Figure 6.7 shows a load profile for finite loading. Notice the load is smoothed so there is no overload condition.

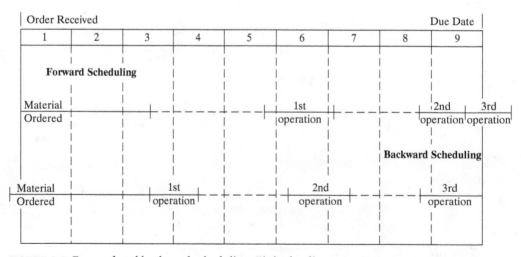

FIGURE 6.6 Forward and backward scheduling. Finite loading.

FIGURE 6.7 Finite load profile.

Chapter 5 gives an example of backward scheduling as it relates to capacity requirements planning. The same process is used in PAC.

Example Problem

A company has an order for 50 brand X to be delivered on day 100. Draw a backward schedule based on the following:

a. Only one machine is assigned to each operation
b. The factory works one 8-hour shift 5 days a week
c. The parts move in one lot of 50.

Part	Operation	Time (days)
A	10	5
A	20	3
B	10	10
X	Assembly	5

ANSWER

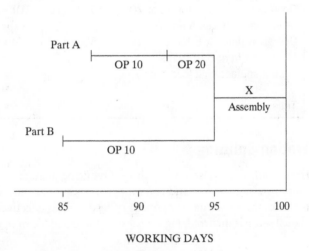

WORKING DAYS

Operation Overlapping

In **operation overlapping**, the next operation is allowed to begin before the entire lot is completed on the previous operation. This reduces the total manufacturing lead times because the second operation starts before the first operation finishes all the parts in the order. Figure 6.8 shows schematically how it works and the potential reduction in lead time.

An order is divided into at least two lots. When the first lot is completed on operation A, it is transferred to operation B. As seen in Figure 6.8, it is assumed that operation B cannot be set up until the first lot is received, but this is not always the case. While operation A continues with the second lot, operation B starts on the first lot. When operation A finishes the second lot, it is transferred to operation B. If the lots are sized properly, there will

Operation A

FIGURE 6.8 Operation overlapping.

be no idle time at operation B. The manufacturing lead time is reduced by the overlap time and the elimination of queue time.

Operation overlapping is a method of expediting an order, but there are some costs involved. First, move costs are increased, especially if the overlapped operations are not close together. Second, it may increase the queue and lead times for other orders. Third, it does not increase capacity but potentially reduces it if the second operation is idle waiting for parts from the first operation.

The problem is deciding the size of the sublot. If the run time per piece on operation B is shorter than that on A, the first batch must be large enough to avoid idle time on operation B.

Example Problem

Refer to the data given in the example problem in the section on manufacturing lead time. It is decided to overlap operations A and B by splitting the lot of 100 into two lots of 70 and 30. Wait time between A and B and between B and stores is eliminated. The move times remain the same. Setup on operation B cannot start until the first batch arrives. Calculate the manufacturing lead time. How much time has been saved?

ANSWER

Operation time for A for lot of 70 = 30 + (70 × 10) =	730 minutes
Move time between A and B =	10 minutes
Operation time for B for lot of 100 = 50 + (100 × 5) =	550 minutes
Move time from B to stores =	15 minutes
Total manufacturing lead time =	1305 minutes
=	21 hours, 45 minutes
Time saved =	13 hours

Operation Splitting

Operation splitting is a second method of reducing manufacturing lead time. The order is split into two or more lots and run on two or more machines simultaneously. If the lot is split in two, the run-time component of lead time is effectively cut in half, although an additional setup is incurred. Figure 6.9 shows a schematic of operation splitting.

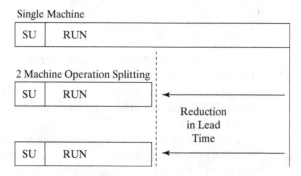

FIGURE 6.9 Operation splitting.

Operation splitting is practical when:

- Setup time is low compared to run time.
- A suitable work center is idle.
- It is possible for an operator to run more than one machine at a time.

The last condition often exists when a machine cycles through its operation automatically, leaving the operator time to set up another machine. The time needed to unload and load must be shorter than the run time per piece. For example, if the unload/load time was two minutes and the run time was three minutes, the operator would have time to unload and load the first machine while the second was running.

Example Problem

A component made on a particular work center has a setup time of 100 minutes and a run time of 3 minutes per piece. An order for 500 is to be processed on 2 machines simultaneously. The machines can be set up at the same time. Calculate the elapsed operation time.

ANSWER

Elapsed operation time = 100 + 3 × 250 = 850 minutes
= 14 hours and 10 minutes

LOAD LEVELING

Load profiles were discussed in Chapter 5 in the section on capacity requirements planning. The load profile for a work center is constructed by calculating the standard hours of operation for each order in each time period and adding them together by time period. Figure 6.10 shows an example of a load report.

This report tells PAC what the load is on the work center. There is a capacity shortage in week 20 of 30 hours. This means there would be no point in releasing all of the planned orders that week. Perhaps some could be released in week 18 or 19, and perhaps some overtime could be worked to help reduce the capacity crunch.

Work Center: 10
Description: Lathes
Number of Machines: 3
Rated Capacity:
    110 standard hours/week

Available Time: 120 hours/week
Efficiency: 115%
Utilization 80%

Week	18	19	20	21	22	23	Total
Released Load	105	100	80	30	0	0	315
Planned Load			60	80	130	80	350
Total Load	105	100	140	110	130	80	665
Rated Capacity	110	110	110	110	110	110	660
(Over)/Under Capacity	5	10	(30)	0	(20)	30	(5)

FIGURE 6.10 Work center load report.

SCHEDULING BOTTLENECKS

In intermittent manufacturing, it is almost impossible to balance the available capacities of the various workstations with the demand for their capacity. As a result, some workstations are overloaded and some underloaded. The overloaded workstations are called **bottlenecks** and, by definition, are those workstations where the required capacity is greater than the available capacity. In the twelfth edition of its dictionary, APICS defines a bottleneck as "a facility, function, department, or resource whose capacity is equal to or less than the demand placed upon it."

Throughput   Throughput is the total volume of production passing through a facility. Bottlenecks control the throughput of all products processed by them. If work centers feeding bottlenecks produce more than the bottleneck can process, excess work-in-process inventory is built up. Therefore, work should be scheduled through the bottleneck at the rate it can process the work. Work centers fed by bottlenecks have their throughput controlled by the bottleneck, and their schedules should be determined by that of the bottleneck.

Example Problem

Suppose a manufacturer makes wagons composed of a box body, a handle assembly, and two wheel assemblies. Demand for the wagons is 500 a week. The wheel assembly capacity is 1200 sets a week, the handle assembly capacity is 450 a week, and final assembly can produce 550 wagons a week.

a. What is the capacity of the factory?

b. What limits the throughput of the factory?

c. How many wheel assemblies should be made each week?

d. What is the utilization of the wheel assembly operation?

e. What happens if the wheel assembly utilization is increased to 100%?

ANSWER

a. 450 units a week.

b. Throughput is limited by the capacity of the handle assembly operation.

c. 900 wheel assemblies should be made each week. This matches the capacity of the handle assembly operation.

d. Utilization of the wheel assembly operation is $900 \div 1200 = 75\%$.

e. Excess inventory builds up.

Some bottleneck principles   Since bottlenecks control the throughput of a facility, some important principles should be noted:

1. **Utilization of a nonbottleneck resource is not determined by its potential but by another constraint in the system.** In the previous example problem, the utilization of the wheel assembly operation was determined by the handle assembly operation.

2. **Using a nonbottleneck 100% of the time does not produce 100% utilization.** If the wheel assembly operation was utilized 100% of the time, it would produce 1200 sets of wheels a week, 300 sets more than needed. Because of the buildup of inventory, this operation would eventually have to stop.

3. **The capacity of the system depends on the capacity of the bottleneck.** If the handle assembly operation breaks down, the throughput of the factory is reduced.

4. **Time saved at a nonbottleneck saves the system nothing.** Suppose, in a flash of brilliance, the industrial engineering department increased the capacity of the wheel assembly operation to 1500 units a week. This extra capacity could not be utilized, and nothing would be gained.

5. **Capacity and priority must be considered together.** Suppose the wagon manufacturer made wagons with two styles of handles. During setup, nothing is produced,

which reduces the capacity of the system. Since handle assembly is the bottleneck, every setup in this operation reduces the throughput of the system. Ideally, the company would run one style of handle for six months, then switch over to the second style. However, customers wanting the second style of handle might not be willing to wait six months. A compromise is needed whereby runs are as long as possible but priority (demand) is satisfied.

6. **Loads can, and should, be split.** Suppose the handle assembly operation (the bottleneck) produces one style of handle for two weeks, then switches to the second style. The batch size is 900 handles. Rather than waiting until the 900 are produced before moving them to the final assembly area, the manufacturer can move a day's production (90) at a time. The process batch size and the transfer batch size are different. Thus, delivery to the final assembly is matched to usage, and work-in-process inventory is reduced.

7. **Focus should be on balancing the flow through the shop.** The key is throughput that ends up in sales.

Managing bottlenecks   Since bottlenecks are so important to the throughput of a system, scheduling and controlling them is extremely important. The following must be done:

1. **Establish a time buffer before each bottleneck.** A time buffer is an inventory (queue) place before each bottleneck. Because it is of the utmost importance to keep the bottleneck working, it must never be starved for material, and it can be starved only if the flow from feeding workstations is disrupted. The time buffer should be only as long as the time of any expected delay caused by feeding workstations. In this way, the time buffer ensures that the bottleneck will not be shut down for lack of work and this queue will be held at a predetermined minimum quantity.

2. **Control the rate of material feeding the bottleneck.** A bottleneck must be fed at a rate equal to its capacity so the time buffer remains constant. The first operation in the sequence of operations is called a **gateway operation**. This operation controls the work feeding the bottleneck and must operate at a rate equal to the output of the bottleneck so the time buffer queue is maintained.

3. **Do everything to provide the needed bottleneck capacity.** Anything that increases the capacity of the bottleneck increases the capacity of the system. Better utilization, fewer setups, and improved methods to reduce setup and run time are some methods for increasing capacity.

4. **Adjust loads.** This is similar to item 3 but puts emphasis on reducing the load on a bottleneck by using such things as alternate work centers and subcontracting. These may be more costly than using the bottleneck, but utilization of nonbottlenecks and throughput of the total system are increased, resulting in more company sales and increased profits.

5. **Change the schedule.** Do this as a final resort, but it is better to be honest about delivery promises.

Once the bottleneck is scheduled according to its available capacity and the market demand it must satisfy, the nonbottleneck resources can be scheduled. When a work order is completed at the bottleneck, it can be scheduled on subsequent operations.

Feeding operations have to protect the time buffer by scheduling backward in time from the bottleneck. If the time buffer is set at four days, the operation immediately preceding the bottleneck is scheduled to complete the required parts four days before they are scheduled to run on the bottleneck. Each preceding operation can be back scheduled in the same way so the parts are available as required for the next operation.

Any disturbances in the feeding operations are absorbed by the time buffer, and throughput is not affected. Also, work-in-process inventory is reduced. Since the queue is limited to the time buffer, lead times are reduced.

THEORY OF CONSTRAINTS AND DRUM-BUFFER-ROPE

The section on managing bottlenecks was developed based on the work of Eliyahu M. Goldratt in his *Theory of Constraints*. It has allowed many people to rethink their approaches to improving and managing their production processes. The fundamental concept behind the work is that every operation producing a product or service is a series of linked processes. Each process has a specific capacity to produce the given defined output for the operation, and in virtually every case, there is one process that limits or constrains the throughput from the entire operation. Refer to Figure 6.11 for an example of an operation producing product A.

The total operation is constrained by process 3 at a capacity of four per hour. No matter how much efficiency there is in the other processes and how many process improvements are made in processes 1, 2, and 4, it will never be possible to exceed the overall operational output of four per hour. Increased efficiency and utilization in processes 1 and 2 will only increase inventory—not sales.

Manage the Constraint

Several fundamental guidelines have been developed for understanding how to manage a constraining process or bottleneck. Some of the more noteworthy include the following: focus on balancing the flow through the shop; time lost at a bottleneck is time lost to the whole system but time lost at a nonconstraint is a mirage; and transfer batches do not have to be the same size as process batches. All of these were discussed in the section Some Bottleneck Principles.

Improve the Process

Once a constraint has been identified, there is a five-step process that is recommended to help improve the performance of the operation. The five steps are summarized as follows:

1. **Identify the constraint.** This implies the need to examine the entire process to determine which process limits the throughput. The concept does not limit this process examination to merely the operational processes. For example, in Figure 6.11, suppose the sales department was selling the output only at the rate of three per hour. In that case, sales would be the constraint and not process 3. It must be remembered that a constraint limits throughput, not inventory or production.

2. **Exploit the constraint.** Find methods to maximize the utilization of the constraint toward productive throughput. For example, in many operations all processes are shut down during lunchtime. If a process is a constraint, the operation should consider rotating lunch periods so that the constraint is never allowed to be idle.

3. **Subordinate everything to the constraint.** Effective utilization of the constraint is the most important issue. Everything else is secondary.

4. **Elevate the constraint.** This means to find ways to increase the available hours of the constraint, including more of it.

5. **Once the constraint is a constraint no longer, find the new one and repeat the steps.** As the effective utilization of the constraint increases, it may cease to be a constraint as another process becomes one. In that case the emphasis shifts to the new process constraint.

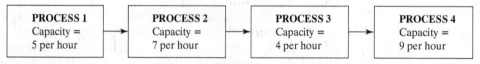

FIGURE 6.11 Process A.

Scheduling with the Theory of Constraints

Even the scheduling system developed for the theory of constraints (TOC) has its own specific approach. It is often described as **Drum-Buffer-Rope**:

- **Drum.** The drum of the system refers to the "drumbeat" or pace of production. It represents the master schedule for the operation, which is focused around the pace of throughput as defined by the constraint.
- **Buffer.** Since it is so important that the constraint never be "starved" for needed inventory, a "time" buffer is often established in front of the constraint. It is called a time buffer because it represents the amount of time that the inventory in the buffer protects the constraint from disruptions.
- **Rope.** The analogy is that the rope "pulls" production to the constraint for necessary processing. Although this may imply a reactive replenishment system, such as a reorder point, it can be done by a well-coordinated release of material into the system at the right time.

Even the scheduling system has its primary focus on effective management of the organization's constraint to throughput and sales.

Four primary plant types are defined, and they are used to specify the flow of materials through a production process. They can therefore be helpful in understanding how to manage the operation using the theory of constraints. They include:

- I-plant, where one raw material is used to make one final product. Processing is usually done in a straight line.
- A-plant, where numerous subassemblies merge into a single final assembly.
- V-plant, where few raw materials can be made into several end products.
- T-plant, where multiple straight lines can split into several assemblies.

The theory of constraints also includes a process to help develop and implement change in an organization. The first step to this is to identify core conflicts, which are then validated by building what is called a *current reality tree*. After those undesirable effects are identified from the core conflicts, a future reality tree is developed, which will lay out a strategy to resolve the problems. The final major step in the process is to build a tactical objective map that will define a strategy to accomplish the future reality.

Example Problem

Parent X requires 1 each of component Y and Z. Both Y and Z are processed on work center 20, which has an available capacity of 40 hours. The setup time for component Y is 1 hour and the run time 0.3 hour per piece. For component Z, setup time is 2 hours and the run time is 0.20 hour per piece. Calculate the number of Ys and Zs that can be produced.

Answer

$$\text{Let } x = \text{number of Ys and Zs to produce}$$
$$\text{Time}_Y + \text{Time}_Z = 40 \text{ hours}$$
$$1 + 0.3x + 2 + 0.2x = 40 \text{ hours}$$
$$0.5x = 37 \text{ hours}$$
$$x = 74$$

Therefore, work center 20 can produce 74 Ys and 74 Zs.

Example Problem

In this problem, parent A is made of one B and 2 Cs. As and Bs are both made on work station 1, which has a capacity of 40 hours per week. The Cs are made on work station 2, which also has a capacity of 40 hours per week.

Product	Setup Time (hours)	Run Time (hours/unit)
A	2	0.1
B	2	0.2
C	1	0.3

Based on the above information calculate the maximum number of As, Bs, and Cs that should be produced per week.

ANSWER

The number of Bs produced should equal the number of As produced to avoid over production. Therefore, the number of Bs can be expressed in a formula as the number of As.

Work station 1

$$Time_A + Time_B = 40 \text{ hours}$$
$$2 + 0.1A + 2 + 0.2A = 40$$
$$0.3A = 36$$
$$A = 120$$

Work station 1 has the capacity to produce enough As and Bs to make 120 As per week.

Work station 2

The number of Cs produced should be twice the number of As produced to avoid over production. Therefore the number of Cs can be represented by 2 × A.

$$Time_C = 40 \text{ Hours}$$
$$1 + 2 \times 0.3A = 40$$
$$0.6A = 39$$
$$A = 65$$

Work station 2 has the capacity to make enough Cs to support production of only 65 As per week, and in this case this is the constraint. To avoid over production, work center 1 should produce 65 As and 65 Bs per week. Work station 2 should produce 130 Cs per week (enough for 65 As).

In this example work station 1 will have very low utilization. However, producing more than 65 Bs per week will only build inventory and work station 1 will be starved by work station 2, which has the capacity to produce only 130 Cs per week.

IMPLEMENTATION

Orders that have tooling, material, and capacity have a good chance of being completed on time and can be released to the shop floor. Other orders that do not have all of the necessary elements should not be released because they only cause excess work-in-process inventory and may interrupt work on orders that can be completed. The process for releasing an order is shown in Figure 6.12.

Implementation is arrived at by issuing a shop order to manufacturing, authorizing them to proceed with making the item. A shop packet is usually compiled and contains the shop order and whatever other information is needed by manufacturing. It may include any of the following:

- Shop order showing the shop order number, part number, name, description, and quantity.
- Engineering drawings.
- Bills of material.
- Route sheets showing the operations to be performed, equipment and accessories needed, materials to use, and setup and run times.
- Material issue tickets that authorize manufacturing to get the required material from stores. These are also used for charging the material against the shop order.

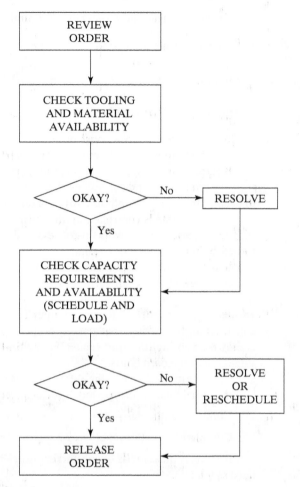

FIGURE 6.12 Order release process.

- Tool requisitions authorizing manufacturing to withdraw necessary tooling from the tool crib.
- Job tickets for each operation to be performed. As well as authorizing the individual operations to be performed, they also can function as part of a reporting system. The worker can log on and off the job using the job ticket, and it then becomes a record of that operation.
- Move tickets that authorize and direct the movement of work between operations.

CONTROL

Once work orders have been issued to manufacturing, their progress has to be controlled. To control progress, performance has to be measured and compared to what is planned. If what is actually happening (what is measured) varies significantly from what was planned, either the plans have to be changed or corrective action must be taken to bring performance back to plan.

The objectives of production activity control are to meet delivery dates and to make the best use of company resources. To meet delivery dates, a company must control the progress of orders on the shop floor, which means controlling the lead time for orders. As discussed previously in this chapter, the largest component of lead time is queue. If queue can be controlled, delivery dates can be met. Intermittent operations have many different products and order quantities and many different routings, each requiring different capacities. In this environment, it is almost impossible to balance the load over all the workstations. Queue exists because of this erratic input and output.

To control queue and meet delivery commitments, production activity control must:

- Control the work going into and coming out of a work center. This is generally called **input/output control**.
- Set the correct priority of orders to run at each work center.

Input/Output Control

Production activity control must balance the flow of work to and from different work centers. This is to ensure that queue, work-in-process, and lead times are controlled. The input/output control system is a method of managing queues and work-in-process lead times by monitoring and controlling the input to, and output from, a facility. It is designed to balance the input rate in hours with the output rate so these will be controlled.

The input rate is controlled by the release of orders to the shop floor. If the rate of input is increased, queue, work-in-process, and lead times increase. The output rate is controlled by increasing or decreasing the capacity of a work center. Capacity change is a problem for manufacturing, but it can be attained by overtime or undertime, shifting workers, and so forth. Figure 6.13 shows the idea graphically.

Input/output report   To control input and output, a plan must be devised, along with a method for comparing what actually occurs against what was planned. This information is shown on an **input/output report**. Figure 6.14 shows an example of such a report. The values are in standard hours.

Cumulative variance is the difference between the total planned for a given period and the actual total for that period. It is calculated as follows:

Cumulative variance = previous cumulative variance + actual − planned

Cumulative input variance week 2 = −4 + 32 − 32 = −4

Backlog is the same as queue and expresses the work to be done in hours. It is calculated as follows:

Planned backlog for period 1 = previous backlog + planned input − planned output
$$= 32 + 38 - 40$$
$$= 30 \text{ hours}$$

The report shows the plan was to maintain a level output in each period and to reduce the queue and lead time by 10 hours, but input and output were lower than expected.

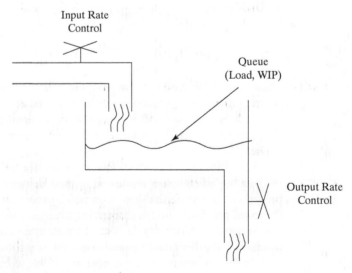

FIGURE 6.13 Input/output control.

Work Center: 201
Capacity per Period: 40 standard hours

Period	1	2	3	4	5	Total
Planned Input	38	32	36	40	44	190
Actual Input	34	32	32	42	40	180
Cumulative Variance	–4	–4	–8	–6	–10	–10

	1	2	3	4	5	Total
Planned Output	40	40	40	40	40	200
Actual Output	32	36	44	44	36	192
Cumulative Variance	–8	–12	–8	–4	–8	–8

		1	2	3	4	5
Planned Backlog	32	30	22	18	18	22
Actual Backlog	32	34	30	18	16	20

FIGURE 6.14 Input/output report.

Planned and actual inputs monitor the flow of work coming to the work center. Planned and actual outputs monitor the performance of the work center. Planned and actual backlogs monitor the queue and lead time performance.

Example Problem

Complete the following input/output report for weeks 1 and 2.

Week		1	2
Planned Input		45	40
Actual Input		42	46
Cumulative Variance			
Planned Output		40	40
Actual Output		42	44
Cumulative Variance			
Planned Backlog	30		
Actual Backlog	30		

ANSWER

Cumulative input variance week 1 = 42 − 45 = −3
Cumulative input variance week 2 = −3 + 46 − 40 = 3
Cumulative output variance week 1 = 42 − 40 = 2
Cumulative output variance week 2 = 2 + 44 − 40 = 6

Planned backlog week 1 = 30 + 45 − 40 = 35
Planned backlog week 2 = 35 + 40 − 40 = 35
Actual backlog week 1 = 30 + 42 − 42 = 30
Actual backlog week 2 = 30 + 46 − 44 = 32

Operation Sequencing

The twelfth edition of the *APICS Dictionary* defines operation sequencing as "a technique for short-term planning of actual jobs to be run in each work center based on capacity (i.e., existing workforce and machine availability) and priorities." Priority, in this case, is the sequence in which jobs at a work center should be worked on.

The material requirements plan establishes proper need dates and quantities. Over time, these dates and quantities change for a variety of reasons. Customers may require different delivery quantities or dates. Deliveries of component parts, either from vendors or internally, may not be met. Scrap, shortages, and overages may occur, and so on. Control of priorities is exercised through dispatching.

Dispatching   **Dispatching** is the function of selecting and sequencing available jobs to be run at individual work centers. The dispatch list is the instrument of priority control. It is a listing by operation of all the jobs available to be run at a work center with the job listed in priority sequence. It normally includes the following information and is updated and published at least daily:

- Plant, department, and work center.
- Part number, shop order number, operation number, and operation description of jobs at the work center.
- Standard hours.
- Priority information.
- Jobs coming to the work center.

Figure 6.15 shows an example of a daily dispatch list.

Dispatching rules   The ranking of jobs for the dispatch list is created through the application of priority rules. There are many rules, some attempting to reduce work-in-process inventory, others attempting to minimize the number of late orders or maximize

---

DISPATCH LIST

Work Center: 10
Rated Capacity: 16 standard hours per day
Shop Date: 250

Order Number	Part Number	Order Quantity	Setup Hours	Run Hours	Total Hours	Quantity Completed	Load Remaining	Operation Dates Start	Finish
123	6554	100	1.5	15	16.5	75	3.75	249	250
121	7345	50	0.5	30	30.5	10	24	249	251
142	2687	500	0.2	75	75.2	0	75	250	259
Total Available Load in Standard Hours							102.75		
Jobs Coming									
145	7745	200	0.7	20	20.7	0	20.7	251	253
135	2832	20	1.2	1.0	2.7	0	2.7	253	254
Total Future Load in Standard Hours							23.4		

FIGURE 6.15 Dispatch list (based on 2 machines working one 8-hour shift per day).

the output of the work center. None is perfect or will satisfy all objectives. Some commonly used rules are:

- **First come, first served (FCFS).** Jobs are performed in the sequence in which they are received. This rule ignores due dates and processing time.
- **Earliest job due date (EDD).** Jobs are performed according to their due dates. Due dates are considered, but processing time is not.
- **Earliest operation due date (ODD).** Jobs are performed according to their operation due dates. Due dates and processing time are taken into account. As well, the operation due date is easily understood on the shop floor.
- **Shortest process time (SPT).** Jobs are sequenced according to their process time. This rule ignores due dates, but it maximizes the number of jobs processed. Orders with long process times tend to be delayed.

Figure 6.16 illustrates how these sequencing rules work. Notice that each rule usually produces a different sequence.

One other rule that should be mentioned is called **critical ratio (CR).** This is an index of the relative priority of an order to other orders at a work center. It is based on the ratio of time remaining to work remaining and is usually expressed as:

$$CR = \frac{\text{due date} - \text{present date}}{\text{lead time remaining}} = \frac{\text{actual time remaining}}{\text{lead time remaining}}$$

Lead time remaining includes all elements of manufacturing lead time and expresses the amount of time the job normally takes to completion.

If the actual time remaining is less than the lead time remaining, it implies there is not sufficient time to complete the job and the job is behind schedule. Similarly, if lead time remaining and actual time remaining are the same, the job is on schedule. If the actual time remaining is greater than the lead time remaining, the job is ahead of schedule. If the actual time remaining is less than 1, the job is late already. The following table summarizes these facts and relates them to the critical ratio:

CR less than 1 (actual time less than lead time).	Order is behind schedule.
CR equal to 1 (actual time equal to lead time).	Order is on schedule.
CR greater than 1 (actual time greater than lead time).	Order is ahead of schedule.
CR zero or less (today's date greater than due date).	Order is already late.

Thus, orders are listed in order of their critical ratio with the lowest one first.

Critical ratio considers due dates and process time. However, it is not easily understood.

Job	Process Time (days)	Arrival Date	Due Date	Operation Due Date	Sequencing Rule			
					FCFS	EDD	ODD	SPT
A	4	223	245	233	2	4	1	3
B	1	224	242	239	3	2	2	1
C	5	231	240	240	4	1	3	4
D	2	219	243	242	1	3	4	2

FIGURE 6.16 Application of sequencing rules.

Example Problem

Today's date is 175. Orders A, B, and C have the following due dates and lead time remaining. Calculate the actual time remaining and the critical ratio for each.

Order	Due Date	Lead Time Remaining (days)
A	185	20
B	195	20
C	205	20

ANSWER

Order A has a due date of 185, and today is day 175. There are 10 actual days remaining. Since the lead time remaining is 20 days,

$$\text{Critical ratio} = \frac{10}{20} = 0.5$$

Similarly, the actual time remaining and the critical ratios are calculated for orders B and C. The following table gives the results:

Order	Due Date	Lead Time Remaining (days)	Actual Time Remaining (days)	CR
A	185	20	10	0.5
B	195	20	20	1.0
C	205	20	30	1.5

Order A has less actual time remaining than lead time remaining, so the CR is less than 1. It is, therefore, behind schedule. Order B has a CR of 1 and is exactly on schedule. Order C has a CR of 1.5—greater than 1—and is ahead of schedule.

Dispatching rules should be simple to use and easy to understand. As shown in Figure 6.16, each rule produces a different sequence and has its own advantages and disadvantages. Whichever rule is selected, it should be consistent with the objectives of the planning system.

PRODUCTION REPORTING

Production reporting provides feedback of what is actually happening on the plant floor. It allows PAC to maintain valid records of on-hand and on-order balances, job status, shortages, scrap, material shortages, and so on. Production activity control needs this information to establish proper priorities and to answer questions regarding deliveries, shortages, and the status of orders. Manufacturing management needs this information to make decisions about plant operation. Payroll needs this information to calculate employees' pay.

Data must be collected, sorted, and reported. The particular data collected depend upon the needs of the various departments. The methods of data collection vary. Sometimes the operator reports the start and completion of an operation, order, movement, and so on, using an online system directly reporting events as they occur via data terminals. In other cases, the operator, supervisor, or timekeeper reports this information on an operation reporting form included in the shop packet. Information about inventory withdrawals and receipts must be reported as well.

Once the data are collected, they must be sorted and appropriate reports produced. Types of information needed for the various reports include:

- Order status.
- Weekly input/output by department or work center.
- Exception reports on such things as scrap, rework, and late shop orders.
- Inventory status.
- Performance summaries on order status, work center and department efficiencies, and so on.

PRODUCT TRACKING

Production control is often responsible for **product tracking** or lot-traceability. This is the process of tracking parts and materials back to their origins. It has a very practical application in the matching of colors in fabrics and paint ensuring the consumer that different units of the product match in color at the time of manufacturing and during the product's lifetime. Traceability may also be legislated in industries such as food, pharmaceutical, or aerospace to ensure the safety of the product. Should a product prove unsafe it is possible for the manufacturer to trace back to find the source of all materials and recall all finished products that used that particular lot. This is a very meticulous process with information collected along with other supply chain information, often by production activity control personnel.

SUMMARY

Production activity control is concerned with converting the material requirements plan into action, reporting the results achieved, and when required, revising the plans and actions to meet the required results. Order release, dispatching, and progress reporting are the three primary functions. To accomplish the plans, PAC must establish detailed schedules for each order, set priorities for work to be done at each work center, and keep them current. Production activity control is also responsible for managing the queue and lead times. The theory of constraints modifies the approach to PAC since it views a production facility, the suppliers, and the market as a series of interdependent functions. TOC attempts to optimize the constraints (bottlenecks) in a system as they affect the overall throughput of the system. As a result, traditional lot sizing rules should be modified to increase the throughput of the entire system and not just the individual work centers. Drum-buffer-rope describes how the TOC works by setting an overall pace of material flow, ensuring bottlenecks never run out of material, and linking the output of one work center to another. If PAC is performing its functions, the company should be able to meet delivery dates, utilize labor and equipment efficiently, and keep inventory levels down.

KEY TERMS

Backward scheduling 123

Bottlenecks 128

Continuous manufacturing 119

Critical ratio (CR) 137

Cumulative variance 134

Cycle time 123

Dispatching 136

Drum-Buffer-Rope 131

Finite loading 124

Flow manufacturing 119

Forward scheduling 123

Gateway operation 129

Infinite loading 124

Input/output control 134

Input/output report 134

Intermittent manufacturing 119

Item master file 120

Manufacturing lead time 122

Operation overlapping 125

Operation splitting 126

Product structure file
(bill of material file) 120

Product tracking 139

Project manufacturing 120

Repetitive manufacturing 119

Routing file 120

Shop order detail file 121

Shop order master file 121

Throughput 128

Throughput time 123

Work center master file 121

QUESTIONS

1. What is the responsibility of production activity control?

2. What are the major functions of planning, implementation, and control?

3. What are the major characteristics of flow, intermittent, and project manufacturing?

4. Why is production activity control more complex in intermittent manufacturing?

5. To plan the flow of materials through manufacturing, what four things must production activity control know? Where will information on each be obtained?

6. What are the four planning files used in production activity control? What information does each contain?

7. What are the two control files? What are their purposes?

8. What should production activity control check before releasing a shop order?

9. What is manufacturing lead time? Name and describe each of its elements.

10. Describe forward and backward scheduling. Why is backward scheduling preferred?

11. Describe infinite and finite loading.

12. What is operation overlapping? What is its purpose?

13. What is operation splitting? What is its purpose?

14. What information does a load report contain? Why is it useful to production activity control?

15. What is a bottleneck operation?

16. What is the definition of throughput?

17. What are the six bottleneck principles discussed in the text?

18. What are the five things discussed in the text that are important in managing bottlenecks?

19. What is a shop order? What kind of information does it usually contain?

20. What two things must be done to control queue and meet delivery commitments?

21. What is an input/output control system designed to do? How is input controlled? How is output controlled?

22. What is dispatching? What is a dispatch list?

23. Describe each of the following dispatching rules giving their advantages and disadvantages.
    a. First come, first served.
    b. Earliest due date.
    c. Earliest operation due date.
    d. Shortest processing time.
    e. Critical ratio.

24. If the time remaining to complete a job is 10 days and the lead time remaining is 12 days, what is the critical ratio? Is the order ahead of schedule, on schedule, or behind schedule?

25. What is the purpose of production reporting? Why is it needed?

26. A student of production inventory management has decided to apply critical ratio to his homework assignments. Describe what is happening if his critical ratio for various assignments is:
    a. negative.
    b. zero.
    c. between zero and 1.
    d. greater than 1.

27. Bottlenecks exist in many business processes that serve the public and are usually indicated by lineups. Choose a business that experiences lineups and identify the constraints in the system. Give specific examples of each of the seven bottleneck principles that apply to that business. Suggest a way to increase the throughput of the bottleneck and describe the benefits to the business and to the customers.

28. What is lot traceability? Why is it important to safety related products?

PROBLEMS

6.1. Shop order 7777 is for 600 of part 8900. From the routing file, it is found that operation 20 is done on work center 300. The setup time is 3.5 hours, and run time is 0.233 hours per piece. What is the required capacity on work center 300 for shop order 7777?

Answer. 143.3 standard hours

6.2. An order for 100 of a product is processed on work centers A and B. The setup time on A is 50 minutes, and run time is 5 minutes per piece. The setup time on B is 60 minutes, and the run time is 5 minutes per piece. Wait time between the two operations is 5 hours. The move time between A and B is 40 minutes. Wait time after operation B is 5 hours, and the move time into stores is 3 hours. Queue at work center A is 25 hours and at B is 35 hours. Calculate the total manufacturing lead time for the order.

Answer. 92 hours and 10 minutes

6.3. In problem 6.2, what percent of the time is the order actually running?

Answer. 18.08%

6.4. An order for 50 of a product is processed on work centers A and B. The setup time on A is 60 minutes, and run time is 5 minutes per piece. The setup time on B is 30 minutes, and the run time is 6 minutes per piece. Wait time between the two operations is 10 hours. The move time between A and B is 60 minutes. Wait time after operation B is 8 hours, and the move time into stores is 2 hours. Queue at work center A is 40 hours and at B is 35 hours. Calculate the total manufacturing lead time for the order.

6.5. In problem 6.4, what percent of time is the order actually running?

6.6. Amalgamated Skyhooks, Inc., has an order for 200 Model SKY3 Skyhooks for delivery on day 200. The Skyhook consists of three parts. Components B and C form subassembly A. Subassembly A and component D form the final assembly. Following are the work centers and times for each operation. Using a piece of graph paper, draw a backward schedule based on the following. When must component C be started to meet the delivery date?

a. Only one machine is assigned to each operation.

b. The factory works one 8-hour shift 5 days a week.

c. All parts move in one lot of 200.

Part	Operation	Standard Time (days)
D	10	5
	20	7
B	10	5
	20	7
C	10	12
	20	5
Subassembly A		7
Final Assembly SKY3		5

Answer. Day 171

6.7. International Door Slammers has an order to deliver 500 door slammers on day 130. Draw up a backward schedule under the following conditions:

a. Only one machine is assigned to each operation.

b. Schedule one 8-hour shift per day for 5 days per week.

c. All parts are to move in one lot of 500 pieces.

d. Allow 8 hours between operations for queue and move times.

A slammer consists of three parts. Purchased components C and D form sub-assembly A. Subassembly A and component B form the final assembly. Part B is machined in three operations. No special tooling is required except for part B, operation 20. It takes 24 hours to make the tooling. Material is available for all parts.

Standard times for the lot of 500 are as follows:

Part	Operation	Standard Time (days)
B	10	10
	20	8
	30	6
Subassembly A		18
Final Assembly		5

6.8. An order for 100 of a product is processed on operation A and operation B. The setup time on A is 50 minutes, and the run time per piece is 9 minutes. The setup time on B is 30 minutes, and the run time is 6 minutes per piece. It takes 20 minutes to move a lot between A and B. Since this is a rush order, it is given top priority (president's edict) and is run as soon as it arrives at either workstation.

It is decided to overlap the two operations and to split the lot of 100 into two lots of 60 and 40. When the first lot is finished on operation A, it is moved to operation B where it is set up and run. Meanwhile, operation A completes the balance of the 100 units (40) and sends the units over to operation B. These 40 units should arrive as operation B is completing the first batch of 60; thus, operation B can continue without interruption until all 100 are completed.

a. Calculate the total manufacturing lead time for operation A and for B without overlapping.

b. Calculate the manufacturing lead time if the operations are overlapped. How much time is saved?

Answer.   a. Total manufacturing lead time = 1600 minutes

b. Total manufacturing lead time = 1240 minutes

Saving in lead time = 360 minutes

6.9. An order for 200 bell ringers is processed on work centers 10 and 20. The setup and run times are as follows. It is decided to overlap the lot on the two work centers and to split the lot into two lots of 75 and 125. Move time between operations is 30 minutes. Work center 20 cannot be set up until the first lot arrives. Calculate the saving in manufacturing lead time.

Setup on A = 50 minutes   Run time on A = 5 minutes per piece
Setup on B = 100 minutes   Run time on B = 7 minutes per piece

6.10. An order for 100 of a product is processed on operation A. The setup time is 50 minutes, and the run time per piece is 9 minutes. Since this is a rush order, it is to be split into two lots of 50 each and run on two machines in the work center. The machines can be set up simultaneously.

a. Calculate the manufacturing lead time if the 100 units are run on one machine.

b. Calculate the manufacturing lead time when run on two machines simultaneously.

c. Calculate the reduction in lead time.

Answer.   a. 950 minutes

b. 500 minutes

c. 450 minutes

6.11. What would be the reduction in MLT if the second machine could not be set up until the setup was completed on the first machine?

6.12. An order for 100 of a product is run on work center 40. The setup time is 4 hours, and the run time is 3 minutes per piece. Since the order is a rush and there are two machines in the work center, it is decided to split the order and run it on both machines. Calculate the manufacturing lead time before and after splitting.

6.13. In problem 6.12, what would be the manufacturing lead time if the second machine could not be set up until the setup on the first machine was completed? Would there be any reduction in manufacturing lead time?

6.14. Complete the following input/output report. What are the planned and actual backlogs at the end of period 4?

Period	1	2	3	4	Total
Planned Input	35	38	36	39	
Actual Input	33	33	31	40	
Cumulative Variance					

Planned Output	40	40	40	40	
Actual Output	38	35	40	38	
Cumulative Variance					

Planned Backlog	32				
Actual Backlog	32				

Answer.   Planned backlog = 20 units. Actual backlog = 18 units

6.15. Complete the following input/output report. What is the actual backlog at the end of period 5?

Period	1	2	3	4	5	Total
Planned Input	78	78	78	78	78	
Actual Input	82	80	74	82	80	
Cumulative Variance						

Planned Output	80	80	80	80	80	
Actual Output	85	83	74	80	84	
Cumulative Variance						

Planned Backlog	45						
Actual Backlog	45						

Answer.   37 units

6.16. Complete the following table to determine the run sequence for each of the sequencing rules.

Job	Process Time (days)	Arrival Date	Due Date	Operation Due Date	Sequencing Rule			
					FCFS	EDD	ODD	SPT
A	5	123	142	132				
B	2	124	144	131				
C	3	131	140	129				
D	6	132	146	135				

6.17. Jobs A, B, and C are in queue at work center 10 before being completed on work center 20. The following information pertains to the jobs and the work centers. For this problem, there is no move time. Today is day 1. If the jobs are scheduled by the earliest due date, can they be completed on time?

Job	Process Time (days)		Due Date
	Work Center 10	Work Center 20	
A	7	3	12
B	5	2	24
C	9	4	18

Job	Work Center 10		Work Center 20	
	Start Day	Stop Day	Start Day	Stop Day
A				
C				
B				

6.18. Calculate the critical ratios for the following orders and establish in what order they should be run. Today's date is 75.

Order	Due Date	Lead Time Remaining (days)	Actual Time Remaining (days)	CR
A	87	12		
B	95	26		
C	100	21		

CASE STYDY 6.1

Johnston Products

No matter how many times Justin Wang, the master scheduler for Johnston Products, tried, he couldn't seem to get it through people's minds. They kept trying to "front load" the production schedule, and the problem appeared to be getting worse.

By "front loading" Justin meant that production supervisors would attempt to catch up with production they failed to make the previous week. It seemed to happen every week, and the only way Justin could get things back to a realistic position was to completely reconstruct the entire master schedule—usually about every three weeks.

Last month could serve as an example. The first week of the month Justin had scheduled production equal to 320 standard hours in the assembly area. The assembly area managed to complete only 291 hours that week because of some equipment maintenance and a few unexpected part shortages. The assembly supervisor then had the workers complete the remaining 29 hours from week 1 at the start of week 2. Since week 2 already had 330 standard hours scheduled, the additional 29 hours really put them in a position of attempting to complete 359 hours. The workers actually completed 302 hours in week 2, leaving 57 hours to front load into week 3, and so forth. Usually by the time Justin came to his three-week review of the master schedule, it was not uncommon for the assembly area to be more than 100 standard hours behind schedule.

Clearly, something needed to be done. Justin decided to review some of the areas that could be causing the problem:

1. **Job standards** Although it had been at least four years since any job standards had been reviewed or changed, Jason felt the standards could not be the problem—quite the opposite. His operations course had taught him about the concept of the learning curve, implying that if anything the standard times for the jobs should be too high, allowing the average worker to complete even more production per hour than that implied by the job standard.

2. **Utilization** The general manager was very insistent on high utilization of the area. He felt that it would help control costs, and consequently used utilization as a major performance measure for the assembly area. The problem was that customer service was also extremely important. With the problems Justin was having with the master schedule, it was difficult to promise order delivery accurately, and equally difficult to deliver the product on time once the order promise was made.

3. **The workers** In an effort to control costs, the hourly wage for the workers was not very high. This caused a turnover in the workforce of almost 70% per year. In spite of this, the facility was located in an area where replacement workers were fairly easy to hire. They were assigned to the production area after they had a minimum of one week's worth of training on the equipment. In the meantime, the company filled vacant positions with temporary workers brought in by a local temporary employment service.

4. **Engineering changes** The design of virtually all the products was changing, with the average product changing with respect to some aspect of the design about every two months. Usually this resulted in an improvement to the products, however, so Justin quickly dismissed the changes as a problem. There were also some engineering changes on the equipment, but in general little in the way of process change had been made. The setup time for a batch of a specific design had remained at about 15 minutes. That forced a batch size of about from 50 to 300 units, depending on the design. The equipment was getting rather old, however, forcing regular maintenance as well as causing an occasional breakdown. Each piece of equipment generally required about three hours of maintenance per week.

Since the computer had done most of his calculations in the past, Justin decided to check to see if the computer was the source of the problem. He gathered information to conduct a manual calculation on a week when there were eight people assigned to the assembly area (one person for each of eight machines) for one shift per day. With no over-time, that would allow 320 hours of production.

Product	Batch Size	Standard Assembly Time (minutes per item)
A174	50	17
G820	100	9
H221	50	19.5
B327	200	11.7
C803	100	21.2
P932	300	14.1
F732	200	15.8
J513	150	17.3
L683	150	12.8

Case Analysis

1. With this information, Justin calculated the total standard time required to be within the 320 hours available. Is he correct? Calculate the time required and check the accuracy of his calculation.

2. List the areas you think are causing trouble in this facility.

3. Develop a plan to deal with the situation and try to get the production schedule back under control under the constraints listed.

PURCHASING

INTRODUCTION

Purchasing is the "process of buying." Many assume purchasing is solely the responsibility of the purchasing department. However, the function is much broader and, if it is carried out effectively, all departments in the company are involved. Obtaining the right material, in the right quantities, with the right delivery (time and place), from the right source, and at the right price are all purchasing functions.

Choosing the right material requires input from the marketing, engineering, manufacturing, and purchasing departments. Quantities and delivery of finished goods are established by the needs of the marketplace. However, manufacturing planning and control (MPC) must decide when to order which raw materials so that marketplace demands can be satisfied. Purchasing is then responsible for placing the orders and for ensuring that the goods arrive on time.

The purchasing department has the major responsibility for locating suitable sources of supply and for negotiating prices. Input from other departments is required in finding and evaluating sources of supply and to help the purchasing department in price negotiation. Environmental responsibility is becoming a major consideration in business due to potential costs and consumer demand. Purchasing departments are in a position to take the lead role in reducing a company's environmental impact since they are familiar with all materials purchased and they have excellent contacts with suppliers for product information. Purchasing, in its broad sense, is everyone's business.

Purchasing and Profit Leverage

On the average, manufacturing firms spend about 50% of their sales dollars in the purchase of raw materials, components, and supplies. This gives the purchasing function tremendous potential to increase profits. As a simple example, suppose a firm spends 50% of its revenue on purchased goods and shows a net profit before taxes of 10%. For every $100 of sales, it receives $10 of profit and spends $50 on purchases. Other expenses are $40. For the moment, assume that all costs vary with sales. These figures are shown in the following as a simplified income statement:

INCOME STATEMENT

Sales		$100
Cost of Goods Sold		
Purchases	$50	
Other Expenses	40	90
Profit Before Tax		$10

To increase profits by $1, a 10% increase in profits, sales must be increased to $110. Purchases and other expenses increase to $55 and $44. The following modified income statement shows these figures:

INCOME STATEMENT (SALES INCREASE)

Sales		$110
Cost of Goods Sold		
Purchases	$55	
Other Expenses	44	99
Profit Before Tax		$11

However, if the firm can reduce the cost of purchases from $50 to $49, a 2% reduction, it would gain the same 10% increase in profits. In this particular example, a 2% reduction in purchase cost has the same impact on profit as a 10% increase in sales.

INCOME STATEMENT (REDUCED PURCHASE COST)

Sales		$100
Cost of Goods Sold		
Purchases	$49	
Other Expenses	40	89
Profit Before Tax		$11

Purchasing Objectives

Purchasing is responsible for establishing the flow of materials into the firm, following up with the supplier, and expediting delivery. Missed deliveries can create havoc for manufacturing and sales, but purchasing can reduce problems for both areas, further adding to the profit.

The objectives of purchasing can be divided into five categories:

- Obtaining goods and services of the required quantity and quality.
- Obtaining goods and services at the lowest cost.
- Ensuring the best possible service and prompt delivery by the supplier.
- Developing and maintaining good supplier relations and developing potential suppliers.
- Selecting products and suppliers that minimize the impact on the environment.

To satisfy these objectives, some basic functions must be performed:

- Determining purchasing specifications: right quality, right quantity, and right delivery (time and place).
- Selecting supplier (right source).
- Negotiating terms and conditions of purchase (right price).
- Issuing and administration of purchase orders.

Outsourcing

APICS (The Association for Operations Management) defines outsourcing as "the process of having suppliers provide goods and services that were previously provided internally." This is a growing trend with North American companies as lower labor costs and an increasingly educated workforce are becoming available offshore. Technical advances in Internet communications and efficient shipping methods make offshore sourcing very attractive. Companies are under pressure to reduce costs and to focus on their core competencies, or, to paraphrase management guru Tom Peters, "stick to the knitting."

The purchasing department is directly affected by the growth in outsourcing. Operations departments add value to goods through supervising employees and efficiently using machines and materials. Many of these components are now purchased rather than produced internally, and there is a shift from internal management of staff to working with outside suppliers through the purchasing department. The outsourcing trend is not just occurring in manufacturing but is also affecting service departments as companies look to have anything from maintenance to IT work outsourced. Outside contractors can often do the same work better, faster, and cheaper.

Purchasing departments have an increasing responsibility with the management of outside operations and the development and administration of contracts. Contracts and legal terms are unfortunately beyond the scope of this text.

Purchasing Cycle

The **purchasing cycle** consists of the following steps:

1. Receiving and analyzing purchase requisitions.
2. Selecting suppliers. Finding potential suppliers, issuing requests for quotations, receiving and analyzing quotations, and selecting the right supplier.
3. Determining the right price.
4. Issuing purchase orders.
5. Following up to ensure delivery dates are met.
6. Receiving and accepting goods.
7. Approving supplier's invoice for payment.

Receiving and analyzing purchase requisition   Purchase requisitions start with the department or person who will be the ultimate user. In the material requirements planning environment, the planner releases a planned order authorizing the purchasing department to go ahead and process a purchase order. At a minimum, the purchase requisition contains the following information:

- Identity of originator, signed approval, and account to which cost is assigned.
- Material specification.
- Quantity and unit of measure.
- Required delivery date and place.
- Any other supplemental information needed.

Electronic requisition systems are now widely used and are often part of enterprise resource planning (ERP) software. The minimum requisition information is still required, and the system can supply much of the details and control of the information. For example, the requisitioner can enter the desired part number and the system database will provide the appropriate description, specification, suggested vendors, shipping instructions, and so on. The system will then forward the requisition for the appropriate approvals with controls in place for account number and spending limits. Once all the approvals have been completed, the requisition is sent to the purchasing department to produce the purchase order without reentering all the information. For items of small value (see C items covered in Chapter 9) that are ordered frequently, the system may send an electronic release of material directly to the approved supplier. The benefits to the company are ease of entry for the requisitioner, reduced paperwork, decreased turnaround time of requisitions, and improved accuracy of information.

Selecting suppliers   Identifying and selecting suppliers are important responsibilities of the purchasing department. For routine items or those that have not been purchased before, a list of approved suppliers is kept. If the item has not been purchased before or there is no acceptable supplier on file, a search must be made. If the order is of small value or for standard items, a supplier can probably be found on the Internet, in a catalogue, trade journal, or directory.

Requesting quotations   For major items, it is usually desirable to issue a request for quotation. This is a written inquiry that is sent to enough suppliers to be sure competitive and reliable quotations are received. *It is not a sales order.* After the suppliers have completed and returned the quotations to the buyer, the quotations are analyzed for price, compliance to specification, terms and conditions of sale, delivery, and payment terms. For items where specifications can be accurately written, the choice is probably made on price, delivery, and terms of sale. For items where specifications cannot be accurately written, the items quoted will vary. The quotations must be evaluated for technical suitability. The final choice is a compromise between technical factors and price. Usually both the issuing and purchasing departments are involved in the decision.

Determining the right price   This is the responsibility of the purchasing department and is closely tied to the selection of suppliers. The purchasing department is also responsible for price negotiation and will try to obtain the best price from the supplier. Price negotiation will be discussed in a later section of this chapter.

Issuing a purchase order   A purchase order is a legal offer to purchase. Once accepted by the supplier, it becomes a legal contract for delivery of the goods according to the terms and conditions specified in the purchase agreement. The purchase order is prepared from the purchase requisition or the quotations and from any other additional information needed. A copy is sent to the supplier; copies are retained by purchasing and are also sent to other departments such as accounting, the originating department, and receiving.

Following up and delivery   The supplier is responsible for delivering the items ordered on time. The purchasing department is responsible for ensuring that suppliers do deliver on time. If there is doubt that delivery dates can be met, purchasing must find out in time to take corrective action. This might involve expediting transportation, alternate sources of supply, working with the supplier to solve its problems, or rescheduling production.

The purchasing department is also responsible for working with the supplier on any changes in delivery requirements. Demand for items changes with time, and it may be necessary to expedite certain items or push delivery back on some others. The buyer must keep the supplier informed of the true requirements so that the supplier is able to provide what is wanted when it is wanted.

Receiving and accepting goods   When the goods are received, the receiving department inspects the goods to be sure the correct ones have been sent, are in the right quantity, and have not been damaged in transit. Using its copy of the purchase order and the bill of lading supplied by the carrier, the receiving department then accepts the goods and writes up a receiving report noting any variance. If further inspection is required, such as by quality control, the goods are sent to quality control or held in receiving for inspection. If the goods are received damaged, the receiving department will advise the purchasing department and hold the goods for further action. Provided the goods are in order and require no further inspection, they will be sent to the originating department or to inventory.

A copy of the receiving report is then sent to the purchasing department, noting any variance or discrepancy from the purchase order. If the order is considered complete, the receiving department closes out its copy of the purchase order and advises the purchasing department. If it is not, the purchase order is held open awaiting completion. If the goods have also been inspected by the quality control department, they, too, will advise the purchasing department whether the goods have been accepted or not.

Approving supplier's invoice for payment   When the supplier's invoice is received, there are three pieces of information that should agree: the purchase order, the receiving report, and the invoice. The items and the quantities should be the same on all; the prices, and extensions to prices, should be the same on the purchase order and the invoice. All discounts and terms of the original purchase order must be checked against the invoice. It is the job of the purchasing department to verify these and to resolve any differences. Once approved, the invoice is sent to accounts payable for payment.

ESTABLISHING SPECIFICATIONS

The first concern of purchasing—what to buy—is not necessarily a simple decision. For example, someone deciding to buy a car should consider how the car will be used, how often, how much one is willing to pay, and so on. Only then can an individual specify the type of car needed to make the "best buy." This section looks at the problems that organizations face when developing specifications of products and the types of specifications that may be used.

In purchasing an item or a service from a supplier, several factors are included in the package bought. These must be considered when specifications are being developed and can be divided into three broad categories:

- Quantity requirements.
- Price requirements.
- Functional requirements.

Quantity Requirements

Market demand first determines the quantity needed. The quantity is important because it will be a factor in the way the product is designed, specified, and manufactured. For example, if the demand was for only one item, it would be designed to be made at least cost, or a suitable standard item would be selected. However, if the demand were for several thousand, the item would be designed to take advantage of economies of scale, thus satisfying the functional needs at a better price.

Price Requirements

The price specification represents the economic value that the buyer puts on the item—the amount the individual is willing to pay. If the item is to be sold at a low price, the manufacturer will not want to pay a high price for a component part. The economic value placed on the item must relate to the use of the item and its anticipated selling price.

Functional Requirements

Functional specifications are concerned with the end use of the item and what the item is expected to do. By their very nature, functional specifications are the most important of all categories and govern the others.

In a sense, functional specifications are the most difficult to define. To be successful, they must satisfy the real need or purpose of an item. In many cases, the real need has both practical and aesthetic elements to it. A coat is meant to keep one warm, but under what circumstances does it do so and what other functions is it expected to perform? How cold must it get before one needs a coat? On what occasions will it be worn? Is it for working or dress wear? What color and style should it be? What emotional needs is it expected to fill? In the same way, we can ask what practical and aesthetic needs a door handle or side-view mirror on a car is expected to satisfy.

Functional specifications and quality Functional specifications are intimately tied to the quality of a product or service. Everyone knows, or thinks he or she knows, what quality is, but there are several misconceptions about what it is and what it is not. Ask someone what is meant by quality, and you will get replies such as "The best there is," "Perfection," "Degree of excellence," and "Very good." All sound great but do not mean very much.

There are many definitions of quality, but they all center on the idea of user satisfaction. On this basis, it can be said that an item has the required quality if it satisfies the needs of the user.

There are four phases to providing user satisfaction:

1. Quality and product planning.
2. Quality and product design.
3. Quality and manufacturing.
4. Quality and use.

Product planning is involved with decisions about which products and services a company is to market. It must decide the market segment to be served, the product features and quality level expected by that market, the price, and the expected sales volume. The basic quality level is thus specified by senior managers according to their understanding of the needs and wants of the marketplace. The success of the product depends on how well they do this.

The result of the firm's market studies is a general specification of the product outlining the expected performance, appearance, price, and sales volume of the product. It is then the job of the product designer to build into the design of the product the quality level described in the general specification. If this is not properly done, the product may not be successful in the marketplace.

For manufactured products, it is the responsibility of manufacturing, at a minimum, to meet the specifications laid down by the product designer. If the item is bought, it is purchasing's responsibility to make sure the supplier can provide the required quality level. For purchasing and manufacturing, quality means conforming to specifications or requirements.

To the final user, quality is related to his or her expectation of how the product should perform. Customers do not care why a product or service is defective. They expect satisfaction. If the product is what the customer wants, well designed, well made, and well serviced, the quality is satisfactory.

Functional specifications should define the quality level needed. They should describe all those characteristics of a product determined by its final use.

Function, quantity, service, and price are interrelated. It is difficult to specify one without consideration of the others. Indeed, the final specification is a compromise of them all, and the successful specification is the best combination of the lot. However, functional specifications ultimately are the ones that drive the others. If the product does not perform adequately for the price, it will not sell.

Value analysis   **Value analysis** as defined by the twelfth edition of the *APICS Dictionary* is "the systematic use of techniques that identify a required function, establish a value for that function, and finally provide that function at the lowest overall cost." Teams of engineers, users, production personnel, and suppliers analyze parts to challenge current specifications and identify redundant or unnecessary features. This can reduce the cost and, more importantly, improve the overall functionality of the part. A good example of value analysis is the evolution of the milk bottle as it went from a heavy glass bottle to a plastic jug. The result is a much cheaper package with improvements in sterility, transportation, and breakage.

FUNCTIONAL SPECIFICATION DESCRIPTION

Functional specification can be described in the following ways or by a combination of them:

1. By brand.
2. By specification of physical and chemical characteristics, material and method of manufacture, and performance.
3. By engineering drawings.
4. Miscellaneous.

Description by Brand

Description by brand is most often used in wholesale or retail businesses but is also used extensively in manufacturing. This is particularly true under the following circumstances:

- Items are patented, or the process is secret.
- The supplier has special expertise that the buyer does not have.
- The quantity bought is so small that it is not worth the buyer's effort to develop specifications.
- The supplier, through advertising or direct sales effort, has created a preference on the part of the buyer's customers or staff.

When buying by brand, the customer is relying on the reputation and integrity of the supplier. The assumption is that the supplier wishes to maintain the brand's reputation and will maintain and guarantee the quality of the product so repeat purchases will give the buyer the same satisfaction.

Most of the objections to purchasing by brand center on cost. Branded items, as a group, usually have price levels that are higher than nonbranded items. It may be less costly to develop specifications for generic products than to rely on brands. The other major disadvantage to specifying by brand is that it restricts the number of potential suppliers and reduces competition. Consequently, the usual practice, when specifying by brand, is to ask for the item by brand name or equivalent. In theory, this allows for competition.

Description by Specification

There are several ways of describing a product, but they usually include one or more of the following. Whatever method is used, description by specification depends on the buyer describing in detail exactly what is wanted:

- **Physical and chemical characteristics.** The buyer must define the physical and chemical properties of the materials wanted. Petroleum products, pharmaceuticals, and paints are often specified in this way.
- **Material and method of manufacture.** Sometimes the method of manufacture determines the performance and use of a product. For example, hot- and cold-rolled steels are made differently and have different characteristics.
- **Performance.** This method is used when the buyer is primarily concerned with what the item is required to do and is prepared to have the supplier decide how performance is to be attained. For example, a water pump might be specified as having to deliver so many gallons per minute. Performance specifications are relatively easy to prepare and take advantage of the supplier's special knowledge.

Whatever the method of specification, there are several characteristics to description by specification:

- To be useful, specifications must be carefully designed. If they are too loosely drawn, they may not provide a satisfactory product. If they are too detailed and elaborate, they are costly to develop, are difficult to inspect, and may discourage possible suppliers.
- Specifications must allow for multiple sources and for competitive bidding.
- If performance specifications are used, the buyer is assured that if the product does not give the desired results, the seller is responsible. They provide a standard for measuring and checking the materials supplied.
- Not all items lend themselves to specification. For example, it may not be easy to specify color schemes or the appearance of an item.
- An item described by specification may be no more suitable, and a great deal more expensive, than a supplier's standard product.
- If the specifications are set by the buyer, they may be expensive to develop. They will be used only when there is sufficient volume of purchases to warrant the cost or where it is not possible to describe what is wanted in any other way.

Sources of specifications   There are two major sources of specifications:

1. Buyer specifications.
2. Standard specifications.

Buyer specifications   **Buyer-developed specifications** are usually expensive and time consuming to develop. Companies usually do not use this method unless there is no suitable standard specification available or unless the volume of work makes it economical to do so.

Standard specifications   **Standard specifications** have been developed as a result of much study and effort by governmental and nongovernmental agencies. They usually apply to raw or semifinished products, component parts, or the composition of material. In many cases, they have become de facto standards used by consumers and by industry. When we buy motor oil for a car and ask for SAE 10W30, we are specifying a standard grade of motor oil established by the Society of Automotive Engineers. Most of the electrical products we buy are manufactured to Underwriters Laboratory (UL) standards. Steel and structural steel members are manufactured to standards set by the American Society of Mechanical Engineers.

There are several advantages to using standard specifications. First, they are widely known and accepted and, because of this, are readily available from most suppliers. Second, because they are widely accepted, manufactured, and sold, they are lower in price than nonstandard items. Finally, because they have been developed with input from a broad range of producers and users, they are usually adaptable to the needs of many purchasers.

Market grades are a type of standard specification usually set by the government and used for commodities and foodstuffs. When we buy eggs, for example, we buy them by market grade—small, medium, or large.

Engineering Drawings

Engineering drawings describe in detail the exact configuration of the parts and the assembly. They also give information on such things as finishes, tolerances, and material to be used. These drawings are a major method of specifying what is wanted and are widely used because often there is no other way to describe the configuration of parts or the way they are to fit together. They are produced by the engineering design department and are expensive to produce, but they give an exact description of the part required.

Miscellaneous

There are a variety of other methods of specification, including the famous phrase, "Gimme one just like the last one." Sometimes samples are used, for example, when colors or patterns are to be specified. Often a variety of methods can be used, and the buyer must select the best one.

The method of description is communication with the supplier. How well it is done will affect the success of the purchase and sometimes the price paid.

SELECTING SUPPLIERS

The objective of purchasing is to get all the right things together: quality, quantity, delivery, and price. Once the decision is made about what to buy, the selection of the right supplier is the next most important purchasing decision. A good supplier is one that has the technology to make the product to the required quality, has the capacity to make the quantities needed, and can run the business well enough to make a profit and still sell a product competitively.

Sourcing

There are three types of sourcing: sole, multiple, and single.

1. *Sole sourcing* implies that only one supplier is available because of patents, technical specifications, raw material, location, and so forth.

2. *Multiple sourcing* is the use of more than one supplier for an item. The potential advantages of multiple sourcing are that competition will result in lower price and better service and that there will be a continuity of supply. In practice there is a tendency toward an adversarial relationship between supplier and customer.

3. *Single sourcing* is a planned decision by the organization to select one supplier for an item when several sources are available. It is intended to produce a long-term partnership. This aspect is discussed at more length in Chapter 15, in the section on supplier partnerships.

Factors in Selecting Suppliers

The previous section discussed the importance of function, quantity, service, and price specifications. These are what the supplier is expected to provide and are the basis for selection and evaluation. Considering this, there are several factors in selecting a supplier.

Technical ability   Does the supplier have the technical ability to make or supply the product wanted? Does the supplier have a program of product development and improvement? Can the supplier assist in improving the products? These questions are important since, often, the buyer will depend upon the supplier to provide product improvements that will enhance or reduce the cost of the buyer's products. Sometimes the supplier can suggest changes in product specification that will improve the product and reduce cost.

Manufacturing capability   Manufacturing must be able to meet the specifications for the product consistently while producing as few defects as possible. This means that the supplier's manufacturing facilities must be able to supply the quality and quantity of the products wanted. The supplier must have a good quality assurance program, competent and capable manufacturing personnel, and good manufacturing planning and control systems to ensure timely delivery. These are important in ensuring that the supplier can supply the quality and quantity wanted.

Reliability   In selecting a supplier, it is desirable to pick one that is reputable, stable, and financially strong. If the relationship is to continue, there must be an atmosphere of mutual trust and assurance that the supplier is financially strong enough to stay in business.

After-sales service   If the product is of a technical nature or likely to need replacement parts or technical support, the supplier must have a good after-sales service. This should include a good service organization and inventory of service parts.

Supplier location   Sometimes it is desirable that the supplier be located near the buyer, or at least maintain an inventory locally. A close location helps shorten delivery times and means emergency shortages can be delivered quickly.

JIT capabilities   Companies competing in a just-in-time (JIT) environment depend on suppliers to quickly deliver small quantities of product. Modern companies operate with very little inventory of raw materials and require accurate, on-time deliveries from their suppliers. JIT suppliers who simply keep extra inventory to meet these demands will soon have increased costs and pressures to increase their prices. Buyers in a JIT environment need suppliers who value their new relationship, working in partnership to remove waste from the system. As a result, JIT suppliers need to have in place information and delivery systems that allow them to quickly ship exactly what the customer needs without increased cost or effort. JIT and lean production are further discussed in Chapter 15.

Other considerations   Sometimes other factors such as credit terms, reciprocal business, and willingness of the supplier to hold inventory for the buyer should be considered.

Price   The supplier should be able to provide competitive prices. This does not necessarily mean the lowest price. It is one that considers the ability of the supplier to provide the necessary goods in the quantity and quality wanted, at the time wanted, as well as any other services needed.

The total acquisition cost of an item includes the price paid plus all the handling and delivery costs associated with getting the product to production. A buyer will often get a price and per unit transportation discount by ordering in larger quantities. However, the total acquisition cost may increase when the costs of storage and inventory are included.

A low acquisition cost still may not be a good decision when the total costs to the company are considered. For example, a carpenter will pay a lower price for a lower grade of wood. However, the time spent on sorting out knots and defects and the decreased yield of good material will incur production-related costs, which will increase the total cost of the final product, perhaps cancelling any savings made in price. The total cost concept looks at the total costs to the system and not at just the price paid for materials.

In a modern business environment, the type of relationship between the supplier and the buyer is crucial to both. Ideally, the relationship will be ongoing with a mutual dependency. The supplier can rely on future business, and the buyer will be ensured of a supply of quality product, technical support, and product improvement. Communications between buyer and supplier must be open and full so both parties understand the problems of the other and can work together to solve problems to their mutual advantage. Thus, supplier selection and supplier relations are of the utmost importance.

Identifying Suppliers

One major responsibility of the purchasing department is to continue to research all available sources of supply. Some aids for identifying sources of supply follow:

- Salespersons of the supplier company.
- Internet.
- Catalogues.
- Trade magazines.
- Trade directories.
- Information obtained by the salespeople of the buyer firm.

Final Selection of Supplier

Some factors in evaluating potential suppliers are quantitative, and a dollar value can be put on them. Price is the obvious example. Other factors are qualitative and demand some judgment to determine them. These are usually set out in a descriptive fashion. The supplier's technical competence might be an example.

The challenge is finding some method of combining these two major factors that will enable a buyer to pick the best supplier. One method is the **ranking method**, described next.

1. Select those factors that must be considered in evaluating potential suppliers.
2. Assign a weight to each factor. This weight determines the importance of the factor in relation to the other factors. Usually a scale of 1 to 10 is used. If one factor is assigned a weight of 5 and another factor a weight of 10, the second factor is considered twice as important as the first. When developing the factors and their weights, the buyer can use input from the people who will be affected by the supplier selection. This will help the buyer in making a more informed decision and will improve the acceptance of the new supplier by the users.
3. Rate the suppliers for each factor. This rating is not associated with the weight. Rather, suppliers are rated on their ability to meet the requirements of each factor. Again, usually a scale of 1 to 10 is used.
4. Rank the suppliers. For each supplier, the weight of each factor is multiplied by the supplier rating for that factor. For example, if a factor had a weight of 8 and a supplier was rated 3 for that factor, the ranking value for that factor would be 24. The supplier rankings are then added to produce a total ranking. The suppliers can then be listed by total ranking and the supplier with the highest ranking chosen.

Figure 7.1 shows an example of this method of selecting suppliers. Supplier B has the highest total of 223; however, supplier D comes in a very close second with 222. The normal practice when using the ranking method is to eliminate the bottom ranking suppliers from consideration, allowing management to make a simpler decision.

The ranking method is an attempt to quantify those things that are not quantified by nature. It attempts to put figures on subjective judgment. It is not a perfect method, but it forces the buying company to consider the relative importance of the various factors.

Factor	Weight	Rating of Suppliers				Ranking of Suppliers			
Suppliers		A	B	C	D	A	B	C	D
Function	10	8	10	6	6	80	100	60	60
Cost	8	3	5	9	10	24	40	72	80
Service	8	9	4	5	7	72	32	40	56
Technical Assistance	5	7	9	4	2	35	45	20	10
Credit Terms	2	4	3	6	8	8	6	12	16
Total (rank of suppliers)						219	223	204	222

FIGURE 7.1 Supplier rating.

When the method includes the input of many people in determining the relative weights, agreement on the final selection will be improved.

PRICE DETERMINATION

Price is not the only factor in making purchasing decisions. However, all other things being equal, it is the most important. In the average manufacturing company, purchases account for about 50% of the cost of goods sold, and any savings made in purchase cost has a direct influence on profits.

However, remember that "you only get what you pay for." The trick is to know what you want and not pay more than necessary. When a purchase is made, the buyer receives a package of function, quantity, service, and price characteristics that are suited to the individual's needs. The idea of "best buy" is the mixture that serves the purpose best.

Basis for Pricing

The term *fair price* is sometimes used to describe what should be paid for an item. But what is a fair price? One answer is that it is the lowest price at which the item can be bought. However, there are other considerations, especially for repeat purchases where the buyer and seller want to establish a good working relationship. One definition of a **fair price** is one that is competitive, gives the seller a profit, and allows the buyer ultimately to sell at a profit. Sellers who charge too little to cover their costs will not stay in business. To survive, they may attempt to cut costs by reducing quality and service. In the end, both the buyer and seller must be satisfied.

Since we want to pay a fair price and no more, it is good to develop some basis for establishing what is a fair price.

Prices have an upper and a lower limit. The market decides the upper limit. What buyers are willing to pay is based on their perception of demand, supply, and their needs. The seller sets the lower limit. It is determined by the costs of manufacturing and selling the product and profit expectation. If buyers are to arrive at a fair price, they must develop an understanding of market demand and supply, competitive prices, and the methods of arriving at a cost.

One widely used method of analyzing costs is to break them down into fixed and variable costs. **Fixed costs** are costs incurred no matter the volume of sales. Examples are equipment depreciation, taxes, insurance, and administrative overhead. **Variable costs** are those directly associated with the amount produced or sold. Examples are direct labor, direct material, and commissions of the sales force.

$$\text{Total cost} = \text{fixed cost} + \text{variable cost per unit (number of units)}$$

$$\text{Unit cost} = \frac{\text{total cost}}{\text{number of units}}$$

$$= \frac{\text{fixed cost}}{\text{number of units}} + \text{variable cost per unit}$$

FIGURE 7.2 Break-even analysis.

The preceding formula shows that as the number of units produced increases, the unit cost decreases. This is an important factor when determining price. Buyers can lower the unit price paid by increasing the volume per order using longer-term contracts or through the standardization of parts. Sellers will offer quantity discounts to encourage larger orders, also taking advantage of this reduction in unit cost. Quantity discounts are discussed later in Chapter 10, and standardization is discussed in Chapter 14.

Figure 7.2 shows the relationship of fixed and variable costs to sales volume and how revenue will behave. The sum of the fixed and variable costs is labeled Total Cost on the graph. The third line represents the sales revenue. Where this line intercepts the total cost line, revenue equals total cost, and profit is zero. This is called the **break-even point.** When the volume is less than the break-even point, a loss is incurred; when the volume is greater, a profit is realized. The break-even point occurs where the revenue equals the total cost.

$$\text{Revenue} = \text{Total cost}$$
$$(\text{Price per unit})(\text{number of units sold}) = \text{fixed cost} + (\text{variable cost per unit})$$
$$\times (\text{number of units})$$

Example Problem

To make a particular component requires an overhead (fixed) cost of $5000 and a variable unit cost of $6.50 per unit. What is the total cost and the average cost of producing a lot of 1000? If the selling price is $15 per unit, what is the break-even point?

Answer

$$\text{Total cost} = \$5000 + (\$6.50 \times \$1000) = \$11,500$$
$$\text{Average cost} = \$11,500 \div 1000 = \$11.50 \text{ per unit}$$
$$\text{Break-even point: Let } X = \text{number of units sold}$$
$$\$15X = \$5000 + \$6.5X$$
$$\$8.50X = \$5000$$

Break-even occurs when 588.2 units are made and sold.

Competitive Bidding

Competitive bidding occurs when a buyer compares the price of a product from various suppliers and simply chooses the lowest price. This can be the formal process of sending out quotations and analyzing the results or simply comparing catalogue or advertised prices. The process does take some time, and a number of sources must be available. At least three sources are desired to make a good comparison. Competitive bidding also requires that the product be well specified and widely available. Items such as nuts and bolts, gasoline, bread, and milk are usually sourced using competitive bidding.

Price Negotiation

Prices can be negotiated if the buyer has the knowledge and the clout to do so. A small retailer probably has little of the latter, but a large buyer may have much. Through negotiation, the buyer and seller try to resolve conditions of purchase to the mutual benefit of both parties. Skill and careful planning are required for the negotiation to be successful. It also takes a great deal of time and effort, so the potential profit must justify the expense.

One important factor in the approach to negotiation is the type of product. There are four categories:

1. **Commodities.** Commodities are materials such as copper, coal, wheat, meat, and metals. Price is set by market supply and demand and can fluctuate widely. Negotiation is concerned with contracts for future prices.

2. **Standard products.** These items are provided by many suppliers. Since the items are standard and the choice of suppliers large, prices are determined on the basis of published prices. There is not much room for negotiation except for large purchases.

3. **Items of small value.** These are items such as maintenance or cleaning supplies and represent purchases of such small value that price negotiation is of little purpose. The prime objective should be to keep the cost of ordering low. Firms will negotiate a contract with a supplier that can supply many items and set up a simple ordering system that reduces the cost of ordering.

4. **Made-to-order items.** This category includes items made to specification or for which quotations from several sources are received. These can generally be negotiated.

IMPACT OF MATERIAL REQUIREMENTS PLANNING ON PURCHASING

The text in this chapter has described the traditional role and responsibilities of purchasing. This section will study the effect material requirements planning has on the purchasing function and the changing role of purchasing.

Purchasing can be separated into two types of activities: (1) procurement and (2) supplier scheduling and follow-up. Much of what has been covered in this chapter is in the area of procurement. Procurement includes the functions of establishing specifications, selecting suppliers, price determination, and negotiation. Supplier scheduling and follow-up are concerned with the release of orders to suppliers, working with suppliers to schedule delivery, and follow-up. The goals of supplier scheduling are the same as those of production activity control: to execute the master production schedule and the material requirements plan (MRP), ensure good use of resources, minimize work-in-process inventory, and maintain the desired level of customer service.

Planner/buyer concept In a traditional system, the material requirements planner releases an order either to production activity control or to purchasing. Purchasing issues purchase orders based on the material requirements plan. Production activity control prepares shop orders, schedules components into the work flow, and controls material progress through the plant. When plans change, as they invariably do, the production planner must advise the buyer of the change, and the buyer must advise the supplier. The production planner is in closer, more continuous contact with material requirements planning and frequently changing schedules than is the buyer. To improve the effectiveness of the planner/buyer activity, many companies have combined the two functions of buying and planning.

Sometimes the planner's job and the buyer's job are combined into a single job done by one person. **Planner/buyers** do the material planning for the items under their control, communicate the schedules to their suppliers, follow up, resolve problems, and work with other planners and the master scheduler when delivery problems arise. The planner/buyer handles fewer components than either a planner or a buyer but has the responsibilities of both. The planner/buyer is responsible for the following:

- Determining material requirements.
- Developing schedules.
- Issuing shop orders.
- Issuing material releases to suppliers.
- Establishing delivery priorities.
- Controlling orders in the factory and to suppliers.
- Handling all the activities associated with the buying and production scheduling functions.
- Maintaining close contact with supplier personnel.

Because the roles of production planning and buying are combined, there is a smoother flow of information and material between the supplier and the factory. The planner/buyer has a keener knowledge of factory needs than the buyer does and can better coordinate the material flow with suppliers. At the same time, the planner/buyer is better able to match material requirements with the supplier's manufacturing capabilities and constraints.

Contract buying   Usually a material requirements planning system generates frequent orders for relatively small quantities. This is particularly true for components that are ordered lot for lot. It is costly, inefficient, and sometimes impossible to issue a new purchase order for every weekly requirement. The alternative is to develop a long-term contract with a supplier and to authorize releases against the contract. Often suppliers are given a copy of the material requirements plan so they are aware of future demands. The buyer then issues a release against the schedule. This approach is efficient and cost-effective but requires close coordination and communication with the supplier. Again, contract buying can be managed very well by a planner/buyer.

Supplier responsiveness and reliability   Because material requirements often change, suppliers must be able to react quickly to change. They must be highly flexible and reliable so they can react quickly to changes in schedules.

Contract buying ensures suppliers a given amount of business and commits them to allocating that amount of their capacity to the customer. Suppliers are more responsive to customer needs and can react quickly to changes in schedules. Because customers know the capacity will be available when needed, they can delay ordering until they are more sure of their requirements.

Close relationship with suppliers   Contract buying and the need for **supplier flexibility and reliability** mean the buyer–supplier relationship must be close and cooperative. There must be excellent two-way communication, cooperation, and teamwork. Both parties have to understand their own and the other's operations and problems.

The planner/buyer and the supplier counterpart (often the supplier's production planner) must work on a weekly basis to ensure both parties are aware of any changes in material requirements or material availability.

Electronic data interchange   Electronic data interchange (**EDI**) enables customers and suppliers to electronically exchange transaction information such as purchase orders, invoices, and material requirements planning information. This eliminates time-consuming paperwork and facilitates easy communication between planner/buyers and suppliers.

Vendor-managed inventory   In recent years there has been a growth in the purchasing approach known as **vendor-managed inventory.** In this concept, a supplier maintains an inventory of certain items in the customer's facility. The supplier "owns" the inventory until the customer actually withdraws it for use, after which the customer then pays for that use. The customer does not have to order any of the inventory, as the supplier is responsible for maintaining an adequate supply in the facility for customer use. This approach is most commonly used for lower-value products that have a relatively standard design, such as fasteners, standard electrical equipment, and so forth. These items are often categorized as C items, which are further discussed in Chapter 9. Vendor-managed inventory reduces the need for many small MRP order releases.

Internet   Internet technology has become the most quickly accepted communications medium ever. There are three variations of networks used: Internet, intranet, and extranet. The **Internet** is most commonly used and is open to the general public. An **intranet** is an internal net that is normally used within the boundaries of a company. It may stretch across many manufacturing sites or even countries. Much of the data shared in this environment is considered sensitive, and therefore access is usually limited to people within the company. **Extranet** is an intranet shared by two or more companies. Each participating company moves certain data outside of a private intranet to the extranet, making it available only to the companies sharing the extranet. [A supplier may be provided with information such as the planned order releases (from the MRP system) or the stock status of an item.]

ENVIRONMENTALLY RESPONSIBLE PURCHASING

The fifth category of purchasing objectives introduced at the beginning of this chapter is the objective for purchasing departments to minimize the impact their organization has on the environment, that is, **environmentally responsible purchasing**. Purchasing is responsible for managing waste products in most organizations since they have:

- First-hand knowledge of price trends for waste products.
- Contact with salespeople who are an excellent source of information as to possible uses of waste material.
- Familiarity with the company's own needs, or uses for materials within the organization.
- Knowledge of legislation involving the transportation and handling of environmentally sensitive materials.

Reduce, Reuse, Recycle is a widely used phrase to guide people in lowering the impact they have on the environment. Properly understood and implemented the 3 Rs can also reduce expenses and increase profits.

Reduce

Reducing the use or generation of materials whether hazardous or scrap is the most profitable of the 3 Rs. The purchasing department, having direct contact with suppliers, is the first to learn of new environmentally friendly materials. Lead-free solder and water-based solvents are just two examples of materials that have been developed by suppliers to help their customers reduce their environmental impact and reduce their costs. JIT (discussed further in Chapter 15), when applied to suppliers, involves reducing waste for all stages of the supply chain. The use of returnable racks or packaging is widely used in the automotive industry, reducing both costs and environmental impact.

Suppliers are also the experts and should be consulted when developing material specifications to reduce costs by cutting waste or recommending bulk storage and handling systems.

Reuse

The next most profitable step is to reuse materials wherever possible. Scrap from one process may be reused directly within the organization or slightly processed for reuse. Corrugated cartons can be slit and crushed for use as packing material in the shipping department. Many manufactured products are cut from a continuous web resulting in waste material. However, smaller products can often be nested between the cut-outs to make other, smaller products, reducing the need for raw materials and also the amount of material to be sent for disposal. Another category of reuse is byproducts, which are saleable products made from what was previously considered waste. It was not too long ago that butchers had to find a use for a non-saleable product, chicken wings!

In the food packaging industry, glass jars are shipped in boxes preprinted with finished product artwork. The empty jars are removed from their containers as they enter the cleaning and filling station. The empty boxes are sent to the end of the filling process, where the finished product is placed in the boxes. A final description and batch code are then printed on each box. The company never has to deal with the handling and disposal of the boxes used to ship the empty jars. The boxes have two uses: the shipment from glass manufacturer to the food processor and from the food processor as finished product. Note that reducing and reusing are the most effective methods in reducing environmental impact.

Recycle

This is the most public and least effective of the 3 Rs, yet purchasing can maximize the benefits of recycling through good management. Suppliers are often the best source of information on the disposal of scrap materials and often will buy materials back for reprocessing. This does require good management to keep materials in their most useful form. Some liquids, notably chlorinated solvents, are difficult to dispose of. They should be kept separate from other valuable liquids, such as used machine oils. Contamination of a waste stream can turn the resale of a valuable waste product into an expense and should be avoided at all costs. All materials destined for recycling should be kept separately from other materials where possible.

EXPANSION OF PURCHASING INTO SUPPLY CHAIN MANAGEMENT

As computers and software (ERP, for example) have become more powerful and effective, information flows have become easier and the ability to handle large amounts of data has become more feasible. This condition has allowed companies to expand their planning and control perspectives to include "upstream" (suppliers) and "downstream" (distributors and customers) entities. This concept of the supply chain has four major components that are managed:

- The flow of physical materials from suppliers, downstream through the company itself, and finally to distributors and/or customers.
- The flow of money upstream from customers back to the companies and suppliers.
- The flow of information up and down through the stream.
- The flow of products back (upstream) from the customers, typically for repairs or recycling.

Other entities also have impact on the supply chain for a company. A major example is governments, which can impact the supply chain both positively and negatively. The word *governments* is plural since many modern supply chains are global in nature, often including companies and customers from many different countries around the world.

Although several impacts on the supply chain perspective have been observed and formalized, two in particular have become formalized and noteworthy:

- **Customer relationship management (CRM)** includes several activities with the intent to build and maintain a strong customer base. Customer wants and needs are assessed and cross-functional teams from the company work to align company activities around those customer needs.
- **Supplier relationship management (SRM)** is similar to CRM, only the focus for these activities is the building and maintaining of close, long-term relationships with key suppliers.

One critical reason for developing formal links and relationships in the supply chain is to help control the **bullwhip effect**. This effect occurs when there is uncertainty in the supply chain based on the use of forecasts, and that uncertainty is then exaggerated by lead-time effects and differences in lot sizes as material moves through the supply chain.

The effect can produce large fluctuations in demand for raw materials based on relatively small changes in demand from the customer end of the supply chain. Managing the supply chain with visibility of data (information flow) and building flexibility and agility across the supply chain can substantially reduce large fluctuations.

The management required to effectively manage the supply chain is heavily based on managing data and inventory, but there are other aspects as well. Good strategic planning focusing on anticipating and preparing for disruptions and sharing those risks among other entities in the supply chain represent examples of the types of supply chain management that have been developed.

Another key issue that has grown in importance with the growth of supply chain is the focus on ethics. People in purchasing and supply chain positions often have responsibility for managing the flow of a great deal of money, and as a result it becomes quite important to have honest and ethical conduct on the part of those people. Many companies, and countries, have developed strict codes and rules of conduct to ensure consistent and ethical treatment of the supply chain activities and reported measures.

SOME ORGANIZATIONAL IMPLICATIONS OF SUPPLY CHAIN MANAGEMENT

Organizations that alter their perspective away from traditional purchasing toward supply chain management must recognize that their perspective toward managing the entire organization must also change. For instance, most organizations that have adopted a supply chain perspective find the following:

- Their cost focus has altered dramatically. Often decisions are not based on just product price but instead on total cost and value. This implies an integrated view of price, quality, serviceability, durability, and any other characteristic that the company places on total value. It also can include transportation, storage, and material handling costs. To accomplish this changed perspective, organizations have adopted techniques of process analysis, value stream analysis, and mutual (between the company and its suppliers) value analysis.

- Cross-functional teams are now used to plan and control the supply chain. These teams are made up of representatives from various departments, including production, quality control, engineering, finance, purchasing. Cross-functional teams make decisions more quickly than traditional departmental organizations and also are likely to consider overall benefits to the company, not just benefits to the individual departments.

- Decision making has changed from the "I say and you do" or a negotiated perspective with suppliers to one of "Let's talk about the best way to handle this and make a mutually advantageous decision." This also implies supplier contracts extending into the long-term future.

- Information sharing has changed from simply giving out information about the order to the perspective of sharing some important information about the business itself.

- Measurement systems look at all aspects of the supply chain and not just supplier performance.

- There is a growth in electronic business (e-business). This implies using the Internet more for handling business information flows and transactions.

- The environment must be considered in the acquisition, storage, use, and disposal of all materials

Savings Can Be Substantial

There are many advantages associated with an effective supply chain perspective. Some of these savings include the following:

- More effective product specification, allowing for efficient product substitutions and product specifications focused on fitness of use.
- Better leveraging of volume discounts and supplier consolidation.
- Long-term contracts with efficient communication systems, significantly reducing the administrative cost of ordering and order tracking.
- More effective use of techniques such as electronic commerce, using credit cards for payments, and blanket ordering.
- Reducing environmental costs by avoiding potentially hazardous materials and exercising the Rs.

SUMMARY

Purchasing has always been an important function in any company, especially manufacturers who use a lot of raw materials or who use materials that are difficult to obtain. Purchasing needs to continue to get the right products at the right time and at the best price but, the function is changing. The steps in the purchasing cycle are still necessary but many manual activities such as writing POs, getting information on products, and communicating with suppliers have been sped up through use of the Internet and computerization. The reduction in routine clerical activity allows time to take a more strategic view of the organization and have an increasing impact on profits. Viewing the supply chain as an integrated function, outsourcing, and lean production are three management influences that have encouraged purchasing to improve their relations with suppliers and to take a more active role in the scheduling and flow of products. Purchasing also has the opportunity to take a lead role in reducing the environmental impact of a company by working with suppliers and the use of environmentally friendly materials.

KEY TERMS

Break-even point 158

Bullwhip effect 163

Buyer-developed specifications 153

Contract buying 160

Customer relationship management (CRM) 162

Electronic data interchange (EDI) 160

Environmentally responsible purchasing 161

Extranet 161

Fair price 157

Fixed costs 157

Functional specifications 151

Internet 161

Intranet 161

Planner/buyers 159

Purchasing cycle 149

Ranking method 156

Reduce, reuse, recycle 161

Standard specifications 153

Supplier flexibility and reliability 160

Supplier relationship management (SRM) 163

Value analysis 152

Variable costs 157

Vendor-managed inventory 161

QUESTIONS

1. What are the five objectives of purchasing?
2. List the seven steps in the purchasing cycle.
3. Describe the purposes, similarities, and differences among purchase requisitions, purchase orders, and requests for quotation.
4. What are the responsibilities of the purchasing department in follow-up?
5. Describe the duties of the receiving department upon receipt of goods.
6. Besides functional specifications, what three other specifications must be determined? Why is each important?
7. Name two sources of specifications.
8. What is the difference between sole sourcing and single sourcing?
9. Describe the advantages and disadvantages of the following ways of describing functional requirements. Give examples of when each is used.
   a. By brand.
   b. By specification of physical and chemical characteristics, material and method of manufacture, and performance.
10. What are the advantages of using standard specifications?
11. Why is it important to select the right supplier and to maintain a relationship with that supplier?
12. Name and describe the three types of sourcing.
13. Describe six factors that should be used in selecting a supplier.
14. What is the concept of "best buy"?
15. Type of product is a factor that influences the approach to negotiation. Name the four categories of products and state what room there is for negotiation.
16. What are four savings that can result from adopting a supply chain management approach?
17. A company would like to reduce the amount of lead time in some of their soldered electronics. How can the purchasing department contribute to this endeavor?
18. Describe which of the 3 Rs of recycling has the most beneficial impact on the environment.

PROBLEMS

7.1. If purchases were 45% of sales and other expenses were 45% of sales, what would be the increase in profit if, through better purchasing, the cost of purchases was reduced to 43% of sales?

7.2. If suppliers were to be rated on the following basis, what would be the ranking of the two suppliers listed?

Factor	Weight	Rating of Suppliers Supplier A	Supplier B	Ranking of Suppliers Supplier A	Supplier B
Function	7	8	9		
Cost	5	9	5		
Technical Assistance	4	5	7		
Credit Terms	1	8	4		

7.3. A company is negotiating with a potential supplier for the purchase of 100,000 widgets. The company estimates that the supplier's variable costs are $5 per unit and that the fixed costs, depreciation, overhead, and so on, are $50,000. The supplier quotes a price of $10 per unit. Calculate the estimated average cost per unit. Do you think $10 is too much to pay? Could the purchasing department negotiate a better price? How?

LET'S PARTY!

"Let's party!" is still echoing in your head as you leave your principles of buying class. Again you ask yourself, "Why did I ever let myself run for class president?" Most of the people in the class were good, level-headed individuals who enjoyed a good time and you enjoyed working with them. But a small group from your class, who were known on campus as The Rowdies, often bullied their way on decisions affecting class activities. The decision to have a year-end party was right up their alley, and class had ended with a chanting session of "Let's party." It sounded like a wrestling match to you. Fortunately, your professor had left the room early to let you discuss with the class the idea of some kind of year-end get-together.

The Rowdies had immediately suggested the Goat's Ear, a local hangout with not much to offer but cheap drinks. The rest of your classmates had put forth some other suggestions, but no consensus on a location could be reached between the members of your executive committee or the rest of the class. If you went to the Goat's Ear most of the sane people in your class wouldn't attend, and even when you suggested more conventional locations, people couldn't agree because of factors such as the type of music played.

Since there were only two weeks left until the end of regular classes, you felt that you had to make arrangements in a hurry. It wasn't difficult to identify the most popular possible locations, but getting agreement from this group was going to be difficult.

One of your recent lectures was on supplier selection, and your professor had demonstrated the technique called the ranking or weighted-point method. It seemed simple enough in the lecture, and you had almost embarrassed yourself by asking the question "Why not just pick the least expensive supplier?" The thought occurred to you that there just might be some solution to your current problem in the professor's response, "One of the hardest things to do in any group, whether a business or a social club, is to get consensus on even the simplest choices."

Case Analysis

For this exercise, put yourself in the position of the class president described in this case and complete one of the two following exercises:

Exercise 1

1. Perform a supplier rating analysis for the situation. Include at least 10 factors and 4 possible locations.
2. Make the selection as indicated by the analysis.
3. Discuss why the analysis led to your selection in step 2 and whether you would change any of the criteria or weights.

Exercise 2

1. Prepare a transparency to be used in class to make a selection for a year-end get-together.
2. Lead a discussion to determine at least 4 possible locations and 10 factors.
3. Have the class agree on weighting factors for each criteria.
4. Perform the calculations and make the selection.
5. Discuss with the class why the analysis led to the selection in step 4 and whether you would change any of the criteria or weights.
6. Ask the class members whether they feel more in agreement with the decision after going through this process.

FORECASTING

INTRODUCTION

Forecasting is a prelude to planning. Before making plans, an estimate must be made of what conditions will exist over some future period. How estimates are made, and with what accuracy, is another matter, but little can be done without some form of estimation.

Why forecast? There are many circumstances and reasons, but forecasting is inevitable in developing plans to satisfy future demand. Most firms cannot wait until orders are actually received before they start to plan what to produce. Customers usually demand delivery in reasonable time, and manufacturers must anticipate future demand for products or services and plan to provide the capacity and resources to meet that demand. Firms that make standard products need to have saleable goods immediately available or at least to have materials and subassemblies available to shorten the delivery time. Firms that make to order cannot begin making a product before a customer places an order but must have the resources of labor and equipment available to meet demand.

Many factors influence the demand for a firm's products and services. Although it is not possible to identify all of them, or their effect on demand, it is helpful to consider some major factors:

- General business and economic conditions.
- Competitive factors.
- Market trends such as changing demand.
- The firm's own plans for advertising, promotion, pricing, and product changes.

DEMAND MANAGEMENT

The prime purpose of an organization is to serve the customer. Marketing focuses on meeting customer needs, but operations, through materials management, must provide the resources. The coordination of plans by these two parties is demand management.

Demand management is the function of recognizing and managing all demands for products. It occurs in the short, medium, and long term. In the long term, demand projections are needed for strategic business planning of such things as facilities. In the medium term, the purpose of demand management is to project aggregate demand for production planning. In the short run, demand management is needed for items and is associated with master production scheduling. We are most concerned with the latter.

If material and capacity resources are to be planned effectively, all sources of demand must be identified. These include domestic and foreign customers, other plants in the same corporation, branch warehouses, service parts and requirements, promotions, distribution inventory, and consigned inventory in customers' locations.

Demand management includes four major activities:

- Forecasting.
- Order processing.
- Making delivery promises. The concept of available-to-promise was discussed in Chapter 3.
- Interfacing between manufacturing planning and control and the marketplace. Figure 8.1 shows this relationship graphically.

FIGURE 8.1 Demand management and the manufacturing planning and control system.

In each of these cases, production (supply) is being planned to react to anticipated demand as shown by the forecast.

Order processing   Order processing occurs when a customer's order is received. The product may be delivered from finished goods inventory or it may be made or assembled to order. If goods are sold from inventory, a sales order is produced authorizing the goods to be shipped from inventory. If the product is made or assembled to order, the sales department must write up a sales order specifying the product. This may be relatively simple if the product is assembled from standard components but can be a lengthy, complex process if the product requires extensive engineering. A copy of the sales order stating the terms and conditions of acceptance of the order is sent to the customer. Another copy, sent to the master planner, is authorization to go ahead and plan for manufacture. The master planner must know what to produce, how much, and when to deliver. The sales order must be written in language that makes this information clear.

DEMAND FORECASTING

Forecasts depend upon what is to be done. They must be made for the strategic business plan, the production plan, and the master production schedule. As discussed in Chapter 2, the purpose, planning horizons, and level of detail vary for each.

The strategic business plan is concerned with overall markets and the direction of the economy over the next 2 to 10 years or more. Its purpose is to provide time to plan for those things that take long to change. For production, the strategic business plan should provide sufficient time for resource planning: plant expansion, capital equipment purchase, and anything requiring a long lead time to purchase. The level of detail is not high, and usually forecasts are in sales units, sales dollars, or capacity. Forecasts and planning will probably be reviewed quarterly or yearly.

Production planning is concerned with manufacturing activity for the next one to three years. For manufacturing, it means forecasting those items needed for production planning, such as budgets, labor planning, long lead time procurement items, and overall inventory levels. Forecasts are made for groups or families of products rather than specific end items. Forecasts and plans will probably be reviewed monthly.

Master production scheduling is concerned with production activity from the present to a few months ahead. Forecasts are made for individual items, as found on a master production schedule, individual item inventory levels, raw materials and component parts, labor planning, and so forth. Forecasts and plans will probably be reviewed weekly.

CHARACTERISTICS OF DEMAND

In this chapter, the term *demand* is used rather than *sales*. The difference is that sales implies what is actually sold whereas demand shows the need for the item. Sometimes demand cannot be satisfied, and sales will be less than demand.

Before discussing forecasting principles and techniques, it is best to look at some characteristics of demand that influence the forecast and the particular techniques used.

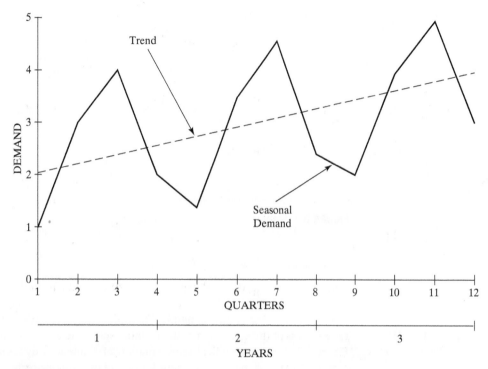

FIGURE 8.2 Demand over time.

Demand Patterns

If historical data for demand are plotted against a time scale, they will show any shapes or consistent patterns that exist. A pattern is the general shape of a time series. Although some individual data points will not fall exactly on the pattern, they tend to cluster around it.

Figure 8.2 shows a hypothetical historical demand pattern. The pattern shows that actual demand varies from period to period. There are four reasons for this: trend, seasonality, random variation, and cycle.

Trend   Figure 8.2 shows that demand is increasing in a steady pattern of demand from year to year. This graph illustrates a linear trend, but there are different shapes, such as geometric or exponential. The **trend** can be level, having no change from period to period, or it can rise or fall.

Seasonality   The demand pattern in Figure 8.2 shows each year's demand fluctuating depending on the time of year. This fluctuation may be the result of the weather, holiday seasons, or particular events that take place on a seasonal basis. **Seasonality** is usually thought of as occurring on a yearly basis, but it can also occur on a weekly or even daily basis. A restaurant's demand varies with the hour of the day, and supermarket sales vary with the day of the week.

Random variation   **Random variation** occurs where many factors affect demand during specific periods and occur on a random basis. The variation may be small, with actual demand falling close to the pattern, or it may be large, with the points widely scattered. The pattern of variation can usually be measured, and this will be discussed in the section on tracking the forecast.

Cycle   Over a span of several years and even decades, wavelike increases and decreases in the economy influence demand. However, forecasting of cycles is a job for economists and is beyond the scope of this text.

FIGURE 8.3 Stable and dynamic demand.

Stable Versus Dynamic

The shapes of the demand patterns for some products or services change over time whereas others do not. Those that retain the same general shape are called **stable** and those that do not are called **dynamic.** Dynamic changes can affect the trend, seasonality, or randomness of the actual demand. The more stable the demand, the easier it is to forecast. Figure 8.3 shows a graphical representation of stable and dynamic demand. Notice the average demand is the same for both stable and dynamic patterns. It is usually the average demand that is forecast.

Dependent Versus Independent Demand

Chapter 4 discussed dependent and independent demand. It was said that demand for a product or service is independent when it is not related to the demand for any other product or service. Dependent demand for a product or service occurs where the demand for the item is derived from that of a second item. Requirements for dependent demand items need not be forecast but are calculated from that of the independent demand item.

Only independent demand items need to be forecasted. These are usually end items or finished goods but should also include service parts and items supplied to other plants in the same company (intercompany transfers).

PRINCIPLES OF FORECASTING

Forecasts have four major characteristics or principles. An understanding of these will allow us to make more effective use of forecasts. They are simple and, to some extent, common sense.

1. **Forecasts are usually wrong.** Forecasts attempt to look into the unknown future and, except by sheer luck, will be wrong to some degree. Errors are inevitable and must be expected.

2. **Every forecast should include an estimate of error.** Since forecasts are expected to be wrong, the real question is "By how much?" Every forecast should include an estimate of error often expressed as a percentage (plus and minus) of the forecast or as a range between maximum and minimum values. Estimates of this error can be made statistically by studying the variability of demand about the average demand.

3. **Forecasts are more accurate for families or groups.** The behavior of individual items in a group is random even when the group has very stable characteristics. For example, the marks for individual students in a class are more difficult to forecast accurately than the class average. High marks average out with low marks. This means that forecasts are more accurate for large groups of items than for individual items in a group.

For production planning, families or groups are based on the similarity of process and equipment used. For example, a firm forecasting the demand for knit socks as a product group might forecast men's socks as one group and women's as another since the markets are different. However, production of men's and women's ankle socks will be done on the same machines and knee socks on another. For production planning, the forecast should be for (a) men's and women's ankle socks and (b) men's and women's knee socks.

4. **Forecasts are more accurate for nearer time periods.** The near future holds less uncertainty than the far future. Most people are more confident in forecasting what they will be doing over the next week than a year from now. As someone once said, tomorrow is expected to be pretty much like today.

    In the same way, demand for the near term is easier for a company to forecast than for a time in the distant future. This is extremely important for long-lead-time items and especially so if their demand is dynamic. Anything that can be done to reduce lead time will improve forecast accuracy.

COLLECTION AND PREPARATION OF DATA

Forecasts are usually based on historical data manipulated in some way using either judgment or a statistical technique. Thus, the forecast is only as good as the data on which it is based. To get good data, three principles of data collection are important.

1. **Record data in the same terms as needed for the forecast.** This is a problem in determining the purpose of the forecast and what is to be forecast. There are three dimensions to this:

    a. If the purpose is to forecast demand on production, data based on demand, not shipments, are needed. Shipments show when goods were shipped and not necessarily when the customer wanted them. Thus, shipments do not necessarily give a true indication of demand.

    b. The forecast period, in weeks, months, or quarters, should be the same as the schedule period. If schedules are weekly, the forecast should be for the same time interval.

    c. The items forecast should be the same as those controlled by manufacturing. For example, if there are a variety of options that can be supplied with a particular product, the demand for the product and for each option should be forecast.

    Suppose a firm makes a bicycle that comes in three frame sizes, three possible wheel sizes, a 3-, 5-, or 10-speed gear changer, and with or without deluxe trim. In all, there are 54 ($3 \times 3 \times 3 \times 2$) individual end items sold. If each were forecast, there would be 54 forecasts to make. A better approach is to forecast (a) total demand and (b) the percentage of the total that requires each frame size, wheel size, and so on. That way there need be only 12 forecasts: 3 frame sizes, 3 wheel sizes, 3 gear changers, 2 levels of trim and the bike itself.

    In this example, the lead time to make the components would be relatively long in comparison to the lead time to assemble a bike. Manufacturing can make the components according to component forecast and can then assemble bikes according to customer orders. This would be ideal for situations where final assembly schedules are used as discussed in Chapter 3.

2. **Record the circumstances relating to the data.** Demand is influenced by particular events, and these should be recorded along with the demand data. For instance, artificial bumps in demand can be caused by sales promotions, price changes, changes in the weather, or a strike at a competitor's factory. It is vital that these factors be related to the demand history so they may be included or removed for future conditions.

3. **Record the demand separately for different customer groups.** Many firms distribute their goods through different channels of distribution, each having its own demand characteristics. For example, a firm may sell to a number of wholesalers that

order relatively small quantities regularly and also sell to a major retailer that buys a large lot twice a year. Forecasts of average demand would be meaningless, and each set of demands should be forecast separately.

FORECASTING TECHNIQUES

There are many forecasting methods, but they can usually be classified into three categories: qualitative, extrinsic, and intrinsic.

Qualitative Techniques

Qualitative techniques are projections based on judgment, intuition, and informed opinions. By their nature, they are subjective. Such techniques are used to forecast general business trends and the potential demand for large families of products over an extended period of time. As such, they are used mainly by senior management. Production and inventory forecasting is usually concerned with the demand for particular end items, and qualitative techniques are seldom appropriate.

When attempting to forecast the demand for a new product, there is no history on which to base a forecast. In these cases, the techniques of market research and historical analogy might be used. Market research is a systematic, formal, and conscious procedure for testing to determine customer opinion or intention. Historical analogy is based on a comparative analysis of the introduction and growth of similar products in the hope that the new product behaves in a similar fashion. Another method is to test-market a product.

There are several other methods of qualitative forecasting. One, called the Delphi method, uses a panel of experts who give their opinions on what is likely to happen.

Extrinsic Techniques

Extrinsic forecasting techniques are projections based on external (extrinsic) indicators that relate to the demand for a company's products. Examples of such data would be housing starts, birth rates, and disposable income. The theory is that the demand for a product group is directly proportional, or correlates, to activity in another field. Examples of correlation follow:

- Sales of bricks are proportional to housing starts.
- Sales of automobile tires are proportional to gasoline consumption.

Housing starts and gasoline consumption are called **economic indicators.** They describe economic conditions prevailing during a given time period. Some commonly used economic indicators are construction contract awards, automobile production, farm income, steel production, and gross national income. Data of this kind are compiled and published by various government departments, financial papers and magazines, trade associations, and banks.

The problem is to find an indicator that correlates with demand and one that preferably leads demand, that is, one that occurs before the demand does. For example, the number of construction contracts awarded in one period may determine the building material sold in the next period. When it is not possible to find a leading indicator, it may be possible to use a nonleading indicator for which the government or an organization forecasts. In a sense, it is basing a forecast on a forecast.

Extrinsic forecasting is most useful in forecasting the total demand for a firm's products or the demand for families of products. As such, it is used most often in business and production planning rather than the forecasting of individual end items.

Intrinsic Techniques

Intrinsic forecasting techniques use historical data to forecast. These data are usually recorded in the company and are readily available. Intrinsic forecasting techniques are based on the assumption that what happened in the past will happen in the future. This assumption has been likened to driving a car by looking out the rearview mirror. Although there is some obvious truth to this, it is also true that lacking any other crystal ball, the best guide to the future is what has happened in the past.

Since intrinsic techniques are so important, the next section will discuss some of the more important intrinsic techniques. They are often used as input to master production scheduling where end-item forecasts are needed for the planning horizon of the plan.

SOME IMPORTANT INTRINSIC TECHNIQUES

Assume that the monthly demand for a particular item over the past year is as shown in Figure 8.4.

Suppose it is the end of December, and we want to forecast demand for January of the coming year. Several rules can be used:

- **Demand this month will be the same as last month.** January demand would be forecast at 84, the same as December. This may appear too simple, but if there is little change in demand month to month, it probably will be quite usable.
- **Demand this month will be the same as demand the same month last year.** Forecast demand would be 92, the same as January last year. This rule is adequate if demand is seasonal and there is little up or down trend.

Rules such as these, based on a single month or past period, are of limited use when there is much random fluctuation in demand. Usually methods that average out history are better because they dampen out some effects of random variation.

As an example, the average of last year's demand can be used as an estimate for January demand. Such a simple average would not be responsive to trends or changes in level of demand. A better method would be to use a moving average.

Average Demand   This raises the question of what to forecast. As discussed previously, demand can fluctuate because of random variation. It is best to forecast the **average demand** rather than second-guess what the effect of random fluctuation will be. The second principle of forecasting discussed previously said that a forecast should include an estimate of error. As we will see, this range can be estimated. Thus, a forecast of average demand should be made, and the estimate of error applied to it.

Moving Averages

One simple way to forecast is to take the average demand for, say, the last three or six periods and use that figure as the forecast for the next period. At the end of the next period, the first-period demand is dropped and the latest-period demand added to determine a new average to be used as a forecast. This forecast would always be based on the average of the actual demand over the specified period.

January	92	July	84
February	83	August	81
March	66	September	75
April	74	October	63
May	75	November	91
June	84	December	84

FIGURE 8.4 A 12-month demand history.

For example, suppose it was decided to use a three-month moving average on the data shown in Figure 8.4. Our forecast for January, based on the demand in October, November, and December, would be:

$$\frac{63 + 91 + 84}{3} = 79$$

Now suppose that January demand turned out to be 90 instead of 79. The forecast for February would be calculated as:

$$\frac{91 + 84 + 90}{3} = 88$$

Example Problem

Demand over the past three months has been 120, 135, and 114 units. Using a three-month moving average, calculate the forecast for the fourth month.

ANSWER

$$\text{Forecast for month 4} = \frac{120 + 135 + 114}{3} = \frac{369}{3} = 123$$

Actual demand for the fourth month turned out to be 129. Calculate the forecast for the fifth month.

$$\text{Forecast for month 5} = \frac{135 + 114 + 129}{3} = 126$$

In the previous discussion, the forecast for January was 79, and the forecast for February was 88. The forecast has risen, reflecting the higher January value and the dropping of the low October value. If a longer period, such as six months, is used, the forecast does not react as quickly. The fewer months included in the moving average, the more weight is given to the latest information, and the faster the forecast reacts to trends. However, the forecast will always lag behind a trend. For example, consider the following demand history for the past five periods:

Period	Demand
1	1000
2	2000
3	3000
4	4000
5	5000

There is a rising trend to demand. If a five-period moving average is used, the forecast for period 6 is $(1000 + 2000 + 3000 + 4000 + 5000) \div 5 = 3000$. It does not look very accurate since the forecast is lagging actual demand by a large amount. However, if a three-month moving average is used, the forecast is $(3000 + 4000 + 5000) \div 3 = 4000$. Not perfect, but somewhat better. The point is that a moving average always lags a trend, and the more periods included in the average, the greater the lag will be.

On the other hand, if there is no trend but actual demand fluctuates considerably due to random variation, a moving average based on a few periods reacts to the fluctuation rather than forecasts the average. Consider the following demand history:

Period	Demand
1	2000
2	5000
3	3000
4	1000
5	4000

The demand has no trend and is random. If a five-month moving average is used, the forecast for the next month is 3000. This reflects all the values. If a two-month average is taken, the forecasts for the third, fourth, fifth, and sixth months are as follows:

$$\text{Forecast for third month} = (2000 + 5000) \div 2 = 3500$$
$$\text{Forecast for fourth month} = (5000 + 3000) \div 2 = 4000$$
$$\text{Forecast for fifth month} = (3000 + 1000) \div 2 = 2000$$
$$\text{Forecast for sixth month} = (1000 + 4000) \div 2 = 2500$$

With a two-month moving average the forecast reacts very quickly to the latest demand and thus is not stable.

Moving averages are best used for forecasting products with stable demand where there is little trend or seasonality. Moving averages are also useful to filter out random fluctuations. This has some common sense since periods of high demand are often followed by periods of low demand since the total market demand is usually constant and consumers often buy goods ahead of time due to sales or other outside influences including the weather and holiday events. Buying early will lower future sales.

One drawback to using moving averages is the need to retain several periods of history for each item to be forecast. This will require a great deal of computer storage or clerical effort. Also, the calculations are cumbersome. A common forecasting technique, called **exponential smoothing**, gives the same results as a moving average but without the need to retain as much data and with easier calculations.

Exponential Smoothing

It is not necessary to keep months of history to get a moving average because the previously calculated forecast has already allowed for this history. Therefore, the forecast can be based on the old calculated forecast and the new data.

Using the data in Figure 8.4, suppose an average of the demand of the last six months (80 units) is used to forecast January demand. If at the end of January, actual demand is 90 units, we must drop July's demand and pick up January's demand to determine the new forecast. However, if an average of the old forecast (80) and the actual demand for January (90) is taken, the new forecast, for February, is 85 units. This formula puts as much weight on the most recent month as on the old forecast (all previous months). If this does not seem suitable, less weight could be put on the latest actual demand and more weight on the old forecast. Perhaps putting only 10% of the weight on the latest month's demand and 90% of the weight on the old forecast would be better. In that case,

$$\text{February forecast} = 0.1(90) + 0.9(80) = 81$$

Notice that this forecast did not rise as much as our previous calculation in which the old forecast and the latest actual demand were given the same weight. One advantage to exponential smoothing is that the new data can be given any weight wanted.

The weight given to latest actual demand is called a **smoothing constant** and is represented by the Greek letter alpha (α). It is always expressed as a decimal and typically ranges from 0 to 0.3.

In general, the formula for calculating the new forecast is as follows:

$$\text{New forecast} = (\alpha)(\text{latest demand}) + (1-\alpha)(\text{Previous forecast})$$

Example Problem

The old forecast for May was 220, and the actual demand for May was 190. If alpha (α) is 0.15, calculate the forecast for June. If June demand turns out to be 218, calculate the forecast for July.

ANSWER

$$\text{June forecast} = (0.15)(190) + (1 - 0.15)(220) = 215.5$$
$$\text{July forecast} = (0.15)(218) + (0.85)(215.5) = 215.9$$

Exponential smoothing provides a routine method for regularly updating item forecasts. It works quite well when dealing with stable items. Generally, it has been found

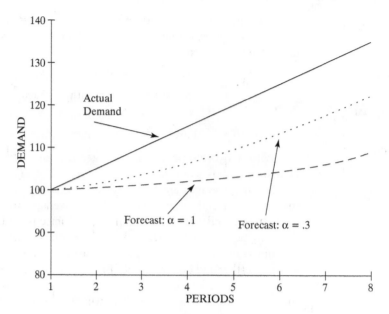

FIGURE 8.5 Exponential forecast where trend exists.

satisfactory for short-range forecasting. It is not satisfactory where the demand is low or intermittent.

Exponential smoothing will detect trends, although the forecast will lag actual demand if a definite trend exists. Figure 8.5 shows a graph of the exponentially smoothed forecast lagging the actual demand where a positive trend exists. Notice the forecast with the larger α follows actual demand more closely.

If a trend exists, it is possible to use a slightly more complex formula, called double exponential smoothing. This technique uses the same principles but notes whether each successive value of the forecast is moving up or down on a trend line. Double exponential smoothing is beyond the scope of this text.

A problem exists in selecting the "best" alpha factor. If a low factor such as 0.1 is used, the old forecast will be heavily weighted, and changing trends will not be picked up as quickly as might be desired. If a larger factor such as 0.4 is used, the forecast will react sharply to changes in demand and will be erratic if there is a sizable random fluctuation. A good way to get the best alpha factor is to use computer simulation. Using past actual demand, forecasts are made with different alpha factors to see which one best suits the historical demand pattern for particular products.

SEASONALITY

Many products have a seasonal or periodic demand pattern: skis, lawnmowers, bathing suits, and Christmas tree lights are examples. Less obvious are products whose demand varies by the time of day, week, or month. Examples of these might be electric power usage during the day or grocery shopping during the week. Power usage peaks between 4:00 P.M. and 7:00 P.M. and supermarkets are most busy toward the end of the week or before certain holidays.

Seasonal Index

A useful indication of the degree of seasonal variation for a product is the **seasonal index.** This index is an estimate of how much the demand during the season will be above or below the average demand for the product. For example, swimsuit demand might average 100 per month, but in July the average could be 175, and in September it could be 35. The index for July demand would be 1.75, and for September it would be 0.35.

Year	Quarter				
	1	2	3	4	Total
1	122	108	81	90	401
2	130	100	73	96	399
3	132	98	71	99	400
Average	128	102	75	95	400

FIGURE 8.6 Seasonal sales history.

The formula for the seasonal index is as follows:

$$\text{Seasonal index} = \frac{\text{period average demand}}{\text{average demand for all periods}}$$

The period can be daily, weekly, monthly, or quarterly depending on the basis for the seasonality of demand.

The average demand for all periods is a value that averages out seasonality. This is called the **deseasonalized demand.** The previous equation can be rewritten as follows:

$$\text{Deseasonalized demand} = \frac{\text{period average demand}}{\text{seasonal index}}$$

Example Problem

A product that is seasonally based on quarterly demand and the demand for the past three years is shown in Figure 8.6. There is no trend, but there is definite seasonality. Average quarterly demand is 100 units. Figure 8.6 also shows a graph of actual seasonal demand and average quarterly demand. The average demand shown is the historical average demand for all periods. Remember we forecast average demand, not seasonal demand.

ANSWER

The seasonal indices can now be calculated as follows:

$$\text{Seasonal index} = \frac{128}{100} = 1.28 \text{ (quarter 1)}$$

$$= \frac{102}{100} = 1.02 \text{(quarter 2)}$$

$$= \frac{75}{100} = 0.75 \text{(quarter 3)}$$

$$= \frac{95}{100} = 0.95 \text{(quarter 4)}$$

$$\text{Total of seasonal indices} = 4.00$$

Note that the total of all the seasonal indices equals the number of periods. This is a good way to check whether the calculations are correct.

Seasonal Forecasts

The equation for developing seasonal indices is also used to forecast seasonal demand. If a company forecasts average demand for all periods, the seasonal indices can be used to calculate the seasonal forecasts. Changing the equation around we get:

$$\text{Seasonal demand} = (\text{seasonal index})(\text{average demand})$$

$$\text{Deseasonalized demand} = \frac{\text{actual seasonal demand}}{\text{seasonal index}}$$

Example Problem

The company in the previous problem forecasts an annual demand next year of 420 units. Calculate the forecast for quarterly sales.

Answer

Expected quarter demand = (seasonal index) (average quarterly demand)

Expected first − quarter demand = 1.28 × 105 = 134.4 units

Expected second − quarter demand = 1.02 × 105 = 107.1 units

Expected third − quarter demand = 0.75 × 105 = 78.75 units

Expected fourth − quarter demand = 0.95 × 105 = 99.75 units

Total forecast demand   = 420   units

Deseasonalized Demand

Forecasts do not consider random variation. They are made for average demand, and seasonal demand is calculated from the average using seasonal indices. Figure 8.7 shows both actual demand and forecast average demand. The forecast average demand is also the deseasonalized demand. Historical data are of actual seasonal demand, and they must be deseasonalized before they can be used to develop a forecast of average demand.

Also, if comparisons are made between sales in different periods, they are meaningless unless deseasonalized data are used. For example, a company selling tennis rackets finds demand is usually largest in the summer. However, some people play indoor tennis, so there is demand in the winter months as well. If demand in January was 5200 units and in June was 24,000 units, how could January demand be compared to June demand to see

FIGURE 8.7 Seasonal demand.

which was the better demand month? If there is seasonality, comparison of actual demand would be meaningless. Deseasonalized data are needed to make a comparison.

The equation to calculate deseasonalized demand for each period is derived from the previous seasonal equation and is as follows:

$$\text{Deseasonalized demand} = \frac{\text{actual seasonal demand}}{\text{seasonal index}}$$

Example Problem

A company selling tennis rackets has a January demand of 5200 units and a June demand of 24,000 units. If the seasonal indices for January were 0.5 and for June were 2.5, calculate the deseasonalized January and June demand. How do the two months compare?

ANSWER

Deseasonalized January demand = 5200 ÷ 0.5 = 10,400 units

Deseasonalized June demand = 24,000 ÷ 2.5 = 9600 units

June and January demand can now be compared. On a deseasonalized basis, January demand is greater than June demand.

Deseasonalized data must be used for forecasting. Forecasts are made for average demand, and the forecast for seasonal demand is *calculated* from the average demand using the appropriate season index.

The rules for forecasting with seasonality follow:

- Use only deseasonalized data to forecast.
- Forecast deseasonalized demand (base forecast), not seasonal demand.
- Calculate the seasonal forecast by applying the seasonal index to the base forecast.

Example Problem

A company uses exponential smoothing to forecast demand for its products. For April, the deseasonalized forecast was 1000, and the actual seasonal demand was 1250 units. The seasonal index for April is 1.2 and for May is 0.7. If α is 0.1, calculate the following:

a. The deseasonalized actual demand for April.

b. The deseasonalized May forecast.

c. The seasonal forecast for May.

ANSWER

a. Deseasonalized actual demand for April $= \dfrac{1250}{1.2} = 1042$

b. Deseasonalized May forecast $= \alpha(\text{latest actual}) + (1 - \alpha)\,(\text{previous forecast})$
$$= 0.1(1042) + 0.9(1000) = 1004$$

c. Seasonalized May forecast = (seasonal index)(deseasonalized forecast)
$$= 0.7(1004) = 703$$

TRACKING THE FORECAST

As noted in the discussion on the principles of forecasting, forecasts are usually wrong. There are several reasons for this, some of which are related to human involvement and others to the behavior of the economy. If there were a method of determining how good a forecast is, forecasting methods could be improved and better estimates could be made accounting for the error. There is no point in continuing with a plan based on poor forecast data. We need to track the forecast. Tracking the forecast is the process of comparing actual demand with the forecast.

Forecast Error

Forecast error is the difference between actual demand and forecast demand. Error can occur in two ways: bias and random variation.

Bias   Cumulative actual demand may not be the same as forecast. Consider the data in Figure 8.8. Actual demand varies from forecast, and over the six-month period, cumulative demand is 120 units greater than expected.

Bias exists when the cumulative actual demand varies from the cumulative forecast. This means the forecast average demand has been wrong. In the example in Figure 8.8, the forecast average demand was 100, but the actual average demand was $720 \div 6 = 120$ units. Figure 8.9 shows a graph of cumulative forecast and actual demand.

Month	Forecast		Actual	
	Monthly	Cumulative	Monthly	Cumulative
1	100	100	110	110
2	100	200	125	235
3	100	300	120	355
4	100	400	125	480
5	100	500	130	610
6	100	600	110	720
Total	600	600	720	720

FIGURE 8.8 Forecast and actual sales with bias.

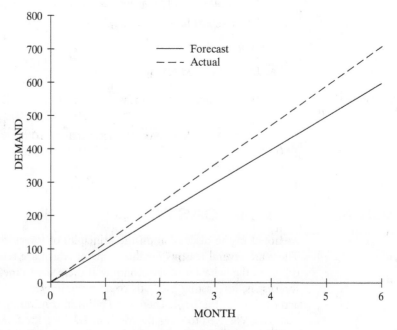

FIGURE 8.9 Forecast and actual demand with bias.

Bias is a systematic error in which the actual demand is consistently above or below the forecast demand. When bias exists, the forecast should be changed to improve its accuracy.

The purpose of tracking the forecast is to be able to react to forecast error by planning around it or by reducing it. When an unacceptably large error or bias is observed, it should be investigated to determine its cause.

Often there are exceptional one-time reasons for error. Examples are machine breakdown, customer shutdown, large one-time orders, and sales promotions. These reasons relate to the discussion on collection and preparation of data and the need to record the circumstances relating to the data. On these occasions, the demand history must be adjusted to consider the exceptional circumstances.

Errors can also occur because of timing. For example, an early or late winter will affect the timing of demand for snow shovels although the cumulative demand will be the same.

Tracking cumulative demand will confirm timing errors or exceptional one-time events. The following example illustrates this. Note that in April the cumulative demand is back in a normal range.

Month	Forecast	Actual	Cumulative Forecast	Cumulative Actual
January	100	95	100	95
February	100	110	200	205
March*	100	155	300	360
April	100	45	400	405
May	100	90	500	495

*Customer foresaw a possible strike and stockpiled.

Random variation   In a given period, actual demand will vary about the average demand. The variability will depend upon the demand pattern of the product. Some products will have a stable demand, and the variation will not be large. Others will be unstable and will have a large variation.

Consider the data in Figure 8.10, showing forecast and actual demand. Notice there is much random variation, but the average error is zero. This shows that the average forecast was correct and there was no bias. The data are plotted in Figure 8.11.

Mean Absolute Deviation

Forecast error must be measured before it can be used to revise the forecast or to help in planning. There are several ways to measure error. One method commonly used due to its ease of calculation is **mean absolute deviation (MAD).**

Month	Forecast	Actual	Variation (error)
1	100	105	5
2	100	94	− 6
3	100	98	− 2
4	100	104	4
5	100	103	3
6	100	96	− 4
Total	600	600	0

FIGURE 8.10 Forecast and actual sales without bias.

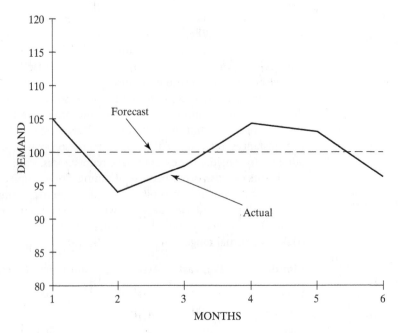

FIGURE 8.11 Forecast and actual sales without bias.

Consider the data on variability in Figure 8.10. Although the total error (variation) is zero, there is still considerable variation each month. Total error would be useless to measure the variation. One way to measure the variability is to calculate the total error ignoring the plus and minus signs and take the average. This is mean absolute deviation:

- *mean* implies an average,
- *absolute* means without reference to plus and minus,
- *deviation* refers to the error:

$$\text{MAD} = \frac{\text{sum of absolute deviations}}{\text{number of observations}}$$

Example Problem

Given the data shown in Figure 8.10, calculate the mean absolute deviation.

Answer

$$\text{Sum of absolute deviations} = 5 + 6 + 2 + 4 + 3 + 4 = 24$$

$$\text{MAD} = \frac{24}{6} = 4$$

Normal distribution The mean absolute deviation measures the difference (error) between actual demand and forecast. Usually, actual demand is close to the forecast but sometimes is not. A graph of the number of times (frequency) actual demand is of a particular value produces a bell-shaped curve. This distribution is called a **normal distribution** and is shown in Figure 8.12. Chapter 11 gives a more detailed discussion of normal distributions and their characteristics.

There are two important characteristics to normal curves: the central tendency, or average, and the dispersion, or spread, of the distribution. In Figure 8.12, the central tendency is the forecast. The dispersion, the fatness or thinness of the normal curve, is measured by the standard deviation. The greater the dispersion, the larger the standard deviation. The mean absolute deviation is an approximation of the standard deviation and is used because it is easy to calculate and apply.

From statistics we know that the error will be within

±1 MAD of the average about 60% of the time;

±2 MAD of the average about 90% of the time;

±3 MAD of the average about 98% of the time.

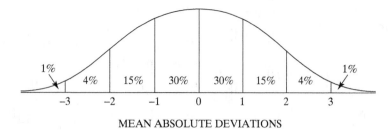

MEAN ABSOLUTE DEVIATIONS

FIGURE 8.12 Normal distribution curve.

Uses of mean absolute deviation   Mean absolute deviation has several uses. Some of the most important follow.

Tracking signal   Bias exists when cumulative actual demand varies from forecast. The problem is in guessing whether the variance is due to random variation or bias. If the variation is due to random variation, the error will correct itself, and nothing should be done to adjust the forecast. However, if the error is due to bias, the forecast should be corrected. Using the mean absolute deviation, we can make some judgment about the reasonableness of the error. Under normal circumstances, the actual period demand will be within ±3 MAD of the average 98% of the time. If actual period demand varies from the forecast by more than 3 MAD, we can be about 98% sure that the forecast is in error.

A **tracking signal** can be used to monitor the quality of the forecast. There are several procedures used, but one of the simpler ones is based on a comparison of the cumulative sum of the forecast errors (the cumulative bias) to the mean absolute deviation. Following is the equation:

$$\text{Tracking signal} = \frac{\text{algebraic sum of forecast errors}}{\text{MAD}}$$

Example Problem

The forecast is 100 units a week. The actual demand for the past six weeks has been 105, 110, 103, 105, 107, and 115. If MAD is 7.5, calculate the sum of the forecast error and the tracking signal.

ANSWER

$$\text{Some of forecast error} = 5 + 10 + 3 + 5 + 7 + 15 = 45$$
$$\text{Tracking signal} = 45 \div 7.5 = 6$$

Example Problem

A company uses a trigger of ±4 to decide whether a forecast should be reviewed. Given the following history, determine in which period the forecast should be reviewed. MAD for the item is 2.

Period	Forecast	Actual	Deviation	Cumulative Deviation	Tracking Signal
				5	2.5
1	100	96			
2	100	98			
3	100	104			
4	100	110			

ANSWER

Period	Forecast	Actual	Deviation	Cumulative Deviation	Tracking Signal
				5	2.5
1	100	96	– 4	1	0.5
2	100	98	– 2	– 1	– 0.5
3	100	104	4	3	1.5
4	100	110	10	13	6.5

The forecast should be reviewed in period 4.

Contingency planning   Suppose a forecast is made that demand for door slammers will be 100 units and that capacity for making them is 110 units. Mean absolute deviation of actual demand about the forecast historically has been calculated at 10 units. This means there is a 60% chance that actual demand will be between 90 and 110 units and a 40% chance that they will not. With this information, manufacturing management might be able to devise a contingency plan to cope with the possible extra demand.

Safety stock   The data can be used as a basis for setting safety stock. This will be discussed in detail in Chapter 11.

P/D Ratio

Because of the inherent error in forecasts, companies that rely on them can run into a variety of problems. For example, the wrong material may be bought and perhaps processed into the wrong goods. A more reliable way of producing what is really needed is the use of the P/D ratio.

P, or **production lead time**, is the stacked lead time for a product. It includes time for purchasing and arrival of raw materials, manufacturing, assembly, delivery, and sometimes the design of the product. Figure 1.1. on page 4 shows various times in different types of industries and is reproduced in Figure 8.13.

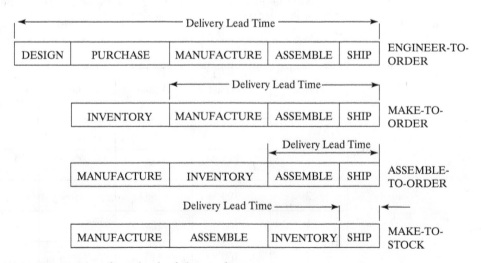

FIGURE 8.13 Manufacturing lead time and strategy.

FIGURE 8.14 Mushroom design.

D, or **demand lead time**, is the customer's lead time. It is the time from when a customer places an order until the goods are delivered. It can be very short, as in a make-to-stock environment, or very long, as in an engineer-to-order company.

The traditional way to guard against inherent error in forecasting is to include safety stock in inventory. There is an added expense to the extra inventory carried "just in case." One other way is to make more accurate predictions. There are five ways to move in this direction.

1. **Reduce P time.** The longer the P time, the more chance there is for error. Ideally, P will be less than D.

2. **Force a match between P and D.** Moving in this direction can be done in two ways:

    a. Make the customer's D time equal to your P time. This is common with custom products when the manufacturer makes the product according to the customer's specification.

    b. *Sell what you forecast.* This will happen while you control the market. One good example is the automobile market. It is common to offer special inducements toward the end of the automotive year in order to sell what the manufacturers have predicted.

3. **Simplify the product line.** The more variety in the product line, the more room for error.

4. **Standardize products and processes.** This means that "customization" can occur closer to final assembly. This technique is also known as postponement, as discussed in Chapter 1. The basic components are identical, or similar, for all components. Figure 8.14 shows this graphically.

5. **Forecast more accurately.** Make forecasts using a well-thought-out, well-controlled process.

SUMMARY

Forecasting is an inexact science that is, nonetheless, an invaluable tool if the following are kept in mind:

- Forecasts should be tracked.
- There should be a measure of reasonableness of error.
- When actual demand exceeds the reasonableness of error, an investigation should be made to discover the cause of the error.
- If there is no apparent cause of error, the method of forecasting should be reviewed to see if there is a better way to forecast.

There are several methods used to forecast, including qualitative, intrinsic, and extrinsic methods.

KEY TERMS

Average demand 173

Bias 180

Demand lead time 185

Demand management 167

Deseasonalized demand 177

Dynamic 170

Economic indicators 172

Exponential smoothing 175

Extrinsic forecasting techniques 172

Forecast error 180

Intrinsic forecasting techniques 172

Mean absolute deviation (MAD) 181

Moving averages 175

Normal distribution 182

Order processing 168

Production lead time 184

Qualitative techniques 172

Random variation 169

Seasonal index 176

Seasonality 169

Smoothing constant 175

Stable 170

Tracking signal 183

Trend 169

QUESTIONS

1. What is demand management? What functions does it include?
2. Why must we forecast?
3. What factors influence the demand for a firm's products?
4. Describe the purpose of forecasting for strategic business planning, production planning, and master production scheduling.
5. The text describes three characteristics of demand. Name and describe each.
6. Describe trend, seasonality, random variation, and cycle as applied to forecasting.
7. The text discusses four principles of forecasting. Name and describe each.
8. Name and describe the three principles of data collection.
9. Describe the characteristics and differences between qualitative, extrinsic, and intrinsic forecasting techniques.
10. Describe and give the advantages and disadvantages of (a) moving averages and (b) exponential smoothing.
11. What is a seasonal index? How is it calculated?
12. What is meant by the term *deseasonalized demand*?
13. What is meant by the term *tracking the forecast*? In which two ways can forecasts go wrong?
14. What is bias error in forecasting? What are some of the causes?
15. What is random variation?
16. What is the mean absolute deviation (MAD)? Why is it useful in forecasting?
17. What action should be taken when unacceptable error is found in tracking a forecast?
18. What is the P/D ratio? How may it be improved?
19. How would a manufacturer with a P/D ration less than 1 schedule production? How would this affect inventories?
20. What might it mean if a forecasting method has no bias yet has a large MAD?

PROBLEMS

8.1. Over the past three months, the demand for a product has been 255, 219, and 231. Calculate the three-month moving average forecast for month 4. If the actual demand in month 4 is 228, calculate the forecast for month 5.

   Answer.   235, 226

8.2. Given the following data, calculate the three-month moving average forecasts for months 4, 5, 6, and 7.

Month	Actual Demand	Forecast
1	60	
2	70	
3	40	
4	50	
5	70	
6	65	
7		

8.3. Monthly demand over the past 10 months is given in what follows.

a. Graph the demand.

b. What is your best guess for the demand for month 11?

c. Using a three-month moving average, calculate the forecasts for months 4, 5, 6, 7, 8, 9, 10, and 11.

Month	Actual Demand	Forecast
1	102	
2	91	
3	95	
4	105	
5	94	
6	100	
7	106	
8	95	
9	105	
10	98	
11		

8.4. If the forecast for February was 122 and actual demand was 135, what would be the forecast for March if the smoothing constant (α) is 0.15? Use exponential smoothing for your calculation.

Answer. Forecast = 123.95 = 124

8.5. If the old forecast is 100 and the latest actual demand is 83, what is the exponentially smoothed forecast for the next period? Alpha is 0.3.

8.6. Using exponential smoothing, calculate the forecasts for months 2, 3, 4, 5, and 6. The smoothing constant is 0.2, and the old forecast for month 1 is 245.

Month	Actual Demand	Forecast Demand
1	260	
2	230	
3	225	
4	245	
5	250	
6		

8.7. Using exponential smoothing, calculate the forecasts for the same months as in problem 8.3c. The old average for month 3 was 96 and $\alpha = 0.2$. What is the difference between the two forecasts for month 11?

Month	Actual Demand	Forecast
1	102	
2	91	
3	95	
4	105	
5	94	
6	100	
7	106	
8	95	
9	105	
10	98	
11		

8.8. Weekly demand for an item averaged 100 units over the past year. Actual demand for the next eight weeks is shown in what follows:

a. Plot the data on graph paper.

b. Letting $\alpha = 0.25$, calculate the smoothed forecast for each week.

c. Comment on how well the forecast is tracking actual demand. Is it lagging or leading actual demand?

Week	Actual Demand	Forecast
1	103	100
2	112	
3	113	
4	120	
5	128	
6	131	
7	140	
8	142	
9		

8.9. If the average demand for the first quarter was 140 and the average demand for all quarters was 175, what is the seasonal index for the first quarter?

Answer.   Seasonal index $= 0.80$

8.10. Using the data in problem 8.9, if the forecast for next year is 800, calculate the forecast for first quarterly demand next year.

Answer.   Forecast for first quarter $= 160$

8.11. The average demand for January has been 80, and the average annual demand has been 1800. Calculate the seasonal index for January. If the company forecasts annual demand next year at 2000 units, what is the forecast for January next year?

8.12. Given the following average demand for each month, calculate the seasonal indices for each month.

Month	Average Demand	Seasonal Index
January	30	
February	50	
March	85	
April	110	
May	125	
June	245	
July	255	
August	135	
September	100	
October	90	
November	50	
December	30	
Total		

Note that your answer, if done correctly, should have all the seasonal indices add up to the number of periods in the entire season, in this case 12.

8.13. Using the data in problem 8.12 and the seasonal indices you have calculated, calculate expected monthly demand if the annual forecast is 2000 units.

Month	Seasonal Index	Forecast
January		
February		
March		
April		
May		
June		
July		
August		
September		
October		
November		
December		

8.14. If the actual demand for April was 1440 units and the seasonal index was 2.5, what would be the deseasonalized April demand?

Answer.   Deseasonalized demand = 576 units

8.15. Calculate the deseasonalized demands for the following:

Quarter	Actual Demand	Seasonal Index	Deseasonalized Demand
1	130	0.62	
2	170	1.04	
3	375	1.82	
4	90	0.52	
Total			

8.16. The old deseasonalized forecast is 100 units, $\alpha = 0.30$, and the actual demand for the last month was 150 units. If the seasonal index for the last month is 1.2 and the next month is 0.8, calculate:

a. The deseasonalized actual demand for the last month.

b. The deseasonalized forecast for next month using exponential smoothing.

c. The forecast of actual demand for the next month.

Answer.   a. Deseasonalized last month's demand = 125

b. Deseasonalized forecast for next month = 107.5

c. Forecast of seasonalized demand = 86

8.17. The Fast Track Ski Shoppe sells ski goggles during the four months of the ski season. Average demand follows:

Month	Average Past Demand	Seasonal Index	Forecast Demand Next Year
December	300		
January	400		
February	220		
March	130		
Total			

a. Calculate the deseasonalized sales and the seasonal index for each of the four months.

b. If next year's demand is forecast at 1200 pairs of goggles, what will be the forecast sales for each month?

8.18. Given the following forecast and actual demand, calculate the mean absolute deviation.

Period	Forecast	Actual Demand	Absolute Deviation
1	110	85	
2	110	105	
3	110	120	
4	110	100	
5	110	90	
Total			

Answer.   MAD = 14

8.19. For the following data, calculate the mean absolute deviation.

Period	Forecast	Actual Demand	Absolute Deviation
1	100	105	
2	105	95	
3	110	90	
4	115	135	
5	120	105	
6	125	120	
Total	675	650	

8.20. A company uses a tracking signal trigger of ±4 to decide whether a forecast should be reviewed. Given the following history, determine in which period the forecast should be reviewed. MAD for the item is 15. Is there any previous indication that the forecast should be reviewed?

Period	Forecast	Actual	Deviation	Cumulative Deviation	Tracking Signal
1	100	110			
2	105	90			
3	110	85			
4	115	110			
5	120	105			
6	125	95			

NORTHCUTT BIKES: THE FORECASTING PROBLEM

Jan Northcutt, owner of Northcutt Bikes, started business in 1995 when she noticed the quality of bikes she purchased for sale in her bike shop declining while the prices went up. She also found it more difficult to obtain the features she wanted on ordered bikes without waiting for months. Her frustration turned to a determination to build her own bikes to her particular customer specifications.

She began by buying all the necessary parts (frames, seats, tires, etc.) and assembling them in a rented garage using two helpers. As the word spread about her shop's responsiveness to options, delivery, and quality, however, the individual customer base grew to include other bike shops in the area. As her business grew and demanded more of her attention, she soon found it necessary to sell the bike shop itself and concentrate on the production of bikes from a fairly large leased factory space.

As the business continued to grow, she backward integrated more and more processes into her operation, so that now she purchases less than 50% of the component value of the manufactured bikes. This not only improves her control of production quality but also helps her control the costs of production and makes the final product more cost attractive to her customers.

The Current Situation

Jan considers herself a hands-on manager and has typically used her intuition and her knowledge of the market to anticipate production needs. Since one of her founding principles was rapid and reliable delivery to customer specification, she felt she needed to begin production of the basic parts for each particular style of bike well in advance of demand. In that way she could have the basic frame, wheels, and standard accessories started in production prior to the recognition of actual demand, leaving only the optional add-ons to assemble once the order came in. Her turnaround time for an order of less than half the industry average is considered a major strategic advantage, and she feels it is vital for her to maintain or even improve on response time if she is to maintain her successful operation.

As the customer base has grown, however, the number of customers Jan knows personally has shrunk significantly as a percentage of the total customer base for Northcutt Bikes, and many of these new customers are expecting or even demanding very short response times, as that is what attracted them to Northcutt Bikes in the first place. This condition, in addition to the volatility of overall demand, has put a strain on capacity planning. She finds that at times there is a lot of idle time (adding significantly to costs), whereas at other times the demand exceeds capacity and hurts customer response time. The production facility has therefore turned to trying to project demand for certain models and actually building a finished goods inventory of those models. This has not proven to be too satisfactory, as it has actually hurt costs and some response times. Reasons include the following:

- The finished goods inventory is often not the "right" inventory, meaning shortages for some goods and excessive inventory of others. This condition both hurts responsiveness and increases inventory costs.
- Often to help maintain responsiveness, inventory is withdrawn from finished goods and reworked, adding to product cost.
- Reworking inventory uses valuable capacity for other customer orders, again resulting in poorer response times and/or increased costs due to expediting. Existing production orders and rework orders are both competing for vital equipment and resources during times of high demand, and scheduling has become a nightmare.

The inventory problem has grown to the point that additional storage space is needed, and that is a cost that Jan would like to avoid if possible.

Another problem Jan faces is the volatility of demand for bikes. Since she is worried about unproductive idle time and yet does not wish to lay off her workers during times of low demand, she has allowed them to continue to work steadily and build finished goods. This makes the problem of building the "right" finished goods even more important, especially given the tight availability of storage space.

Past Demand

The following shows the monthly demand for one major product line: the standard 26-inch 10-speed street bike. Although it is only one of Jan's products, it is representative of most of the major product lines currently being produced by Northcutt Bikes. If Jan can find a way to use this data to more constructively understand her demand, she feels she can probably use the same methodologies to project demand for other major product families. Such knowledge can allow her, she feels, to plan more effectively and continue to be responsive while still controlling costs.

ACTUAL DEMAND

Month	2008	2009	2010	2011
January	437	712	613	701
February	605	732	984	1291
March	722	829	812	1162
April	893	992	1218	1088
May	901	1148	1187	1497
June	1311	1552	1430	1781
July	1055	927	1392	1843
August	975	1284	1481	839
September	822	1118	940	1273
October	893	737	994	912
November	599	983	807	996
December	608	872	527	792

Tasks

1. Plot the data and describe what you see. What does it mean and how would you use the information from the plot to help you develop a forecast?

2. Use at least two different methodologies to develop as accurate a forecast as possible for the demand. Use each of those methods to project the next four months demand.

3. Which method from question 2 is "better"? How do you know that?

4. How, if at all, could we use Jan's knowledge of the market to improve the forecast? Would it be better to forecast in quarterly increments instead of monthly? Why or why not?

5. Are there other possible approaches that might improve Jan's operation and situation? What would they be and how could they help?

6. Has Jan's operation grown too large for her to control well? Why or why not? What would you suggest she do? What additional information would you suggest she look for to help her situation?

INVENTORY FUNDAMENTALS

INTRODUCTION

Inventories are materials and supplies that a business or institution carries either for sale or to provide inputs or supplies to the production process. All businesses and institutions require inventories. Often they are a substantial part of total assets.

Financially, inventories are very important to manufacturing companies. On the balance sheet, they usually represent from 20% to 60% of total assets. As inventories are used, their value is converted into cash, which improves cash flow and return on investment. There is a cost for carrying inventories, which increases operating costs and decreases profits. Good inventory management is essential.

Inventory management is responsible for planning and controlling inventory from the raw material stage to the customer. Since inventory either results from production or supports it, the two cannot be managed separately and, therefore, must be coordinated. Inventory must be considered at each of the planning levels and is thus part of production planning, master production scheduling, and material requirements planning. Production planning is concerned with overall inventory, master planning with end items, and material requirements planning with component parts and raw material.

AGGREGATE INVENTORY MANAGEMENT

Aggregate inventory management deals with managing inventories according to their classification (raw material, work-in-process, and finished goods) and the function they perform rather than at the individual item level. It is financially oriented and is concerned with the costs and benefits of carrying the different classifications of inventories. As such, aggregate inventory management involves:

- Flow and kinds of inventory needed.
- Supply and demand patterns.
- Functions that inventories perform.
- Objectives of inventory management.
- Costs associated with inventories.

ITEM INVENTORY MANAGEMENT

Inventory is managed not only at the aggregate level but also at the item level. Management must establish decision rules about inventory items so the staff responsible for inventory control can do their job effectively. These rules include the following:

- Which individual inventory items are most important.
- How individual items are to be controlled.
- How much to order at one time.
- When to place an order.

This chapter will study aggregate inventory management and some factors influencing inventory management decisions, which include the following:

- Types of inventory based on the flow of material.
- Supply and demand patterns.
- Functions performed by inventory.
- Objectives of inventory management.
- Inventory costs.

Finally, this chapter will conclude with a study of the first two decisions, deciding the importance of individual end items and how they are controlled. Subsequent chapters will discuss the question of how much stock to order at one time and when to place orders.

INVENTORY AND THE FLOW OF MATERIAL

There are many ways to classify inventories. One often-used classification is related to the flow of materials into, through, and out of a manufacturing organization, as shown in Figure 9.1

- **Raw materials.** These are purchased items received that have not entered the production process. They include purchased materials, component parts, and subassemblies.
- **Work-in-process (WIP).** Raw materials that have entered the manufacturing process and are being worked on or waiting to be worked on.
- **Finished goods.** The finished products of the production process that are ready to be sold as completed items. They may be held at a factory or central warehouse or at various points in the distribution system.

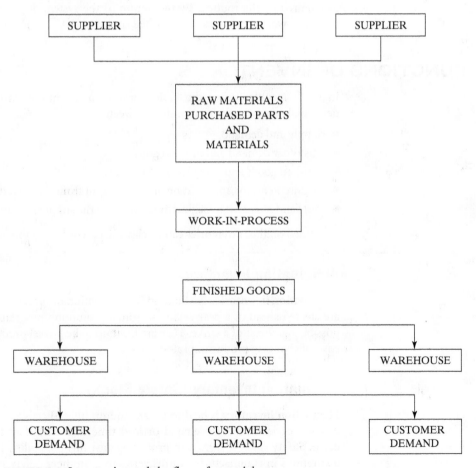

FIGURE 9.1 Inventories and the flow of materials.

- **Distribution inventories.** Finished goods located in the distribution system.
- **Maintenance, repair, and operational supplies (MROs).** Items used in production that do not become part of the product. These include hand tools, spare parts, lubricants, and cleaning supplies.

Classification of an item into a particular inventory depends on the production environment. For instance, sheet steel or tires are finished goods to the supplier but are raw materials and component parts to the car manufacturer.

SUPPLY AND DEMAND PATTERNS

If supply met demand exactly, there would be little need for inventory. Goods could be made at the same rate as demand, and no inventory would build up. For this situation to exist, demand must be predictable, stable, and relatively constant over a long time period.

If this is so, manufacturing can produce goods on a line-flow basis, matching production to demand. Using this system, raw materials are fed to production as required, work flow from one workstation to another is balanced so little work-in-process inventory is required, and goods are delivered to the customer at the rate the customer needs them. Flow manufacturing systems were discussed in Chapter 1. Because the variety of products they can make is so limited, demand has to be large enough to justify economically setting up the system. These systems are characteristic of just-in-time manufacturing, which will be discussed in Chapter 15.

Demand for most products is neither sufficient nor constant enough to warrant setting up a line-flow system, and these products are usually made in lots or batches. Workstations are organized by function—for example, all machine tools in one area, all welding in another, and assembly in another. Work moves in lots from one workstation to another as required by the routing. By the nature of the system, inventory will build up in raw materials, work-in-process, and finished goods.

FUNCTIONS OF INVENTORIES

In batch manufacturing, the basic purpose of inventories is to decouple supply and demand. Inventory serves as a buffer between

- Supply and demand.
- Customer demand and finished goods.
- Finished goods and component availability.
- Requirements for an operation and the output from the preceding operation.
- Parts and materials to begin production and the suppliers of materials.

Based on this, inventories can be classified according to the function they perform.

Anticipation Inventory

Anticipation inventories are built up in anticipation of future demand. For example, they are created ahead of a peak selling season, a promotion program, vacation shutdown, or possibly the threat of a strike. They are built up to help level production and to reduce the costs of changing production rates.

Fluctuation Inventory (Safety Stock)

Fluctuation inventory is held to cover random unpredictable fluctuations in supply and demand or lead time. If demand or lead time is greater than forecast, a **stockout** will occur. **Safety stock** is carried to protect against this possibility. Its purpose is to prevent disruptions in manufacturing or deliveries to customers. Safety stock is also called buffer stock or reserve stock.

Lot-Size Inventory

Items purchased or manufactured in quantities greater than needed immediately create **lot-size inventories**. This is to take advantage of quantity discounts; to reduce shipping, clerical, and setup costs; and in cases where it is impossible to make or purchase items at the same rate that they will be used or sold. Lot-size inventory is sometimes called **cycle stock**. It is the portion of inventory that depletes gradually as customers' orders come in and is replenished cyclically when suppliers' orders are received.

Transportation Inventory

Transportation inventories exist because of the time needed to move goods from one location to another, such as from a plant to a distribution center or a customer. They are sometimes called **pipeline or movement inventories**. The average amount of inventory in transit is

$$I = \frac{tA}{365}$$

where I is the average annual inventory in transit, t is transit time in days, and A is annual demand. Notice that the transit inventory does not depend upon the shipment size but on the transit time and the annual demand. The only way to reduce the inventory in transit, and its cost, is to reduce the transit time.

Example Problem

Delivery of goods from a supplier is in transit for 10 days. If the annual demand is 5200 units, what is the average annual inventory in transit?

Answer

$$I = \frac{10 \times 5200}{365} = 142.5 \text{ units}$$

The problem can be solved in the same way using dollars instead of units.

Hedge Inventory

Some products such as minerals and commodities—for example, grains or animal products—are traded on a worldwide market. The price for these products fluctuates according to world supply and demand. If buyers expect prices to rise, they can purchase **hedge inventory** when prices are low. Hedging is complex and beyond the scope of this text.

Maintenance, Repair, and Operating Supplies

MROs are items used to support general operations and maintenance but do not become directly part of a product. They include maintenance supplies, spare parts, and consumables such as cleaning compounds, lubricants, pencils, and erasers.

OBJECTIVES OF INVENTORY MANAGEMENT

A firm wishing to maximize profit will have at least the following objectives:

- Maximum customer service.
- Low-cost plant operation.
- Minimum inventory investment.

Customer Service

In broad terms, customer service is the ability of a company to satisfy the needs of customers. In inventory management, the term is used to describe the availability of items when needed and is a measure of inventory management effectiveness. The customer can be a purchaser, a distributor, another plant in the organization, or the workstation where the next operation is to be performed.

There are many different ways to measure customer service, each with its strengths and weaknesses, but there is no one best measurement. Some measures are percentage of orders shipped on schedule, percentage of line items shipped on schedule, and order-days out of stock.

Inventories help to maximize customer service by protecting against uncertainty. If we could forecast exactly what customers want and when, we could plan to meet demand with no uncertainty. However, demand and the lead time to get an item are often uncertain, possibly resulting in stockouts and customer dissatisfaction. For these reasons, it may be necessary to carry extra inventory to protect against uncertainty. This inventory is called safety stock and will be discussed in Chapter 11.

Operating Efficiency

Inventories help make a manufacturing operation more productive in four ways:

1. Inventories allow operations with different rates of production to operate separately and more economically. If two or more operations in a sequence have different rates of output and are to be operated efficiently, inventories must build up between them.

2. Chapter 2 discussed production planning for seasonal products in which demand is nonuniform throughout the year. One strategy discussed was to level production and build anticipation inventory for sale in the peak periods. This would result in the following:

   - Lower overtime costs.
   - Lower hiring and firing costs.
   - Lower training costs.
   - Lower subcontracting costs.
   - Lower capacity required.

   By leveling production, manufacturing can continually produce an amount equal to the average demand. The advantage of this strategy is that the costs of changing production levels are avoided. Figure 9.2 shows this strategy.

3. Inventories allow manufacturing to run longer production runs, which result in the following:

   - **Lower setup costs per item.** The cost to make a lot or batch depends upon the setup costs and the run costs. The setup costs are fixed, but the run costs vary with the number produced. If larger lots are run, the setup costs are absorbed over a larger number, and the average (unit) cost is lower.

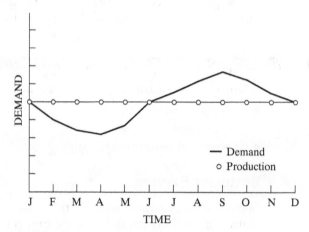

FIGURE 9.2 Operation leveling.

- **An increase in production capacity due to production resources being used at a greater portion of the time for processing as opposed to setup.** Time on a work center is taken up by setup and by run-time. Output occurs only when an item is being worked on and not when setup is taking place. If larger quantities are produced at one time, there are fewer setups required to produce a given annual output, and thus more time is available for producing goods. This is most important with bottleneck resources. Time lost on setup on these resources is lost throughput (total production) and lost capacity.

4. Inventories allow manufacturing to purchase in larger quantities, which results in lower ordering costs per unit and quantity discounts.

But all of this is at a price. The problem is to balance inventory investment with the following:

1. **Customer service.** The lower the inventory, the higher the likelihood of a stockout and the lower the level of customer service. The higher the inventory level, the higher customer service will be.

2. **Costs associated with changing production levels.** Excess equipment capacity, overtime, hiring, training, and layoff costs will all be higher if production fluctuates with demand.

3. **Cost of placing orders.** Lower inventories can be achieved by ordering smaller quantities more often, but this practice results in higher annual ordering costs.

4. **Transportation costs.** Goods moved in small quantities cost more to move per unit than those moved in large quantities. However, moving large lots implies higher inventory.

If inventory is carried, there has to be a benefit that exceeds the costs of carrying that inventory. Someone once said that the only good reason for carrying inventory beyond current needs is if it costs less to carry it than not. This being so, we should turn our attention to the costs associated with inventory.

INVENTORY COSTS

The following costs are used for inventory management decisions:

- Item cost.
- Carrying costs.
- Ordering costs.
- Stockout costs.
- Capacity-associated costs.

Item Cost

Item cost is the price paid for a purchased item, which consists of the cost of the item and any other direct costs associated in getting the item into the plant. These could include such things as transportation, custom duties, and insurance. The inclusive cost is often called the **landed price**. For an item manufactured in-house, the cost includes direct material, direct labor, and factory overhead. These costs can usually be obtained from either purchasing or accounting.

Carrying Costs

Carrying costs include all expenses incurred by the firm because of the volume of inventory carried. As inventory increases, so do these costs. They can be broken down into three categories:

1. **Capital costs.** Money invested in inventory is not available for other uses and as such represents a lost opportunity cost. The minimum cost would be the interest lost by

not investing the money at the prevailing interest rate, and it may be much higher depending on investment opportunities for the firm.

2. **Storage costs.** Storing inventory requires space, workers, and equipment. As inventory increases, so do these costs.

3. **Risk costs.** The risks in carrying inventory are as follows:

   a. Obsolescence; loss of product value resulting from a model or style change or technological development.

   b. Damage; inventory damaged while being held or moved.

   c. Pilferage; goods lost, strayed, or stolen.

   d. Deterioration; inventory that rots or dissipates in storage or whose shelf life is limited.

What does it cost to carry inventory? Actual figures vary from industry to industry and company to company. Capital costs may vary depending upon interest rates, the credit rating of the firm, and the opportunities the firm may have for investment. Storage costs vary with location and type of storage needed. Risk costs can be very low or can be close to 100% of the value of the item for perishable goods. The carrying cost is usually defined as a percentage of the dollar value of inventory per unit of time (usually one year). Textbooks tend to use a figure of 20–30% in manufacturing industries. This is realistic in many cases but not with all products. For example, the possibility of obsolescence with fad or fashion items is high, and the cost of carrying such items is greater.

Example Problem

A company carries an average annual inventory of $2,000,000. If it estimates the cost of capital is 10%, storage costs are 7%, and risk costs are 6%, what does it cost per year to carry this inventory?

ANSWER

Total cost of carrying inventory = 10% + 7% + 6% = 23%
Annual cost of carrying inventory = 0.23 × $2,000,000 = $460,000

Ordering Costs

Ordering costs are those costs associated with placing an order either with the factory or with a supplier. The cost of placing an order does not depend upon the quantity ordered. Whether a lot of 10 or 100 is ordered, the costs associated with placing the order are essentially the same. However, the annual cost of ordering depends upon the number of orders placed in a year.

Ordering costs in a factory include the following:

- **Production control costs.** The annual cost and effort expended in production control depends on the number of orders placed, not on the quantity ordered. The fewer orders per year, the less cost. The costs incurred are those of issuing and closing orders, scheduling, loading, dispatching, and expediting.

- **Setup and teardown costs.** Every time an order is issued, work centers have to set up to run the order and tear down the setup at the end of the run. These costs do not depend upon the quantity ordered but on the number of orders placed per year.

- **Lost capacity cost.** Every time an order is placed at a work center, the time taken to set up is lost as productive output time. This represents a loss of capacity and is directly related to the number of orders placed. It is particularly important and costly with bottleneck work centers.

- **Purchase order cost.** Every time a purchase order is placed, costs are incurred to place the order. These costs include order preparation, follow-up, expediting, receiving, authorizing payment, and the accounting cost of receiving and paying the invoice.

The annual cost of ordering depends upon the number of orders placed in a year. This can be reduced by ordering more at one time, resulting in the placing of fewer orders. However, this drives up the inventory level and the annual cost of carrying inventory.

Example Problem

Given the following annual costs, calculate the average cost of placing one order.

Production control salaries = $60,000
Supplies and operating expenses for production control department = $15,000
Cost of setting up work centers for an order = $120
Orders placed each year = 2000

ANSWER

$$\text{Average cost} = \frac{\text{fixed costs}}{\text{number of orders}} + \text{variable cost}$$

$$= \frac{\$60,000 + \$15,000}{2000} + \$120 = \$157.50$$

Stockout Costs

If demand during the lead time exceeds forecast, we can expect a **stockout**. A stockout can potentially be expensive because of back-order costs, lost sales, and possibly lost customers. Stockouts can be reduced by carrying extra inventory to protect against those times when the demand during lead time is greater than forecast.

Capacity-Associated Costs

When output levels must be changed, there may be costs for overtime, hiring, training, extra shifts, and layoffs. These **capacity-associated costs** can be avoided by leveling production, that is, by producing items in slack periods for sale in peak periods. However, this builds inventory in the slack periods.

Example Problem

A company makes and sells a seasonal product. Based on a sales forecast of 2000, 3000, 6000, and 5000 per quarter, calculate a level production plan, quarterly ending inventory, and average quarterly inventory.

If inventory carrying costs are $3 per unit per quarter, what is the annual cost of carrying inventory? Opening and ending inventories are zero.

ANSWER

	Quarter 1	Quarter 2	Quarter 3	Quarter 4	Total
Forecast Demand	2000	3000	6000	5000	16,000
Production	4000	4000	4000	4000	16,000
Ending Inventory 0	2000	3000	1000	0	
Average Inventory	1000	2500	2000	500	
Inventory Cost (dollars)	3000	7500	6000	1500	18,000

FINANCIAL STATEMENTS AND INVENTORY

The two major financial statements are the balance sheet and the income statement. The balance sheet shows assets, liabilities, and owners' equity. The income statement shows the revenues made and the expenses incurred in achieving that revenue.

Balance Sheet

An **asset** is something that has value and is expected to benefit the future operation of the business. An asset may be tangible, such as cash, inventory, machinery, and buildings, or may be intangible, such as accounts receivable or a patent.

Liabilities are obligations or amounts owed by a company. Accounts payable, wages payable, and long-term debt are examples of liabilities.

Owners' equity is the difference between assets and liabilities. After all the liabilities are paid, it represents what is left for the owners of the business. Owners' equity is created either by the owners investing money in the business or through the operation of the business when it earns a profit. It is decreased when owners take money out of the business or when the business loses money.

The **accounting equation** is the relationship between assets, liabilities, and owners' equity is expressed by the balance sheet equation:

$$\text{Assets} = \text{liabilities} + \text{owners' equity}$$

This is a basic accounting equation. Given two of the values, the third can always be found.

Example Problem

a. If the owners' equity is $1,000 and liabilities are $800, what are the assets?

b. If the assets are $1,000 and liabilities are $600, what is the owners' equity?

ANSWER

a. Assets = Liabilities + owners' equity

   Assets = $800 + $1000 = $1800

b. Owners' equity = assets − liabilities

   $$= \$1,000 - \$600 = \$400$$

Balance sheet   The **balance sheet** usually has the assets on the left side and the liabilities and owners' equity on the right side, as shown.

Assets		Liabilities	
Cash	$100,000	Notes payable	$5,000
Accounts receivable	$300,000	Accounts payable	$20,000
Inventory	$500,000	Long-term debt	$500,000
Fixed assets	$1,000,000	Total liabilities	$525,000
		Owners' equity	
		Capital	$1,000,000
		Retained earnings	$375,000
Total assets	$1,900,000	Total liabilities and owners' equity	$1,900,000

Capital is the amount of money the owners have invested in the company.

Retained earnings are increased by the revenues a company makes and decreased by the expenses incurred. The summary of revenues and expenses is shown on the income statement.

Income Statement

Income (profit). The primary purpose of a business is to increase the owners' equity by making a profit. For this reason, owners' equity is broken down into a series of accounts, called revenue accounts, which show what increased owners' equity, and expense accounts, which show what decreased owners' equity.

$$\text{Income} = \text{revenue} - \text{expenses}$$

Revenue comes from the sale of goods or services. Payment is sometimes immediate in the form of cash, but often is made as a promise to pay at a later date, called an account receivable.

Expenses are the costs incurred in the process of making revenue. They are usually categorized into the cost of goods sold and general and administrative expenses.

Cost of goods sold are costs that are incurred to make the product. They include direct labor, direct material, and factory overhead. Factory overhead is all other factory costs except direct labor and direct material.

General and administrative expenses include all other costs in running a business. Examples of these are advertising, insurance, property taxes, and wages and benefits other than direct material, direct labor, and factory overhead costs.

The following is an example of an income statement.

Revenue		$1,000,000
Cost of goods sold		
Direct labor	$200,000	
Direct material	400,000	
Factory overhead	200,000	$800,000
Gross margin (profit)		$200,000
General and administrative expenses		$100,000
Net income (profit)		$100,000

Example Problem

Given the following data, calculate the gross margin and the net income.

Revenue	= $1,500,000
Direct labor	= $ 300,000
Direct material	= $ 500,000
Factory overhead	= $ 400,000
General and administrative expenses	= $ 150,000

How much would profits increase if, through better materials management, material costs are reduced by $50,000?

Revenue		$1,500,000
Cost of goods sold		
Direct labor	$300,000	
Direct material	500,000	
Overhead	400,000	$1,200,000
Gross margin (gross profit)		$300,000
General and administrative expenses		$150,000
Net income (profit)		$150,000

If material costs are reduced by $50,000, income increases by $50,000. Materials management can have a direct impact on the bottom line—net income.

Cash Flow Analysis

When inventory is purchased as raw material, it is recorded as an asset. When it enters production, it is recorded as work-in-process inventory, and as it is processed, its value increases by the amount of direct labor applied to it and the overhead attributed to its processing. The material is said to absorb overhead. When the goods are ready for sale, they do not become revenue until they are sold. However, the expenses incurred in producing the goods must be paid for. This raises another financial issue: Businesses must have the cash to pay their bills. Cash is generated by sales, and the flow of cash into a business must be sufficient to pay bills as they become due. Businesses develop financial statements showing the cash flows into and out of the business. Any shortfall of cash must be provided for, perhaps by borrowing or in some other way. This type of analysis is called cash flow analysis.

Financial Inventory Performance Measures

From a financial point of view, inventory is an asset and represents money that is tied up and cannot be used for other purposes. As we saw previously in this chapter, inventory has a carrying cost—the costs of capital, storage, and risk. Finance wants as little inventory as possible and needs some measure of the level of inventory. Total inventory investment is one measure, but in itself does not relate to sales. Two measures that do relate to sales are the inventory turns ratio and days of supply.

Inventory turns   Ideally, a manufacturer carries no inventory. This is impractical, since inventory is needed to support manufacturing and often to supply customers. How much inventory is enough? There is no one answer. A convenient measure of how effectively inventories are being used is the **inventory turns** ratio:

$$\text{Inventory turns} = \frac{\text{annual cost of goods sold}}{\text{average inventory in dollars}}$$

The calculation of average inventory can be complicated and is a subject for cost accounting. In this text it will be taken as a given.

For example, if the annual cost of goods sold is $1 million and the average inventory is $500,000, then

$$\text{Inventory turns} = \frac{\$1,000,000}{\$500,000} = 2$$

What does this mean? At the very least, it means that with $500,000 of inventory a company is able to generate $1 million in sales. If, through better materials management, the firm is able to increase its turns ratio to 10, the same sales are generated with only $100,000 of average inventory. If the annual cost of carrying inventory is 25% of the inventory value, the reduction of $400,000 in inventory results in a cost reduction (and profit increase) of $100,000.

Example Problem

a. What will be the inventory turns ratio if the annual cost of goods sold is $24 million a year and the average inventory is $6 million?

ANSWER

$$\text{Inventory turns} = \frac{\text{annual cost of goods sold}}{\text{average inventory in dollars}}$$

$$= \frac{24,000,000}{6,000,000} = 4$$

b. What would be the reduction in inventory if inventory turns were increased to 12 times per year?

ANSWER

$$\text{Average inventory} = \frac{\text{annual cost of goods sold}}{\text{inventory turns}}$$

$$= \frac{24,000,000}{12}$$

$$= \$2,000,000$$

$$\text{Reduction in inventory} = 6,000,000 - 2,000,000 = \$4,000,000$$

c. If the cost of carrying inventory is 25% of the average inventory, what will the savings be?

ANSWER

$$\text{Reduction in inventory} = \$4,000,000$$

$$\text{Savings} = \$4,000,000 \times 0.25 = \$1,000,000$$

Days of supply   Companies need to know how much inventory they have in order to make effective decisions at both the management and operational level. One of the easiest tools to use and understand is **days of supply**. It is essentially a measure of how long in days, at the rate of anticipated demand, it will take for the current inventory level to reach zero or a set safety stock level. This is useful for deciding when to order and also to balance item inventory levels to have equal days of supply. On the next order cycle, items with an equal time-value of inventory can be ordered at the same time. Days of supply is also one of the most easily understood measures for first line workers and avoids the calculations of other measures such as inventory turns. The equation to calculate the days of supply is

$$\text{Days of supply} = \frac{\text{inventory on hand}}{\text{average daily usage}}$$

Example Problem

A company has 9000 units on hand and the annual usage is 48,000 units. There are 240 working days in the year. What is the days of supply?

ANSWER

$$\text{Average daily usage} = \frac{48,000}{240} = 200 \text{ units}$$

$$\text{Days of supply} = \frac{\text{inventory on hand}}{\text{average daily usage}} = \frac{9000}{200} = 45 \text{ days}$$

Methods of Evaluating Inventory

There are four methods accounting uses to "cost" inventory: first in first out, last in first out, average cost, and standard cost. Each has implications for the value placed on inventory. If there is little change in the price of an item, any of the four ways will produce about the same results. However, in rising or falling prices, there can be a pronounced difference. There is no relationship with the actual physical movement of actual items in any of the methods. Whatever method is used is only to account for usage.

First in first out (FIFO) This method assumes that the oldest (first) item in stock is sold first. In rising prices, replacement is at a higher price than the assumed cost. This method does not reflect current prices, and replacement will be understated. The reverse is true in a falling price market.

Last in first out (LIFO) This method assumes the newest (last) item in stock is the first sold. In rising prices, replacement is at the current price. In a falling price market existing inventory is overvalued. However, the company is left with an inventory that may be grossly understated in value.

Average cost This method assumes an average of all prices paid for the article. The problem with this method in changing prices (rising or falling) is that the cost used is not related to the actual cost.

Standard cost This method uses cost determined before production begins. The cost includes direct material, direct labor, and overhead. Any difference between the standard cost and actual cost is stated as a variance.

ABC INVENTORY CONTROL

Control of inventory is exercised by controlling individual items, which is called stock-keeping units (SKUs). In controlling inventory, four questions must be answered:

1. What is the importance of the inventory item?
2. How are they to be controlled?
3. How much should be ordered at one time?
4. When should an order be placed?

The **ABC inventory** classification system answers the first two questions by determining the importance of items and thus allowing different levels of control based on the relative importance of items.

Most companies carry a large number of items in stock. To have better control at a reasonable cost, it is helpful to classify the items according to their importance. Usually this is based on annual dollar usage, but other criteria may be used.

The ABC principle is based on the observation that a small number of items often dominate the results achieved in any situation. This observation was first made by an Italian economist, Vilfredo Pareto, and is called **Pareto's law**. As applied to inventories, it is usually found that the relationship between the percentage of items and the percentage of annual dollar usage follows a pattern in which three groups can be defined:

Group A   About 20% of the items account for about 80% of the dollar usage.
Group B   About 30% of the items account for about 15% of the dollar usage.
Group C   About 50% of the items account for about 5% of the dollar usage.

The percentages are approximate and should not be taken as absolute. This type of distribution can be used to help control inventory.

Steps in Making an ABC Analysis

1. Establish the item characteristics that influence the results of inventory management. This is usually annual dollar usage but may be other criteria, such as scarcity of material.
2. Classify items into groups based on the established criteria.
3. Apply a degree of control in proportion to the importance of the group.

The factors affecting the importance of an item include annual dollar usage, unit cost, and scarcity of material. For simplicity, only annual dollar usage is used in this text. The procedure for classifying by annual dollar usage is as follows:

1. Determine the annual usage for each item.
2. Multiply the annual usage of each item by its cost to get its total annual dollar usage.
3. List the items according to their annual dollar usage.
4. Calculate the cumulative annual dollar usage and the cumulative percentage of items.
5. Examine the annual usage distribution and group the items into A, B, and C groups based on percentage of annual usage.

Example Problem

A company manufactures a line of 10 items. The usage and unit cost are shown in the following table, along with the annual dollar usage. The latter is obtained by multiplying the unit usage by the unit cost.

a. Calculate the annual dollar usage for each item.
b. List the items according to their annual dollar usage.
c. Calculate the cumulative annual dollar usage and the cumulative percentage of items.
d. Group items into an A, B, C classification.

ANSWER

a. Calculate the annual dollar usage for each item.

Part Number	Unit Usage	Unit Cost $	Annual $ Usage
1	1100	2	2200
2	600	40	24,000
3	100	4	400
4	1300	1	1300
5	100	60	6000
6	10	25	250
7	100	2	200
8	1500	2	3000
9	200	2	400
10	500	1	500
Total	5510		$38,250

b. **b, c**, and **d**.

Part Number	Annual $ Usage	Cumulative $ Usage	Cumulative % $ Usage	Cumulative % of Items	Class
2	24,000	24,000	62.75	10	A
5	6000	30,000	78.43	20	A
8	3000	33,000	86.27	30	B
1	2200	35,200	92.03	40	B
4	1300	36,500	95.42	50	B
10	500	37,000	96.73	60	C
9	400	37,400	97.78	70	C
3	400	37,800	98.82	80	C
6	250	38,050	99.48	90	C
7	200	38,250	100.00	100	C

The percentage of value and the percentage of items are often shown as a graph, as in Figure 9.3.

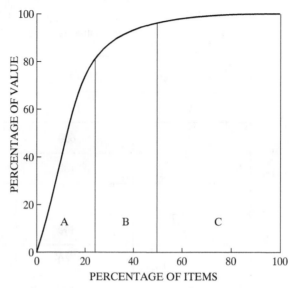

FIGURE 9.3 ABC curve: percentage of value versus percentage of items.

Control Based on ABC Classification

Using the ABC approach, there are two general rules to follow:

1. **Have plenty of low-value items** (plenty in terms of days of supply). **C items** represent about 50% of the items but account for only about 5% percent of the total inventory value. Carrying extra stock of C items adds little to the total value of the inventory. C items are really only important if there is a shortage of one of them—when they become extremely important—so a supply should always be on hand. For example, order a year's supply at a time and carry plenty of safety stock. That way there is only once a year when a stockout is even possible.

2. **Use the money and control effort saved to reduce the inventory of high-value items. A items** represent about 20% of the items and account for about 80% of the value. They are extremely important and deserve the tightest control and the most frequent review.

   Different controls used with different classifications might be the following:

- **A items: high priority.** Tight control including complete accurate records, regular and frequent review by management, frequent review of demand forecasts, and close follow-up and expediting to reduce lead time.
- **B items: medium priority.** Normal controls with good records, regular attention, and normal processing.
- **C items: lowest priority.** Simplest possible controls—make sure there are plenty. Simple or no records; perhaps use a two-bin system or periodic review system. Order large quantities and carry safety stock.

SUMMARY

There are benefits as well as costs to having inventory. The problem is to balance the cost of carrying inventory with the following:

- **Customer service.** The lower the inventory level, the higher the likelihood of a stockout and the potential cost of back orders, lost sales, and lost customers. The higher the inventory level, the higher the level of customer service.

- **Operating efficiency.** Inventories decouple one operation from another and allow manufacturing to operate more efficiently. They allow leveling production and avoid the costs of changing production levels. Carrying inventory allows longer production runs and reduces the number of setups. Finally, inventories let manufacturing purchase in larger quantities. The ABC inventory classification system prioritizes individual items so that inventory and costs can be better controlled.

- **Cost of placing orders.** Inventory can be reduced by ordering less each time an order is placed. However, this increases the annual cost of ordering.

- **Transportation and handling costs.** The more often goods have to be moved and the smaller the quantities moved, the greater the transportation and material handling costs.

Inventory management is influenced by several factors:

- The classification of the inventory, whether raw material, work-in-process, or finished goods.
- The functions that inventory serves: anticipation, fluctuation, lot size, or transportation.
- Supply and demand patterns.
- The costs associated with carrying (or not carrying) inventory.

Besides managing inventory at the aggregate level, it must also be managed at the item level. Management needs to establish decision rules about inventory items so inventory control personnel can do their job effectively.

KEY TERMS

A items 210	Income 204
ABC inventory 208	Inventory turns 206
Accounting equation 204	Item cost 201
Anticipation inventories 198	Landed price 201
Asset 203	Last in first out (LIFO) 207
Average cost 207	Liabilities 204
Balance sheet 204	Lot-size inventories 199
C items 210	Maintenance, repair, and operational supplies (MROs) 198
Capacity-associated costs 203	
Capital 204	Owners' equity 204
Carrying costs 201	Pareto's law 208
Cost of goods sold 205	Pipeline or movement inventories 199
Cycle stock 199	Raw materials 197
Days of supply 206	Retained earnings 204
Distribution inventories 198	Revenue 204
Expenses 204	Safety stock 198
Finished goods 197	Standard cost 207
First in first out (FIFO) 207	Stockout 198
Fluctuation inventory 198	Transportation inventories 199
General and administrative expenses 205	Work-in-process (WIP) 197
Hedge inventory 199	

QUESTIONS

1. What are inventories? Why are they important to manufacturing companies?
2. What are the responsibilities of inventory management?
3. What is aggregate inventory management? With what is it concerned?

4. What are decision rules? Why are they necessary?

5. According to the flow of material, what are the four classifications of inventories?

6. Why is less inventory needed in a line-flow manufacturing system than in lot or batch manufacturing?

7. What is the basic purpose of inventories? In what four areas do they provide a buffer?

8. Describe the function and purpose of the following kinds of inventories:
   a. Anticipation.
   b. Fluctuation.
   c. Lot size.
   d. Transportation.

9. Describe how inventories influence each of the following:
   a. Customer service.
   b. Plant operations.

10. What are the five costs associated with inventories?

11. Name and describe the categories of inventory-carrying costs.

12. Name and describe the categories of ordering costs found in a factory.

13. What are stockout costs and capacity-associated costs? What is their relationship to inventories?

14. What are the balance sheet equation and the income statement equation?

15. What is the purpose of cash flow analysis?

16. What do inventory turns and days of supply measure?

17. What is the basic premise of ABC analysis? What are the three steps in making an ABC inventory analysis?

18. What are the five steps in the procedure for classifying inventory by annual dollar usage?

19. Using the items in your own kitchen, classify them in to A, B, and C categories. Are you practicing good control based on ABC classification? How?

20. What is the difference between FIFO and LIFO?

21. During times of inflation why does the value of inventory change between FIFO and LIFO evaluation?

PROBLEMS

9.1. If the transit time is 11 days and the annual demand for an item is 10,000 units, what is the average annual inventory in transit?

   Answer. 301.4 units

9.2. A company is using a carrier to deliver goods to a major customer. The annual demand is $2,500,000, and the average transit time is 10 days. Another carrier promises to deliver in 7 days. What is the reduction in transit inventory?

9.3. Given the following percentage costs of carrying inventory, calculate the annual carrying cost if the average inventory is $1 million. Capital costs are 10%, storage costs are 6%, and risk costs are 7%.

   Answer. $230,000

9.4. A florist carries an average inventory of $12,000 in cut flowers. The flowers require special storage and are highly perishable. The florist estimates capital costs at 10%, storage costs at 25%, and risk costs at 50%. What is the annual carrying cost?

9.5. Annual purchasing salaries are $65,000, operating expenses for the purchasing department are $25,000, and inspecting and receiving costs are $25 per order. If the purchasing department places 9000 orders a year, what is the average cost of ordering? What is the annual cost of ordering?

   Answer. Average ordering cost = $35
   Annual cost = $315,000

9.6. An importer operates a small warehouse that has the following annual costs. Wages for purchasing are $45,000, purchasing expenses are $30,000, customs and brokerage costs are $25 per order, the cost of financing the inventory is 8%, storage costs are 6%, and the risk costs are 10%. The average inventory is $300,000, and 6000 orders are placed in a year. What are the annual ordering and carrying costs?

9.7. A company manufactures and sells a seasonal product. Based on the sales forecast that follows, calculate a level production plan, quarterly ending inventories, and average quarterly inventories. Assume that the average quarterly inventory is the average of the starting and ending inventory for the quarter. If inventory carrying costs are $3 per unit per quarter, what is the annual cost of carrying this anticipation inventory? Opening and ending inventories are zero.

	Quarter 1	Quarter 2	Quarter 3	Quarter 4	Totals
Sales	1000	2000	3000	2000	
Production					
Ending Inventory					
Average Inventory					
Inventory Cost					

Answer.   Annual inventory costs = $6000

9.8. Given the following data, calculate a level production plan, quarterly ending inventory, and average quarterly inventory. If inventory carrying costs are $6 per unit per quarter, what is the annual carrying cost? Opening and ending inventory are zero.

	Quarter 1	Quarter 2	Quarter 3	Quarter 4	Totals
Forecast Demand	5000	7000	8500	9500	
Production					
Ending Inventory					
Average Inventory					
Inventory Cost					

If the company always carries 100 units of safety stock, what is the annual cost of carrying it?

9.9. Given the following data, calculate a level production plan, quarterly ending inventory, and average quarterly inventory. If inventory carrying costs are $3 per unit per quarter, what is the annual carrying cost? Opening and ending inventory are zero.

	Quarter 1	Quarter 2	Quarter 3	Quarter 4	Totals
Forecast Demand	3000	4000	6500	6500	
Production					
Ending Inventory					
Average Inventory					
Inventory Cost					

9.10. If the assets are $2,000,000 and liabilities are $1,600,000, what is the owners' equity?

Answer. $400,000

9.11. If the liabilities are $4,000,000 and the owners' equity is $1,200,000, what are the assets worth?

9.12. Given the following data, calculate the gross margin and the net income.

$$Revenue = \$3,000,000$$
$$Direct\ labor = \$700,000$$
$$Direct\ material = \$900,000$$
$$Factory\ overhead = \$700,000$$
$$General\ and\ administrative\ expense = \$300,000$$

Answer.   Gross margin = $700,000
Net income = $400,000

9.13. In question 9.12, how much would profit increase if the materials costs are reduced by $200,000?

9.14. If the annual cost of goods sold is $12,000,000 and the average inventory is $2,250,000:

a. What is the inventory turns ratio?

b. What would be the reduction in average inventory if, through better materials management, inventory turns were increased to 10 times per year?

c. If the cost of carrying inventory is 20% of the average inventory, what is the annual savings?

Answer.   a. 5.3
b. $1,050,000
c. $210,000

9.15. If the annual cost of goods sold is $30,000,000 and the average inventory is $10,000,000:

a. What is the inventory turns ratio?

b. What would be the reduction in average inventory if, through better materials management, inventory turns were increased to 10 times per year?

c. If the cost of carrying inventory is 25% of the average inventory, what is the annual savings?

9.16. A company has 600 units on hand and the annual usage is 7200 units. There are 240 working days in the year. What is the days of supply?

Answer.   20 days

9.17. Over the past year, a company has sold the following 10 items. The following table shows the annual sales in units and the cost of each item.

a. Calculate the annual dollar usage of each item.

b. List the items according to their total annual dollar usage.

c. Calculate the cumulative annual dollar usage and the cumulative percentage of items.

d. Group the items into A, B, and C groups based on percentage of annual dollar usage.

Part Number	Annual Unit Usage	Unit Cost $	Annual $ Usage
1	21,000	1	
2	5000	40	
3	1600	3	
4	12,000	1	
5	1000	100	
6	50	50	
7	800	2	
8	10,000	3	
9	4000	1	
10	5000	1	

Answer. A items   2, 5
B items   8, 1, 4
C items   10, 3, 9, 6, 7

9.18. Analyze the following data to produce an ABC classification based on annual dollar usage.

Part Number	Annual Unit Usage	Unit Cost $	Annual $ Usage
1	200	10	
2	17,000	4	
3	60,000	6	
4	15,000	15	
5	1500	10	
6	120	50	
7	25,000	2	
8	700	3	
9	25,000	1	
10	7500	1	

CASE STYDY 9.1

Randy Smith, Inventory Control Manager

Randy Smith was very proud of his new position as inventory control manager for the Johnson Trinket Company. His primary responsibility had been fairly clearly defined: Maintain an inventory level in the warehouse that ensures that production will not run out of stock, yet also maintain an inventory level that will minimize inventory holding and control costs. Since Randy had recently had a course in materials management, he knew an approach that should help him. He decided to make a list of inventory items in one small section of the warehouse to see if he could develop a good plan for inventory control. If it worked in the one small section, he could expand it to the rest of the more than 30,000 part numbers in the warehouse.

The following is the data Randy compiled:

Part Number	Part unit value in $	Quantity currently in inventory	Average annual usage
1234	$2.50	300	3000
1235	$0.20	550	900
1236	$15.00	400	1000
1237	$0.75	50	7900
1238	$7.60	180	2800
1239	$4.40	20	5000
1240	$1.80	200	1800
1241	$0.05	10	1200
1242	$17.20	950	2000
1243	$9.00	160	2500
1244	$3.20	430	7000
1245	$0.30	500	10000
1246	$1.10	25	7500
1247	$8.10	60	2100
1248	$5.00	390	4000
1249	$0.90	830	6500
1250	$6.00	700	3100
1251	$2.20	80	6000
1252	$1.20	480	4500
1253	$5.90	230	900

When Randy scanned the list, he noticed several things that disturbed him, and he asked one of the experienced inventory clerks. The following list summarizes the part number issues that concerned Randy, and the explanation from the clerk:

Part number 1236, a very expensive part with almost half-a-year's worth of inventory. This part is used for a product that has very cyclical demand, and the busy time of the year is about to start.

Part number 1241 is very inexpensive, yet the inventory is very small. This part has a supplier with an erratic delivery history, and the part also has a very long lead time. A lot of 150 has been on order for some time, and is now several days past due.

Part number 1242, like 1236, is expensive with almost half a year worth of inventory—this part is shipped to a location on the other side of the country and is being accumulated into a large lot to save shipping costs.

Part number 1246 is not too expensive, with a low inventory. This part is produced in-house, and has a quality tolerance that the older equipment, which was used to produce it, had a difficult time meeting. The last batch was rejected by the quality department.

Part number 1253 is moderately expensive with a large inventory compared to usage. This part was subject to a recent quality audit, and almost 150 of the items were rejected as a result of that audit.

Once Randy understood some of the issues, suddenly he did not feel quite as confident that he had the best approach in mind to control the inventory to meet the expectations of his boss.

Assignment

Use the information above to evaluate the current situation.

Given your evaluation, try to develop an integrated inventory control policy that Randy should consider.

Is there other information that you would like to see that might help you to make a more effective policy? If so, what would that information be and how would you use it to help you?

ORDER QUANTITIES

INTRODUCTION

The objectives of inventory management are to provide the required level of customer service and to reduce the sum of all costs involved. To achieve these objectives, two basic questions must be answered:

1. How much should be ordered at one time?
2. When should an order be placed?

Management must establish decision rules to answer these questions so inventory management personnel know when to order and how much. Lacking any better knowledge, decision rules are often made based on what seems reasonable. Unfortunately, such rules do not always produce the best results.

This chapter will examine methods of answering the first question, and the next chapter will deal with the second question. First, we must decide what we are ordering and controlling.

Stock-Keeping Unit (SKU)

Control is exercised through individual items in a particular inventory. These are called **stock-keeping units (SKUs)**. Two white shirts in the same inventory but of different sizes or styles would be two different SKUs. The same shirt in two different inventories would be two different SKUs.

Lot-Size Decision Rules

The twelfth edition of the *APICS Dictionary* defines a lot, or batch, as "a quantity produced together and sharing the same production costs and specifications." Following are some common decision rules for determining what lot size to order at one time.

Lot-for-lot The **lot-for-lot** rule says to order exactly what is needed—no more—no less. The order quantity changes whenever requirements change. This technique requires time-phased information such as that provided by a material requirements plan or a master production schedule. Since items are ordered only when needed, this system creates no unused lot-size inventory. Because of this, it is the best method for planning A items (see Chapter 9) and is also used in a just-in-time environment.

Fixed-order quantity **Fixed-order quantity** rules specify the number of units to be ordered each time an order is placed for an individual item or SKU. The quantity is usually arbitrary, such as 200 units at a time. The advantage to this type of rule is that it is easily understood. The disadvantage is that it does not minimize the costs involved.

A variation on the fixed-order quantity system is the **min-max system**. In this system, an order is placed when the quantity available falls below the order point (discussed in the next chapter). The quantity ordered is the difference between the actual quantity available at the time of order and the maximum. For example, if the order point is 100 units, the maximum is 300 units, and the quantity actually available when the order is placed is 75, the order quantity is 225 units. If the quantity actually available is 80 units, an order for 220 units is placed.

One commonly used method of calculating the quantity to order is the economic-order quantity, which is discussed in the next section.

Order *n* periods supply   Rather than ordering a fixed quantity, inventory management can order enough to satisfy future demand for a given period of time. The question is how many periods should be covered? The answer is given later in this chapter in the discussion on the period-order quantity system.

Costs

As shown in Chapter 9, the cost of ordering and the cost of carrying inventory both depend on the quantity ordered. Ideally, the ordering decision rules used will minimize the sum of these two costs. The best-known system is the economic-order quantity.

ECONOMIC-ORDER QUANTITY

Assumptions

The assumptions on which the economic-order quantity (EOQ) is based are as follows:

1. Demand is relatively constant and is known.
2. The item is produced or purchased in lots or batches and not continuously.
3. Order preparation costs and inventory-carrying costs are constant and known.
4. Replacement occurs all at once.

These assumptions are usually valid for finished goods whose demand is independent and fairly uniform. However, there are many situations where the assumptions are not valid and the EOQ concept is of no use. For instance, there is no reason to calculate the EOQ for make-to-order items in which the customer specifies the order quantity, the shelf life of the product is short, or the length of the run is limited by tool life or raw material batch size. In material requirements planning, the lot-for-lot decision rule is often used, but there are also several rules used that are variations of the economic-order quantity.

Development of the EOQ Formula

Under the assumptions given, the quantity of an item in inventory decreases at a uniform rate. Suppose for a particular item that the order quantity is 200 units and the usage rate is 100 units a week. Figure 10.1 shows how inventory would behave.

The vertical lines represent stock arriving all at once as the stock on hand reaches zero. The quantity of units in inventory then increases instantaneously by Q, the quantity

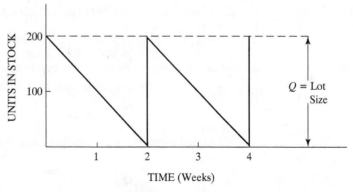

FIGURE 10.1 Inventory on hand over time.

ordered. This is an accurate representation of the arrival of purchased parts or manufactured parts where all parts are received at once.

From the preceding,

$$\text{Average lot size inventory} = \frac{\text{order quantity}}{2} = \frac{200}{2} = 100 \text{ units}$$

$$\text{Number of orders per year} = \frac{\text{annual demand}}{\text{order quantity}} = \frac{100 \times 52}{200}$$

$$= 26 \text{ times per year}$$

Example Problem

The annual demand for an SKU is 10,075 units, and it is ordered in quantities of 650 units. Calculate the average inventory and the number of orders placed per year.

ANSWER

$$\text{Average cycle inventory} = \frac{\text{order quantity}}{2} = \frac{650}{2} = 325 \text{ units}$$

$$\text{Number of orders per year} = \frac{\text{annual demand}}{\text{order quantity}} = \frac{10{,}075}{650} = 15.5$$

Notice in the example problem that the number of orders per year is rounded neither up nor down. It is an average figure, and the actual number of orders per year will vary from year to year but will average to the calculated figure. In the example, 16 orders will be placed in one year and 15 in the second.

Relevant costs   The relevant costs are as follows:

- Annual cost of placing orders.
- Annual cost of carrying inventory.

As the order quantity increases, the average inventory and the annual cost of carrying inventory increase, but the number of orders per year and the ordering cost decrease. It is a bit like a seesaw where one cost can be reduced only at the expense of increasing the other. The trick is to find the particular order quantity in which the total cost of carrying inventory and the cost of ordering will be a minimum.

Let

A = annual usage in units

S = ordering cost in dollars per order

i = annual carrying cost rate as a decimal or a percentage

c = unit cost in dollars

Q = order quantity in units

Then:

Annual ordering cost = number of orders $\times$ costs per order

$$= \frac{A}{Q} \times S$$

Annual carrying cost = average inventory $\times$ cost of carrying 1 unit for 1 year

$$= \text{average inventory} \times \text{unit cost} \times \text{carrying cost}$$

$$= \frac{Q}{2} \times c \times i$$

Total annual costs = annual ordering costs + annual carrying costs

$$= \frac{A}{Q} \times S + \frac{Q}{2} \times c \times i$$

Example Problem

The annual demand is 10,000 units, the ordering cost is $30 per order, the carrying cost is 20%, and the unit cost is $15. The order quantity is 600 units. Calculate:

a. Annual ordering cost.

b. Annual carrying cost.

c. Total annual cost.

ANSWER

$A = 10{,}000$ units

$S = \$30$

$i = 0.20$

$c = \$15$

$Q = 600$ units

a. annual ordering cost $= \dfrac{A}{Q} \times S \quad = \dfrac{10{,}000}{600} \times 30 \quad = \quad \$500$

b. annual carrying cost $= \dfrac{Q}{2} \times c \times i = \dfrac{600}{2} \times 15 \times 0.2 = \quad \underline{\$900}$

c. total annual cost $\qquad\qquad\qquad\qquad\qquad = \$1400$

Ideally, the total cost will be a minimum. For any situation in which the annual demand (A), the cost of ordering (S), and the cost of carrying inventory (i) are given, the total cost will depend upon the order quantity (Q).

Trial-and-Error Method

Consider the following example:

A hardware supply distributor carries boxes of 3-inch bolts in stock. The annual usage is 1000 boxes, and demand is relatively constant throughout the year. Ordering costs are $20 per order, and the cost of carrying inventory is estimated to be 20%. The cost per unit is $5.

Let:

$A = 1000$ units

$S = \$20$ per order

$c = \$5$ per unit

$i = 20\% = 0.20$

Then:

$$\text{Annual ordering cost} = \frac{A}{Q} \times S = \frac{1000}{Q} \times 20$$

$$\text{Annual carrying cost} = \frac{Q}{2} \times c \times i = \frac{Q}{2} \times 5 \times 0.20$$

$$\text{Total annual cost} = \text{annual ordering cost} + \text{annual carrying cost}$$

Figure 10.2 shows a tabulation of the costs for different order quantities. The results from the table in Figure 10.2 are represented on the graph in Figure 10.3.

Figures 10.2 and 10.3 show the following important facts:

1. There is an order quantity in which the sum of the ordering costs and carrying costs is a minimum.

2. This EOQ occurs when the cost of ordering equals the cost of carrying.

3. The total cost varies little for a wide range of lot sizes about EOQ.

Order Quantity (Q)	Ordering Costs (AS/Q)	Carrying Costs (Qci/2)	Total Cost
50	$400	$25	$425
100	200	50	250
150	133	75	208
200	100	100	200
250	80	125	205
300	67	150	217
350	57	175	232
400	50	200	250

FIGURE 10.2 Costs for different lot sizes.

FIGURE 10.3 Cost versus lot size.

The last point is important for two reasons. First, it is usually difficult to determine accurately the cost of carrying inventory and the cost of ordering. Since the total cost is relatively flat around the EOQ, it is not critical to have exact values. Good approximations are sufficient. Second, parts are often ordered in convenient packages such as pallet loads, cases, or dozens, and it is adequate to pick the package quantity closest to the EOQ.

Economic-Order Quantity Formula

The previous section showed that the EOQ occurred at an order quantity in which the ordering costs equal the carrying costs. If these two costs are equal, the following formula can be derived:

$$\text{Carrying costs} = \text{ordering costs}$$

$$\frac{Qic}{2} = \frac{AS}{Q}$$

Solving for Q gives

$$Q^2 = \frac{2\,AS}{ic}$$

$$Q = \sqrt{\frac{2\,AS}{ic}}$$

This value for the order quantity is the economic-order quantity. Using the formula to calculate the EOQ in the preceding example yields:

$$EOQ = \sqrt{\frac{2AS}{ic}} = \sqrt{\frac{2 \times 1000 \times 20}{0.20 \times 5}} = 200 \text{ units}$$

How to Reduce Lot Size

The EOQ formula has four variables. The EOQ will increase as the annual demand (A) and the cost of ordering (S) increase, and it will decrease as the cost of carrying inventory (i) and the unit cost (c) increase.

The annual demand (A) is a condition of the marketplace and is beyond the control of manufacturing. The cost of carrying inventory (i) is determined by the product itself and the cost of money to the company. As such, it is beyond the control of manufacturing.

The unit cost (c) is either the purchase cost of the SKU or the cost of manufacturing the item. Ideally, both costs should be as low as possible. In any event, as the unit cost decreases, the EOQ increases.

The cost of ordering (S) is either the cost of placing a purchase order or the cost of placing a manufacturing order. The cost of placing a manufacturing order is made up from production control costs and setup costs. Anything that can be done to reduce these costs reduces the EOQ.

Just-in-Time manufacturing emphasizes reduction of setup time. There are several reasons why this is desirable, and the reduction of order quantities is one. Chapter 15 discusses just-in-time manufacturing further.

VARIATIONS OF THE EOQ MODEL

There are several modifications that can be made to the basic EOQ model to fit particular circumstances. Two that are often used are the monetary unit lot-size model and the non-instantaneous receipt model.

Monetary Unit Lot Size

The EOQ can be calculated in monetary units rather than physical units. The same EOQ formula given in the preceding section can be used, but the annual usage changes from units to dollars.

A_D = annual usage in dollars

S = ordering costs in dollars

i = carrying cost rate as a decimal or a percent

Because the annual usage is expressed in dollars, the unit cost is not needed in the modified EOQ equation.

The EOQ in dollars is:

$$EOQ = \sqrt{\frac{2 A_D S}{i}}$$

Example Problem

An item has an annual demand of $5000, preparation costs of $20 per order, and a carrying cost of 20%. What is the EOQ in dollars?

$A_D = \$5000$

$S = \$20$

$i = 20\% = 0.20$

$$EOQ = \sqrt{\frac{2 A_D S}{i}} = \sqrt{\frac{2 \times \$5000 \times \$20}{0.2}} = \$1000$$

Non-instantaneous Receipt Model

In some cases when a replenishment order is made, the order is not all received at one time. The most common reason for this is that the ordered material is being produced over an extended period of time, yet material is received for the order as it is being produced. In this case the EOQ is modified to reflect the rate of production as related to rate of demand:

$$EOQ = \sqrt{\frac{2AS}{ic}\left(\frac{p}{p-d}\right)}$$

where

p = the rate of production (in units per day) and

d = the rate of demand (in units per day)

The units of time for p and d (shown above as units per day) can be any unit of time as long as that unit of time is the same for both.

Example Problem

An item has a setup cost for production of $500 per order, and the inventory carrying costs for the item is $12 per year. The demand for the item is constant at 11 units per day. The production rate is 50 units per day while the item is being produced. What is the noninstantaneous economic-order quantity?

$$\text{Annual demand } (A) = (11 \text{ units per day}) \times (365 \text{ days per year})$$
$$= 4015 \text{ units per year}$$
$$EOQ = \sqrt{\frac{2(4015)\,500}{12}\left(\frac{50}{50-11}\right)}$$
$$= \sqrt{334{,}583.3(1.3)}$$
$$= 655 \text{ units}$$

QUANTITY DISCOUNTS

When material is purchased, suppliers often give a discount on orders over a certain size. This can be done because larger orders reduce the supplier's costs; to get larger orders, suppliers are willing to offer volume discounts. The buyer must decide whether to accept the discount, and in doing so must consider the relevant costs:

- Purchase cost.
- Ordering costs.
- Carrying costs.

Example Problem

An item has an annual demand of 25,000 units, a unit cost of $10, an order preparation cost of $10, and a carrying cost of 20%. It is ordered on the basis of an EOQ, but the supplier has offered a discount of 2% on orders of $10,000 or more. Should the offer be accepted?

ANSWER

$$A_D = 25{,}000 \times \$10 = \$250{,}000$$
$$S = \$10$$
$$i = 20\%$$

$$EOQ = \sqrt{\frac{2 \times 250{,}000 \times 10}{0.2}} = \$5000$$

Discounted order quantity = $10,000 × 0.98 = $9800

	No discount	Discount lot size
Unit Price	$10	$9.80
Lot Size	$5000	$9800
Average Lot-Size Inventory ($Qc \div 2$)	$2500	$4900
Number of Orders per Year	50	25
Purchase Cost	$250,000	$245,000
Inventory Carrying Cost (20%)	500	980
Order Preparation Cost ($10 each)	500	250
Total Cost	$251,000	$246,230

From the preceding example problem, it can be said that taking the discount results in the following:

- There is a saving in purchase cost.
- Ordering costs are reduced because fewer orders are placed since larger quantities are being ordered.
- Inventory-carrying costs rise because of the larger order quantity.

The buyer must weigh the first two against the last and decide what to do. What counts is the total cost. Depending on the figures, it may or may not be best to take the discount. When considering a quantity discount, the total costs of using the discount are usually compared with the total costs of using the EOQ method.

ORDER QUANTITIES FOR FAMILIES OF PRODUCT WHEN COSTS ARE NOT KNOWN

The EOQ formula depends upon the cost of ordering and the cost of carrying inventory. In practice, these costs are not necessarily known or easy to determine. However, the formula can still be used to advantage when applied to a family of items.

For a family of items, the ordering costs and the carrying costs are generally the same for each item. For instance, if we were ordering hardware items—nuts, bolts, screws, nails, and so on—the carrying costs would be virtually the same (storage, capital, and risk costs) and the cost of placing an order with the supplier would be the same for each item. In cases such as this, the cost of placing an order (S) is the same for all items in the family as is cost of carrying inventory (i).

Now

$$Q = \sqrt{\frac{2 A_D S}{i}}$$

where A (annual demand) is in *dollars*.

Since S is the same for all the items and i is the same for all items, the ratio $2S \div i$ must be the same for all items in the family. For convenience, let:

$$K = \sqrt{\frac{2S}{i}}$$

Then $$Q = K\sqrt{A_D}$$

Also $$Q = \frac{\text{annual demand}}{\text{orders per year}} = \frac{A_D}{N}$$

Therefore $$K\sqrt{A_D} = \frac{A_D}{N}$$

$$K = \frac{\sqrt{A_D}}{N}$$

Let's see how this can be applied.

Example Problem

Suppose there were a family of items for which the decision rule was to order each item four times a year. Since the cost of ordering (S) and the cost of carrying inventory (i) are not known, ordering four times a year is not based on an EOQ. Can we come up with a better decision rule even if the EOQ cannot be calculated?

Item	Annual Usage	Orders per Year	Present Lot Size	$\sqrt{A_D}$	$K = \dfrac{\sqrt{A_D}}{N}$
A	$10,000	4	$2500	$100	25
B	400	4	100	20	5
C	144	4	36	12	3
		12	$2636	$132	33
Average inventory =			$1318		

The sum of all the lots is $2636. Since the average inventory is equal to half the order quantity, the average inventory is $2636 \div 2 = \$1318$.

Since this is a family of items where the preparation costs are the same and the carrying costs are the same, the values for $K = (2S \div i)^{\frac{1}{2}}$ should be the same for all items. The preceding calculations show that they are not. The correct value for K is not known, but a better value would be the average of all the values:

$$K = \frac{\sum \sqrt{A_D}}{\sum N}$$

$$= \frac{132}{12}$$

$$= 11$$

This value of K can be used to recalculate the order quantities for each item.

Item	Annual Usage	Present Orders per Year	Present Lot Size	$\sqrt{A_D}$	New Lot Size = $K\sqrt{A_D}$	New Orders per Year $N = A_D/Q$
A	$10,000	4	$2500	$100	$1100	9.09
B	400	4	100	20	220	1.82
C	144	4	36	12	132	1.09
	$10,544	12	$2636	$132	$1452	12.00
Average inventory			$1318		$726	

Item A: New lot size = $K\sqrt{A_D} = 11 \times 100 = \$1100$

$$\text{New orders per year} = \frac{A_D}{Q} = \frac{10,000}{1100} = 9.09$$

The average inventory has been reduced from $1318 to $726 while the number of orders per year (12) remains the same. Thus, the total costs associated with inventory have been reduced.

PERIOD-ORDER QUANTITY

The economic-order quantity attempts to minimize the total cost of ordering and carrying inventory and is based on the assumption that demand is uniform. Often demand is not uniform, particularly in material requirements planning (MRP), and using the EOQ does not produce a minimum cost. The order quantity will often exceed the demand expected for the next few periods, which may result in inventory carried over periods of non-demand to avoid the cost of placing another order. However, the quantity ordered may not be exactly enough to cover the demand in the next few periods resulting in the placement of another order even while a remnant of the last order is available. Keeping inventory to avoid placing orders is a good idea but not keeping enough inventory to avoid placing orders defeats the goal of EOQ. A change in the application is required and this is demonstrated in the period-order quantity method.

The period-order quantity (POQ) lot-size rule is based on the same theory as the economic-order quantity. It uses the EOQ formula to calculate an economic **time between orders**. Note that POQ does not calculate a "quantity" but actually calculates the number of "periods" that are to be covered. The POQ is calculated by dividing the EOQ by the demand rate. This produces a time interval for which orders are placed. Instead of ordering the same quantity (EOQ), orders are placed to satisfy requirements for the calculated time interval. The number of orders placed in a year is approximately the same as for an economic-order quantity, but the amount ordered each time varies. Thus, the ordering cost is the same as it would be using the EOQ but because the order quantities are determined by actual demand, the carrying cost is reduced.

$$\text{Period order quantity} = \frac{\text{EOQ}}{\text{average weekly usage}}$$

Note that although POQ calculates an order interval say of 2 weeks, this does not mean that there is an order placed every two weeks. It actually means that when an order needs to be placed then enough inventory is ordered to cover the next two weeks. This is especially important in discontinuous demand, as shown in the following example.

Example Problem

The EOQ for an item is 2800 units, and the annual usage is 52,000 units. What is the period-order quantity?

ANSWER

$$\text{Average weekly usage} = 52{,}000 \div 52 = 1000 \text{ per week}$$

$$\text{Periodorder quantity} = \frac{\text{EOQ}}{\text{average weekly usage}}$$

$$= \frac{2800}{1000} = 2.8 \text{ weeks} \longrightarrow 3 \text{ weeks}$$

When an order is placed it will cover the requirements for the next three weeks.

Notice the calculation is approximate. Precision is not important.

Example Problem

Given the following MRP record and an EOQ of 250 units, calculate the planned order receipts using the economic-order quantity. Next, calculate the period-order quantities and the planned order receipts. In both cases, calculate the ending inventory and the total inventory carried over the 10 weeks.

Week	1	2	3	4	5	6	7	8	9	10	Total
Net Requirements	100	50	150		75	200	55	80	150	30	890
Planned Order Receipt											

ANSWER

EOQ = 250 units

Week	1	2	3	4	5	6	7	8	9	10	Total
Net Requirements	100	50	150		75	200	55	80	150	30	890
Planned Order Receipt	250		250			250			250		
Ending Inventory	150	100	200	200	125	175	120	40	140	110	1360

Period-order quantity:

Weekly average demand = 890 ÷ 10 = 89 units

POQ = 250 ÷ 89 = 2.81 → 3 weeks

Week	1	2	3	4	5	6	7	8	9	10	Total
Net Requirements	100	50	150		75	200	55	80	150	30	890
Planned Order Receipt	300				330			260			
Ending Inventory	200	150	0	0	255	55	0	180	30	0	870

Notice in the example problem the total inventory is reduced from 1360 units to 870 units over the 10-week period. Note also that an order is not placed in week 4 since there is no demand in period 4 and that the period before each order has zero inventory having used up the previous order entirely.

Practical Considerations When Using the EOQ

Lumpy demand The EOQ assumes that demand is uniform and replenishment occurs all at once. When this is not true, the EOQ will not produce the best results. It is better to use the period-order quantity.

Anticipation inventory Demand is not uniform, and stock must be built ahead of periods of high demand. It is better to plan a buildup of inventory based on capacity and future demand.

Minimum order Some suppliers require a minimum order. This minimum may be based on the total order rather than on individual items. Often these are C items where the rule is to order plenty, not an EOQ.

Transportation inventory As will be discussed in Chapter 13, carriers give rates based on the amount shipped. A full load costs less per ton to ship than a partial load. This is similar to the price break given by suppliers for large quantities. The same type of analysis can be used.

Multiples Sometimes, order size is constrained by package size. For example, a supplier may ship only in skid-load lots. In these cases, the unit used should be multiples of the minimum package size.

Order quantities and just-in-time As will be discussed in Chapter 15, lean production has a profound effect on the amount of inventory to be produced at one time. The replenishment quantity of an item is adjusted to match the demand of the next operation in the supply chain. This adjustment leads to smaller lot sizes and is often determined by the frequency of shipments to a customer or the size of an easily moved container rather than by calculation.

SUMMARY

The economic-order quantity is based on the assumption that demand is relatively uniform. This is appropriate for some inventories, and the EOQ formula can be used with reasonable results. One problem in using the EOQ formula is in determining the cost of ordering and the cost of carrying inventory. Since the total cost curve is flat at the bottom, good guesses very often will produce an order quantity that is economical. We have also seen that the EOQ concept can be used effectively with groups of items when the costs of carrying and ordering are not known.

The two costs influenced by the order quantity are the cost of ordering and the cost of carrying inventory. All methods of calculating order quantities attempt to minimize the sum of these two costs. The period-order quantity does this. It has the advantage over the EOQ in that it is better for lumpy demand because it looks forward to see what is actually needed.

KEY TERMS

Economic order quantity EOQ 219	Period Order Quantity 227
Fixed-order quantity 218	Quantity Discounts 224
Lot-for-lot 218	Stock-keeping units (SKUs) 218
Min-max system 218	Time between orders 227
Non-instantaneous receipt model 224	

QUESTIONS

1. What are the two basic questions in inventory management discussed in the text?

2. What are decision rules? What is their purpose?

3. What is an SKU?

4. What is the lot-for-lot decision rule? What is its advantage? Where would it be used?

5. What are the four assumptions on which economic-order quantities are based? For what kind of items are these assumptions valid? When are they not?

6. Under the assumptions on which EOQs are based, what are the formulas for average lot size and the number of orders per year?

7. What are the relevant costs associated with the two formulas? As the order quantities increase, what happens to each cost? What is the objective in establishing a fixed-order quantity?

8. Define each of the following in your own words and as a formula:
   a. Annual ordering cost.
   b. Annual carrying cost.
   c. Total annual cost.

9. What is the economic-order quantity (EOQ) formula? Define each term and give the units used. How do the units change when monetary units are used?

10. What are the relevant costs to be considered when deciding whether to take a quantity discount? On what basis should the decision be made?

11. What is the period-order quantity? How is it established? When can it be used?

12. How do each of the following influence inventory lot-size decisions?
    a. Lumpy demand.
    b. Minimum orders.
    c. Transportation costs.
    d. Multiples.

13. A company working toward JIT will have smaller lot sizes when compared to using traditional methods. Discuss how this will affect the costs associated with inventory. What are the controllable and the uncontrollable costs?

PROBLEMS

10.1. An SKU costing $10 is ordered in quantities of 500 units, annual demand is 5200 units, carrying costs are 20%, and the cost of placing an order is $50. Calculate the following:

a. Average inventory.

b. Number of orders placed per year.

c. Annual inventory-carrying cost.

d. Annual ordering cost.

e. Annual total cost.

Answer.   a. 250 units
             b. 10.4 orders per year
             c. Inventory-carrying cost = $500
             d. Annual ordering cost = $520
             e. Annual total cost = $1020

10.2. If the order quantity is increased to 1000 units, recalculate problems 10.1a to 10.1e and compare the results.

10.3. A company decides to establish an EOQ for an item. The annual demand is 400,000 units, each costing $8, ordering costs are $32 per order, and inventory-carrying costs are 20%. Calculate the following:

a. The EOQ in units.

b. Number of orders per year.

c. Cost of ordering, cost of carrying inventory, and total cost.

Answer.   a. EOQ = 4000 units
             b. Number of orders per year = 100
             c. Annual cost of ordering = $3200
                Annual cost of carrying = $3200
                Annual total cost = $6400

10.4. A company wishes to establish an EOQ for an item for which the annual demand is $800,000, the ordering cost is $32, and the cost of carrying inventory is 20%. Calculate the following:

a. The EOQ in dollars.

b. Number of orders per year.

c. Cost of ordering, cost of carrying inventory, and total cost.

d. How do the costs of carrying inventory compare with the costs of ordering?

Answer.   a. EOQ = $16,000
             b. Number of orders per year = 50
             c. Annual cost of ordering = $1600

Annual cost of carrying = $1600
Annual total cost = $3200

    d. The costs of carrying equal the costs of ordering since the order quantity used was the EOQ.

10.5. An SKU has an annual demand of 10,000 units, each costing $15, ordering costs are $80 per order, and the cost of carrying inventory is 25%. Calculate the EOQ in units and then convert to dollars.

10.6. A company is presently ordering on the basis of an EOQ. The demand is 10,000 units a year, unit cost is $10, ordering cost is $30, and the cost of carrying inventory is 20%. The supplier offers a discount of 3% on orders of 1000 units or more. What will be the saving (loss) of accepting the discount?

Answer. Savings = $2825.45

10.7. Refer to problem 10.3. The supplier offers a 2% discount on orders of 5000 units. Calculate the purchase cost, the cost of ordering, the cost of carrying, and the total cost if orders of 5000 are placed. Compare the results and calculate the savings if the discount is taken.

10.8. The local fire department uses 10,000 alkaline flashlight batteries per year, which cost $4 each. The cost of ordering batteries is estimated to be $50. The current interest rate suggested by the city council is 25%. The sales rep has recently suggested that you could get a discount of 2% for orders of 2000 batteries at a time. Should you take advantage of this special offer?

10.9. Calculate the new lot size for the following if $K = 5$

Item	Annual Demand	$\sqrt{A_D}$	New Lot Size
1	2500		
2	900		
3	121		

Answer. Item 1   250
           Item 2   150
           Item 3   55

10.10. Calculate K for the following data:

Item	Annual Demand	Orders per Year	$\sqrt{A_D}$
11	$14,400	5	
2	4900	5	
3	1600	5	
Totals			

Answer. $K = 15.33$

10.11. A company manufactures three sizes of lightning rods. Ordering costs and carrying costs are not known, but it is known that they are the same for each size. Each size is produced six times per year. If the demand for each size is as follows, calculate order quantities to minimize inventories and maintain the same total number of runs. Calculate the old and new average inventories. Is there any change in the number of orders per year?

Item	Annual Usage	Present Orders per Year	Present Lot Size	$\sqrt{A_D}$	New Lot Size $= K\sqrt{A_D}$	New Orders per Year $N = A_D/Q$
1	$22,500	6				
2	$7225	6				
3	$1600	6				
Totals						
Average Inventory						

Answer.   Average inventory with present lot sizes = $2610.40

Average inventory with new lot sizes = $2100.70

10.12. A company manufactures five sizes of screwdrivers. Ordering costs and carrying costs are not known, but it is known that they are the same for each size. At present, each size is produced four times per year. If the demand for each size is as follows, calculate order quantities to minimize inventories and maintain the same total number of runs. Calculate the old and new average inventories. Is there any change in the number of orders per year?

Item	Annual Usage	Present Orders per Year	Present Lot Size	$\sqrt{A_D}$	New Lot Size $= K\sqrt{A_D}$	New Orders per Year $N = A_D/Q$
1	$12,100					
2	$8100					
3	$3600					
4	$1600					
5	$225					
Totals						
Average Inventory						

10.13. The EOQ for an item is 900 units, and the annual usage is 2900 units. What is the period-order quantity?

Answer.   POQ = 3 weeks

10.14. Given the following net requirements, calculate the planned order receipts based on the period-order quantity. The EOQ is 250 units, and the annual demand is 4200 units.

Week	1	2	3	4	5	6	7	8	
Net Requirements	100	85	90	0	85	80	90	100	630
Planned Order Receipts									

Answer.   POQ = 3 weeks

Planned order period 1 = 275 units

Planned order period 5 = 255 units

Planned order period 8 = 100 units

10.15. Given the following MRP record and an EOQ of 200 units, calculate the planned order receipts using the economic-order quantity. Next, calculate the period-order quantities and the planned order receipts. In both cases, calculate the ending inventory and the total inventory carried over the 10 weeks.

Week	1	2	3	4	5	6	7	8	9	10	Total
Net Requirements	75	70	60	0	100	80	70	65	0	80	
Planned Order Receipt											
Ending Inventory											

Answer.   POQ = 3 weeks

EOQ total ending inventory = 985 units

POQ total ending inventory = 570 units

10.16. An item has a weekly demand of 240 units throughout the year. The item has a unit value of $42 and the company uses 20% of the item value for the annual inventory cost. When ordered, the setup cost to produce an order is $600, and the production process is able to produce 500 per week and deliver them weekly as produced. What is the economic-order quantity?

CASE STYDY 10.1

Carl's Computers

There was no question about Carl's genius. Seven years ago he decided to enter the competitive nightmare that the personal computer business had become. Although on the surface that appeared to be a rather nongenius-like move, the genius came in the unique designs and features that he developed for his computer. He also figured a way to promise delivery in only two days for the local and regional market. Other computer makers also had rapid production and delivery, but they were national competitors, and the delivery time from distant locations generally made Carl able to outcompete them on delivery.

Carl soon had a loyal following, especially among the many small businesses in the area. Not only could Carl deliver quickly, but he also had very rapid service to deal with any technical problems. That service feature became critical for the local businesses whose very livelihood depended on the computers, and soon that rapid service capability became more important than the initial product delivery. Since most of these businesses were fairly small, they could not afford to have their own in-house computer experts, so they depended heavily on Carl.

The Current Situation

All was not totally rosy at Carl's Computers, however. Recently they had hired Rosa Chang for the newly developed position of Inventory Manager for Aftermarket Service. In the first week Rosa got a good idea of the challenges facing her after she interviewed several of the people at Carl's.

RANDY SMITH, CUSTOMER SERVICE MANAGER: "I'm not sure what you need to do, but whatever it is needs to be done fast! At this point our main competitive edge other than product delivery is service response, and I'm always hearing that we can't get a unit in the field serviced because some critical part is missing. Both the customers and the field service people are complaining about it. They make a service call, find out they need a certain part, but in many cases we're out of the part. The customers tend to be fairly loyal, but their patience is wearing thin—our policy is to provide at least a 98% customer service level, and we're not even close. That's not the only problem, though. Since our service is declining, the customers are looking more closely at our prices. I'd like to cut them a break, but our financial people tell us our margins are already too thin, and get this—one major reason is that our inventory and associated inventory costs are too high! It looks to me as if we have a very large amount of the wrong stuff here. I don't know that for sure, but I sure hope you can find a solution, and fast!"

ELLEN BEDROSIAN, CHIEF ENGINEER: "Boy, am I glad you're here! The inventory problems are killing us in engineering. Carl's has always been known for unique designs, and we've been trying hard to keep ahead of the competitive curve on that issue. The problem is that most of the time when we push hard to get a new design out, the inventory and financial people tell us we have to wait. It seems like they always have too much of the old design inventory around, and the financial "hit" to make it immediately obsolete would be too severe. We're told that as soon as we announce a new design many of our customers would want it, so that tends to make most existing old design material—even for service—obsolete. We try to tell the service inventory people when we have a new design coming so they can use up the old material, but somehow it never seems to work out."

JIM HUGHES, PURCHASING MANAGER: "Well, Rosa, I wish you luck—you'll need it. I'm getting pressure from so many directions, sometimes I don't know how to respond. First, the financial people are always telling me to cut or control costs. The engineers then are always coming out with new designs, most of which represent purchased parts. A lot of our time is spent working with suppliers on the new designs, while trying to get them to have very rapid delivery with low prices. Although most can live with that, where we really jerk them around is with the changes in orders. One minute our field service people tell us they've run out of something and they need delivery immediately. In many cases they don't even have an order for that part on the books. The next thing you know they want us to cancel an order for something that only a day before they said was critical. Our buyers and suppliers are good, but they're not miracle workers and they can't do everything at once. Some of our suppliers are even threatening to refuse our business if we don't get our act together. We've tried to offer solutions for the field service people, but nothing seems to work. Maybe they just don't care."

MARY SHOULTON, CHIEF FINANCIAL OFFICER: "If you can help us with this inventory problem, you'll be well worth your salary, and then some! Here we are being competitively crunched for price, delivery, and efficient service, and our service inventory costs seem to have gone completely out of control. The total inventory has climbed more than 200% in the last two years while our service revenues have only grown 15%. On top of that, we have had an increase in obsolete material write-off of 80% in that same two-year period. In addition, significant inventory-related costs have come from expediting. Premium freight shipments, such as flying in parts, caused by critical part shortages cost us over $67,000 last year alone. Do you realize that represents almost 20% of our gross profit margin from the service business? With our interest rates, warehousing, and obsolete inventory costs, we recognize a 23% inventory holding cost. Given our huge inventory level, that takes another big bite out of profits. All this suggests to me we need to get control of the situation or we may find ourselves out of business!"

FRANKLIN KNOWLES, FIELD SERVICE SUPERVISOR: "Until they hired you, the other production supervisor and I had been in charge of inventory. I hate to discourage you, but it looks like an impossible job. The purchasing people bought a bunch of standard-size bins, and they told us that as soon as we had a week's average part usage for each part to order more—specifically, "enough to fill up the bin." Since most of their lead times were a week or less, it sure made sense. All the records were kept on computer, therefore the computer could be programmed to tell us when we had only the week's supply. It made great sense to me, but something kept going wrong. First, field service technicians seemed to frequently grab parts without filling out a transaction. That made our records go to pot. As a matter of fact, we had a complete physical inventory a couple of months ago, and it showed our records to be less than 30% accurate! I suspect our records are almost that bad again, and we don't have another physical inventory scheduled for another nine months.

"Second, with our records so bad the field service technicians can never tell if we really have the parts or not. Several of them have started to take large quantities of critical parts and are keeping their own inventory. When it comes time to replace their own "private stock," they take a bunch more. That has made the demand on the central inventory appear very erratic. One day we have plenty, and the next day we're out! You can imagine how happy purchasing is when the first time they see a purchase order it is requesting an immediate urgent shipment. We've made a policy that the technicians are only supposed to have a few specifically authorized parts with them, but I'm sure many of the technicians are violating that policy big time."

Quentin Bates, Field Service Technician: "Something is drastically wrong with our inventory, and it's driving me and the other techs crazy. We're not supposed to keep much inventory with us, only a few commonly used parts. If we have a field problem requiring a part, we're supposed to be getting it from the central inventory. Problem is, much of the time it's not there. We have to take time to pressure purchasing for it, and then have to try to calm our customers while we wait for delivery. In the meantime, the customers' systems are often unusable, and they're losing business. It doesn't take too long before they're really mad at us. I guess the people at purchasing don't care, since we have to take all the heat. Lately I've been taking and keeping a bunch of parts I'm not really supposed to have in my inventory, and I know the other field technicians do also. That's saved us a few times, but the situation seems to be getting worse."

Now that Rosa had some real information as to the nature of the problems, she needed to start developing solutions—and it appeared that it was important to come up with good solutions fast! The first thing she tried to do was take a couple of part numbers at random and see if she could improve on the ordering approach.

The first number she selected was the A233 circuit board. The average weekly usage was 32. The lead time was given as one week. The board cost $18, and the cost to place an order was given as $16. The quantity ordered to fill the bin was usually 64. The second number was the P656 power supply. It cost $35, but since the supplier only required a fax to order the cost was only $2 per order. Even with the fax the delivery lead time was two weeks. The average weekly demand for the power supply was 120. The company typically ordered 350 units at a time. Recently the supplier for the circuit board hinted that it might be able to give Carl's a price break of $2 per board if Carl's would order 200 or more at a time.

Case Analysis

1. Using the data on the two part numbers given, provide a comprehensive evaluation of the ordering policies. Compare the present annual average cost with the cost of using a system such as EOQ, and discuss any other order policies as appropriate.

2. Should Carl's pursue the price break? Why or why not?

3. What do you think the sources of the other problems are? Be specific and analyze as completely as possible.

4. Develop a comprehensive plan to help Rosa get the inventory back under control.

INDEPENDENT DEMAND ORDERING SYSTEMS

INTRODUCTION

The concept of an economic-order quantity, covered in Chapter 10, addresses the question of how much to order at one time. Another important question is when to place a replacement order. If stock is not reordered soon enough, there will be a stockout and a potential loss in customer service. However, stock ordered earlier than needed will create extra inventory. The problem is how to balance the costs of carrying extra inventory against the costs of a stockout.

No matter what the items are, some rules for reordering are needed and can be as simple as order when needed, order every month, or order when stock falls to a predetermined level. We all use rules of some sort in our own lives, and they vary depending on the significance of the item. A homemaker uses some intuitive rules to make up the weekly shopping list. Order enough meat for a week, order salt when the box is empty, order vanilla extract if it will be needed over the next week, and so on.

In industry there are many inventories that involve a large investment and have high stockout costs. Controlling these inventories requires effective reorder systems. Three basic systems are used to determine when to order:

- Order point system.
- Periodic review system.
- Material requirements planning.

The first two are for independent demand items; the last is for dependent demand items.

ORDER POINT SYSTEM

When the quantity of an item on hand in inventory falls to a predetermined level, called an **order point**, an order is placed. The quantity ordered is usually precalculated and based on economic-order-quantity concepts.

Using this system, an order must be placed when there is enough stock on hand to satisfy demand from the time the order is placed until the new stock arrives (called the **lead time**). Suppose that for a particular item the average demand is 100 units a week and the lead time is four weeks. If an order is placed when there are 400 units on hand, on the average there will be enough stock on hand to last until the new stock arrives. However, demand during any one lead-time period probably varies from the average—sometimes more and sometimes less than the 400. Statistically, half the time the demand is greater than average, and there is a stockout; half the time the demand is less than average, and there is extra stock. If it is necessary to provide some protection against a stockout, safety stock can be added. The item is ordered when the quantity on hand falls to a level equal to the demand during the lead time plus the safety stock:

FIGURE 11.1 Quantity on hand versus time: independent demand item.

$$OP = DDLT + SS$$

where

OP = order point

DDLT = demand during the lead time

SS = safety stock

It is important to note that it is the *demand (and the variation in demand) during the lead time that is important*. The only time a stockout is possible is during the lead time. If demand during the lead time is greater than expected, there will be a stockout unless sufficient safety stock is carried.

Example Problem

Demand is 200 units a week, the lead time is 3 weeks, and safety stock is 300 units. Calculate the order point.

ANSWER

$$OP = DDLT + SS$$
$$= 200 \times 3 + 300$$
$$= 900 \text{ units}$$

Figure 11.1 shows the relationship between safety stock, lead time, order quantity, and order point. With the order point system,

- Order quantities are usually fixed.
- The order point is determined by the average demand during the lead time. If the average demand or the lead time changes and there is no corresponding change in the order point, effectively there has been a change in safety stock.
- The intervals between replenishment are not constant but vary depending on the actual demand during the reorder cycle.
- The average inventory for a period is equal to the opening inventory plus the ending inventory, divided by 2.

Period opening inventory = order quantity plus safety stock

Period ending inventory = safety stock

$$\text{Average inventory} = \frac{\text{order quantity} + \text{safety stock} + \text{safety stock}}{2}$$

$$= \frac{\text{order quantity}}{2} + \text{safety stock}$$

$$= \frac{Q}{2} + SS$$

Example Problem

Order quantity is 1000 units and safety stock (SS) is 300 units. What is the average inventory?

ANSWER

$$\text{Average inventory} = \frac{Q}{2} + \text{SS}$$

$$= \frac{1000}{2} + 300$$

$$= 800 \text{ units}$$

Determining the order point depends on the demand during the lead time and the safety stock required.

Methods of estimating the demand during the lead time were discussed in Chapter 8. We now look at the factors to consider when determining safety stock.

DETERMINING SAFETY STOCK

Safety stock is intended to protect against uncertainty in supply and demand. Uncertainty may occur in two ways: quantity uncertainty and timing uncertainty. Quantity uncertainty occurs when the amount of supply or demand varies; for example, if the demand is greater or less than expected in a given period. Timing uncertainty occurs when the time of receipt of supply or demand differs from that expected. A customer or a supplier may change a delivery date, for instance.

There are two ways to protect against uncertainty: carry extra stock, called **safety stock**, or order early, called safety lead time. **Safety stock** is a calculated extra amount of stock carried and is generally used to protect against quantity uncertainty. **Safety lead time** is used to protect against uncertainty in delivery lead time by planning order releases and order receipts earlier than required. Safety stock and safety lead time both result in extra inventory, but the methods of calculation are different.

Safety stock is the most common way of buffering against uncertainty and is the method described in this text. The safety stock required depends on the following:

- Variability of demand during the lead time. The higher the variability the greater the need for safety stock

- Frequency of reorder. If orders are placed frequently, changes to the demand or variability of the demand will be detected earlier.

- Service level desired. Higher service levels require more inventory, to accommodate periods of increased demand.

- Length of the lead time. The longer the lead time, the more safety stock has to be carried to provide a specified service level. This is one reason it is important to reduce lead times as much as possible.

Variation in Demand During Lead Time

Chapter 8 discussed forecast error and said that actual demand varies from forecast for two reasons: bias error in forecasting the average demand and random variations in demand about the average. It is the latter with which we are concerned in determining safety stock.

Suppose two items, A and B, have a 10-week sales history, as shown in Figure 11.2. Average demand over the lead time of one week is 1000 per week for both items. (Note that, for simplicity, the lead time and the sales history interval are both expressed as one week. This is unusual, and the difference between order lead time and sales interval will be accommodated later in this chapter.) However, the weekly demand for item A has a range from 700 to 1400 units a week and for item B the range is from 200 to 1600 units per week. The demand for B is more erratic than that for A. If the order point is 1200 units for both items, there will be one stockout for A and four for B, which will occur when the demand during any one week exceeds 1200 units. If the same service level is to be provided (the same chance of stockout for all items), some method of estimating the randomness of item demand is needed.

Week	Item A	Item B
1	1200	400
2	1000	600
3	800	1600
4	900	1300
5	1400	200
6	1100	1100
7	1100	1500
8	700	800
9	1000	1400
10	800	1100
Total	10,000	10,000
Average	1000	1000

FIGURE 11.2 Actual demand for two items.

Variation in Demand About the Average

Suppose over the past 100 weeks a history of weekly demand for a particular item shows an average demand of 1000 units. As expected, most of the demands are around 1000; a smaller number would be farther away from the average, and still fewer would be farthest away. If the weekly demands are classified into groups or ranges about the average, a picture of the distribution of demand about the average appears. Suppose the demand is distributed as follows:

Weekly Demand	Number of Weeks
725–774	2
775–824	3
825–874	7
875–924	12
925–974	17
975–1024	20
1025–1074	17
1075–1124	12
1125–1174	7
1175–1224	3
1225–1274	2

These data are plotted to give the results shown in Figure 11.3. This is a histogram.

Normal distribution   Everything in life varies—even identical twins in some respects. The pattern of demand distribution about the average will differ for different products and markets. Some method is needed to describe the distribution—its shape, center, and spread.

The shape of the histogram in Figure 11.3 indicates that although there is variation in the distribution, it follows a definite pattern, as shown by the smooth curve. Such a natural pattern shows predictability. As long as the demand conditions remain the same, we can expect the pattern to remain very much the same. If the demand is erratic, so is the demand pattern, making it difficult to predict with any accuracy. Fortunately, most demand patterns are stable and predictable.

FIGURE 11.3 Histogram of actual demand.

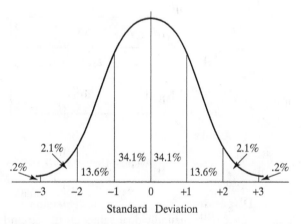

FIGURE 11.4 Normal distribution.

The most common predictable pattern is similar to the one outlined by the histogram in Figure 11.3 and is called a **normal curve,** or **bell curve,** because its shape resembles a bell. The shape of a perfectly normal distribution is shown in Figure 11.4.

The **normal distribution** has most of the values clustered near a central point with progressively fewer results occurring away from the center. It is symmetrical about this central point in that it spreads out evenly on both sides.

The normal curve is described by two characteristics. One relates to its central tendency, or average, and the other to the variation, or dispersion, of the actual values about the average.

Average or mean   The **average** or **mean** value is at the high point of the curve. It is the central tendency of the distribution. The symbol for the mean is $\bar{x}$ (pronounced "x bar"). It is calculated by adding the data and dividing by the total number of data. In mathematical terms, it can be written as:

$$\bar{x} = \frac{\sum x}{n}$$

where x stands for the individual data [(in this case, the individual demands) $\sum$ (capital Greek letter sigma) is the summation sign and n is the number of data (demands)].

Example Problem

Given the following actual demands for a 10-week period, calculate the average ($\bar{x}$) of the distribution.

Period	Actual Demand
1	1200
2	1000
3	800
4	900
5	1400
6	1100
7	1100
8	700
9	1000
10	800
Total	10,000

ANSWER

$$\text{Average Demand} = \bar{x} = \frac{\sum x}{n} = \frac{10,000}{10} = 1000 \text{ units}$$

Dispersion   The variation, or **dispersion**, of actual demands about the average refers to how closely the individual values cluster around the mean or average. It can be measured in several ways:

- As a range of the maximum minus the minimum value.
- As the mean absolute deviation (MAD), which is a measure of the average forecast error. (Calculation of MAD was discussed in Chapter 8.)
- As a standard deviation.

Standard Deviation (σ)

The **standard deviation** is a statistical value that measures how closely the individual values cluster about the average. It is represented by the Greek letter sigma (σ). The standard deviation is calculated as follows:

1. Calculate the deviation for each period by subtracting the actual demand from the forecast demand.
2. Square each deviation.
3. Add the squares of the deviations.
4. Divide the value in step 3 by the number of periods to determine the average of the squared deviations.
5. Calculate the square root of the value calculated in step 4. This is the standard deviation (σ).

6. Most calculators and spreadsheet applications have a statistical function that can calculate sigma (σ) directly and have two variations of sigma: σ_n, which is based on a population and σ_{n-1}, which is based on a sample estimating the population. We will use sigma based on n (σ_n). Further explanation of this difference is unfortunately beyond the scope of this text.

Note that previous versions of this text have used MAD as the measure of dispersion since it is easier to calculate manually. However, standard deviation is a more widely accepted technique, which we will use in the calculation of safety stocks. One standard deviation is approximately equal to 1.25 MADs.

It is also important to note that in our discussion of safety stock the deviations in demand are still calculated for the same time intervals as the lead time. If the lead time is one week, then the variation in demand over a one-week period is needed to determine the safety stock. Differences in the lead time and forecast interval will be discussed later in this chapter.

Example Problem

Given the data from the previous example problem, calculate the standard deviation (σ).

ANSWER

Period	Forecast demand	Actual demand	Deviation	Deviation squared
1	1000	1200	200	40000
2	1000	1000	0	0
3	1000	800	-200	40000
4	1000	900	-100	10000
5	1000	1400	400	160000
6	1000	1100	100	10000
7	1000	1100	100	10000
8	1000	700	-300	90000
9	1000	1000	0	0
10	1000	800	-200	40000
Total	10000	10000	0	400000

Average of the squares of the deviation = 400,000 ÷ 10 = 40,000

Sigma = $\sqrt{40,000}$ = 200 units

From statistics, we can determine that:

The actual demand will be within ± 1 sigma (± 200 units) of the forecast average approximately 68% of the time.

The actual demand will be within ± 2 sigma (± 400 units) of the forecast average approximately 98% of the time.

The actual demand will be within ± 3 sigma (± 600 units) of the forecast average approximately 99.88% of the time.

Determining the Safety Stock and Order Point

Now that we have calculated the standard deviation, we must decide how much safety stock is needed.

One property of the normal curve is that it is symmetrical about the average. This means that half the time the actual demand is less than the average and half the time it is greater. Safety stocks are needed to cover only those periods in which the demand during the lead time is greater than the average. Thus, a service level of 50% can be attained with no safety stock. If a higher service level is needed, safety stock must be provided to protect against those times when the actual demand is greater than the average.

As stated, we know from statistics that the error is within ±1 sigma of the forecast about 68% of the time (34% of the time less and 34% of the time greater than the forecast).

Suppose the standard deviation of demand during the lead time is 100 units and this amount is carried as safety stock. This much safety stock provides protection against stock-out for the 34% of the time that actual demand is greater than expected. In total, there is enough safety stock to provide protection for the 84% of the time (50% + 34% = 84%) that a stockout is possible.

The service level is a statement of the percentage of time there is no stockout. But what exactly is meant by supplying the customer 84% of the time? It means being able to supply when a stockout is possible, and a stockout is possible only during the time interval between when an order is to be placed and when the replenishment is received. If we order 100 times a year, there are 100 chances of a stockout. With safety stock equivalent to one standard deviation, on the average we would expect no stockouts about 84 of the 100 times.

Example Problem

Using the figures in the last example problem in which the standard deviation was calculated as 200 units,

a. Calculate the safety stock and the order point for an 84% service level.

b. If a safety stock equal to two standard deviations is carried, calculate the safety stock and the order point.

ANSWER

a. Safety stock = 1 sigma

$$= 1 \times 200$$

$$= 200 \text{ units}$$

Order point = DDLT + SS

$$= 1000 + 200 = 1200 \text{ units}$$

where DDLT and SS are as defined previously. With this order point and level of safety stock, on the average there are no stockouts 84% of the time when a stockout is possible.

b. SS = 2 × 200

$$= 400 \text{ units}$$

OP = DDLT + SS

$$= 1000 + 400$$

$$= 1400 \text{ units}$$

Safety factor   The service level is directly related to the number of standard deviations provided as safety stock and is usually called the **safety factor.** In our earlier discussions, we have used the normal curve to determine the service level produced by one, two, or three standard deviations. Safety factors are the inverse of this procedure, wherein we determine a desired service level and look up the corresponding number of standard deviations required.

Figure 11.5 shows safety factors for various service levels. Note that the service level is the percentage of order cycles without a stockout. For values not shown on the table, you

Service Level (%)	Safety Factor
50	0.00
75	0.67
80	0.84
85	1.04
90	1.28
94	1.56
95	1.65
96	1.75
97	1.88
98	2.05
99	2.33
99.86	3.00
99.99	4.00

FIGURE 11.5 Table of safety factors.

can make a close approximation of the safety factor by interpolating the factors given. For example, to find the safety factor for a desired service level of 77%, calculate the average safety factor for a 75% service level (0.67) and an 80% service level (0.84). The safety factor for a 77% service level would be approximately

$$\frac{0.67 + 0.84}{2} = 0.76$$

Example Problem

If the standard deviation is 200 units, what safety stock should be carried to provide a service level of 90%? If the expected demand during the lead time is 1500 units, what is the order point?

ANSWER

From Figure 11.5, the safety factor for a service level of 90% is 1.28. Therefore,

$$\text{Safety stock} = \sigma \times \text{safety factor}$$
$$= 200 \times 1.28$$
$$= 256 \text{ units}$$
$$\text{Order point} = \text{DDLT} + \text{SS}$$
$$= 1500 + 256$$
$$= 1756 \text{ units}$$

DETERMINING SERVICE LEVELS

Theoretically, we want to carry enough safety stock on hand so the cost of carrying the extra inventory plus the cost of stockouts is a minimum. Stockouts cost money for the following reasons:

- Back-order costs.
- Lost sales.
- Lost customers.

The cost of a stockout varies depending on the item, the market served, the customer, and competition. In some markets, customer service is a major competitive tool, and a stockout can be very expensive. In others, it may not be a major consideration. Stockout costs are difficult to establish. Usually the decision about what the service level should be is a senior management decision and is part of the company's corporate and marketing strategy. As such, it is beyond the scope of this text.

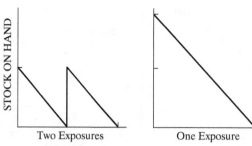

FIGURE 11.6 Exposures to stockout.

The only time it is possible for a stockout to occur is when stock is running low, and this happens every time an order is to be placed. Therefore, the chances of a stockout are directly proportional to the frequency of reorder. The more often stock is reordered, the more often there is a chance of a stockout. Figure 11.6 shows the effect of the order quantity on the number of exposures per year. Note also that when the order quantity is increased, exposure to stockout decreases. The safety stock needed decreases, but because of the larger order quantity, the average inventory increases.

It is the responsibility of management to determine the number of stockouts per year that are tolerable. Then the service level, safety stock, and order point can be calculated.

Example Problem

Suppose management stated that it could tolerate only one stockout per year for a specific item.

For this particular item, the annual demand is 52,000 units, it is ordered in quantities of 2600, and the standard deviation of demand during the lead time is 100 units. The lead time is one week. Calculate:

a. Number of orders per year.

b. Service level.

c. Safety stock.

d. Order point.

ANSWER

a. Number of orders per year $= \dfrac{\text{annual demand}}{\text{order quantity}}$

$$= \frac{52{,}000}{2600} = 20 \text{ times per year}$$

b. Since one stockout per year is tolerable, there must be no stockouts 19 $(20 - 1)$ times per year.

$$\text{Service level} = \frac{20 - 1}{20} = 95\%$$

c. From Figure 11.5

$$\text{Safety factor} = 1.65$$
$$\text{Safety stock} = \text{safety factor} \times \sigma$$
$$= 1.65 \times 100 = 165 \text{ units}$$

d. Demand during lead time (1 week) $= \dfrac{(52{,}000)}{52} = 1000 \text{ units}$

$$\text{Order point} = \text{demand during lead time} + SS$$
$$= 1000 + 165 = 1165 \text{ units}$$

DIFFERENT FORECAST AND LEAD-TIME INTERVALS

Usually, there are many items in an inventory, each with different lead times. Records of actual demand and forecasts are normally made on a weekly or monthly basis for all items regardless of what the individual lead times are. It is almost impossible to measure the variation in demand about the average for each of the lead times. Some method of adjusting standard deviation for the different time intervals is needed.

If the lead time is zero, the standard deviation of demand is zero. As the lead time increases, the standard deviation increases. However, it will not increase in direct proportion to the increase in time. For example, if the standard deviation is 100 for a lead time of one week, then for a lead time of four weeks it will not be 400, since it is very unlikely that the deviation would be high for four weeks in a row. As the time interval increases, there is a smoothing or canceling effect, and the longer the time interval, the more smoothing takes place.

The following adjustment can be made to the standard deviation or the safety stock to compensate for differences between lead-time interval (LTI) and forecast interval (FI). It states that the standard deviation changes as the square root of the change in the interval. Although not exact, the formula gives a good approximation

$$\text{sigma for LTI} = (\text{sigma for FI})\sqrt{\frac{\text{LTI}}{\text{FI}}}$$

Example Problem

The forecast interval is 4 weeks, the lead time interval is 2 weeks, and sigma for the forecast interval is 150 units. Calculate the standard deviation for the lead-time interval.

ANSWER

$$\text{sigma for LTI} = 150 \sqrt{\tfrac{2}{4}} = 150 \times 0.707 = 106 \text{ units}$$

The preceding relationship is also useful where there is a change in the LTI. Now it is probably more convenient to work directly with the safety stock rather than the standard deviation. The relationship is as follows:

$$\text{New safety stock} = \text{old safety stock} \sqrt{\frac{\text{new interval}}{\text{old interval}}}$$

Example Problem

The safety stock for an item is 150 units, and the lead time is 2 weeks. If the lead time changes to 3 weeks, calculate the new safety stock.

ANSWER

$$\text{SS (new)} = 150\sqrt{\tfrac{3}{2}}$$
$$= 150 \times 1.22 = 183 \text{ units}$$

It should also be noted that as the lead time is decreased the amount of safety stock is also decreased. This is one of the many direct benefits of just-in-time and lean production discussed in Chapter 15.

DETERMINING WHEN THE ORDER POINT IS REACHED

There must be some method to show when the quantity of an item on hand has reached the order point. In practice, there are many systems, but they all are inclined to be variations or extensions of three basic systems: the two-bin system, the Kanban system, and the perpetual inventory record system.

Two-Bin System

A quantity of an item equal to the order point quantity is set aside (frequently in a separate or second bin) and not touched until all the main stock is used up. When this stock needs to be used, the production control or purchasing department is notified and a replenishment order is placed.

There are variations on this system, such as the red-tag system, where a tag is placed in the stock at a point equal to the order point. Bookstores frequently use this system. A tag or card is placed in a book that is in a stack in a position equivalent to the order point. When a customer takes that book to the checkout, the store is effectively notified that it is time to reorder that title.

The **two-bin system** is a simple way of keeping control of C items. Because they are of low value, it is best to spend the minimum amount of time and money controlling them. However, they do need to be managed, and someone should be assigned to ensure that when the reserve stock is reached an order must be placed. When it is out of stock, a C item becomes an A item.

Kanbans

The **Kanban system** is a simple system that signals the need for more product. It normally consists of a card or ticket that has information on the item and the quantity to be produced. It avoids the need for formal record keeping and, like the two-bin system, makes a visual signal of the need for more product when the inventory falls below a preset level. It is used to replenish all items and not just low-value C items. Kanbans are discussed in detail in Chapter 15.

Perpetual Inventory Record System

A **perpetual inventory record** is a continual account of inventory transactions as they occur. At any instant, it holds an up-to-date record of transactions. At a minimum, it contains the balance on hand, but it may also contain the quantity on order but not received, the quantity allocated but not issued, and the available balance. The accuracy of the record depends upon the speed with which transactions are recorded and the accuracy of the input. Because manual systems rely on the input of humans, they are more likely to have slow response and inaccuracies. Computer-based systems have a higher transaction speed and reduce the possibility of human error.

An inventory record contains variable and permanent information. Figure 11.7 shows an example of a perpetual inventory record.

Permanent or static information is shown at the top of Figure 11.7. Although not absolutely permanent, this information does not change frequently. Any alteration is usually

426254 SCREW				ORDER QUANTITY 500		ORDER POINT 100
DATE	ORDERED	RECEIVED	ISSUED	ON HAND	ALLOCATED	AVAILABLE
01				500		500
02				500	400	100
03	500			500		100
04			400	100	0	100
05		500		600	0	600

FIGURE 11.7 Perpetual inventory record.

the result of an engineering change, manufacturing process change, or inventory management change. It includes data such as the following:

- Part number, name, and description.
- Storage location.
- Order point.
- Order quantity.
- Lead time.
- Safety stock.
- Suppliers.

Variable or dynamic information changes with each transaction and includes the following:

- Quantities ordered: dates, order numbers, and quantities.
- Quantities received: dates, order numbers, and quantities.
- Quantities issued: dates, order numbers, and quantities.
- Balance on hand.
- Allocated: dates, order numbers, and quantities.
- Available balance.

The information depends on the needs of the company and the particular circumstances.

PERIODIC REVIEW SYSTEM

In the order point system, an order is placed when the quantity on hand falls to a predetermined level called the order point. The quantity ordered is usually predetermined on some basis such as the economic-order quantity. The interval between orders varies depending on the demand during any particular cycle. In most retail environments and especially supermarkets, there are thousands of items, and each item could be reaching its order point at any time. It is impractical to place many individual orders and it is anticipated that many items will be delivered on one truck at a time. In this way the ordering cost, which includes the price of transportation, is spread over many small items. The periodic review system makes the timing of each order a regular interval.

Using the periodic review system, the quantity on hand of a particular item is determined at specified, fixed-time intervals, and an order is placed. Figure 11.8 illustrates this system.

Figure 11.8 shows that the review intervals (t_1, t_2, and t_3) are equal and that Q_1, Q_2, and Q_3 are not necessarily the same. Thus the review period is fixed, and the order

FIGURE 11.8 Periodic review system: units in stock versus time.

quantity is allowed to vary. The quantity on hand plus the quantity ordered must be sufficient to last until the *next shipment* is received. That is, the quantity on hand plus the quantity ordered must equal the sum of the demand during the lead time plus the demand during the review period plus the safety stock.

Target-Level or Maximum-Level Inventory

The quantity equal to the demand during the lead time plus the demand during the review period plus safety stock is called the **target-level or maximum-level inventory**:

$$T = D(R + L) + SS$$

where

T = target (maximum) inventory level

D = demand per unit of time

L = lead-time duration

R = review-period duration

SS = safety stock

Note that, as illustrated in Figure 11.8, inventory rarely actually reaches the target or maximum level inventory since product will continue to be consumed during the lead time interval.

The order quantity is equal to the maximum-inventory level minus the quantity on hand at the review period:

$$Q = T - I$$

where

Q = order quantity

I = inventory on hand

The periodic review system is useful for the following:

- Where there are many small issues from inventory, and posting transactions to inventory records are very expensive. Supermarkets and retailers are in this category.

- Where ordering costs per item need to be kept small. This occurs when many different items are ordered from one source. A regional distribution center may order most or all of its stock from a central warehouse in regular, large, multi-item shipments.

- Where many items are ordered together to make up a production run or fill a truckload. A good example of this is a regional distribution center that orders a truckload once a week from a central warehouse.

Example Problem

A hardware company stocks nuts and bolts and orders them from a local supplier once every 2 weeks (10 working days). Lead time is 2 days. The company has determined that the average demand for ½-inch bolts is 150 per week (5 working days), and it wants to keep a safety stock of 3 days' supply on hand. An order is to be placed this week, and stock on hand is 130 bolts.

a. What is the target level?

b. How many ½-inch bolts should be ordered this time?

ANSWER

Let

D = demand per unit of time = 150 ÷ 5 = 30 per working day

L = lead-time duration = 2 days

R = review period duration = 10 days

SS = safety stock = 3 days' supply = 3 × 30 = 90 units

I = inventory on hand = 130 units

Then

    a.   Target level $T = D(R + L) + SS$

$$= 30(10 + 2) + 90$$

$$= 450 \text{ units}$$

    b. Order quantity $Q = T - I$

$$= 450 - 130 = 320 \text{ units}$$

DISTRIBUTION INVENTORY

Distribution inventory includes all the finished goods held anywhere in the distribution system. The purpose of holding inventory in distribution centers is to improve customer service by locating stock near the customer and to reduce transportation costs by allowing the manufacturer to ship full loads rather than partial loads over long distances. This will be studied in Chapter 13.

The objectives of distribution inventory management are to provide the required level of customer service, to minimize the costs of transportation and handling, and to be able to interact with the factory to minimize scheduling problems.

Distribution systems vary considerably, but in general they have a central supply facility that is supported by a factory, a number of distribution centers, and, finally, customers. Figure 11.9 shows a schematic of such a system. The customers may be the final consumer or some intermediary in the distribution chain.

Unless a firm delivers directly from factory to customer, demand on the factory is created by central supply. In turn, demand on central supply is created by the distribution centers. This can have severe repercussions on the pattern of demand on central supply and the factory. Although the demand from customers may be relatively uniform, the demand on central supply is not, because it is dependent on when the distribution centers place replenishment orders. In turn, the demand on the factory depends on when central supply places orders. Figure 11.10 shows the process schematically.

Notice in Figure 11.10 how continuous, steady demand at the distribution center has changed, due to lot sizing into discontinuous or lumpy demand at the central supply. The distribution system is the factory's customer, and the way the distribution system interfaces with the factory has a significant effect on the efficiency of factory operations.

Distribution inventory management systems can be classified into decentralized, centralized, and distribution requirements planning.

FIGURE 11.9 Schematic of a distribution system.

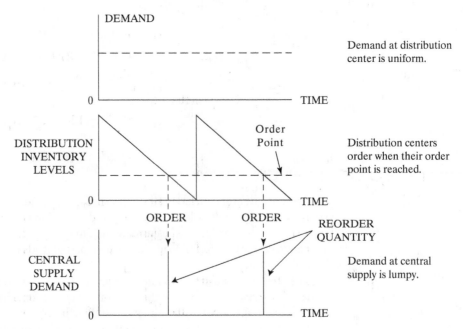

FIGURE 11.10 Distribution inventory.

Decentralized System

In a **decentralized system**, each distribution center first determines what it needs and when, and then places orders to central supply. Each center orders on its own to service local demand without regard for the needs of other centers, available inventory at central supply, or the production schedule of the factory.

The advantage of the decentralized system is that each center can operate on its own and thus reduce communication and coordination expense. The disadvantage is the lack of coordination and the effect this may have on overall inventories, customer service, and factory schedules. Because of these deficiencies, many distribution systems have moved toward more central control.

A number of ordering systems can be used at each distribution center, including the order point and periodic review systems. The decentralized system is sometimes called the pull system because orders are placed on central supply and "pulled" through the system.

Centralized System

In a **centralized system**, all forecasting and order decisions are made centrally. Stock is "pushed" out into the system from central supply. Distribution centers have no say about what they receive.

Different ordering systems can be used, but generally an attempt is made to replace the stock that has been sold and to provide for special situations such as seasonality or sales promotions. These systems attempt to balance the available inventory with the needs of each distribution center.

The advantage of these systems is the coordination between factory, central supply, and distribution center needs. The disadvantage is the inability to react to local demand, thus lowering the level of service.

Distribution Requirements Planning

Distribution requirements planning is a system that forecasts when the various demands will be made by the system on central supply. This gives central supply and the factory the opportunity to plan for the goods that will actually be needed and when. It is able both to respond to local customer demand and coordinate planning and control.

FIGURE 11.11 Distribution requirements planning.

The system translates the logic of material requirements planning to the distribution system. Planned order releases from the various distribution centers become the input to the material plan of central supply. The planned order releases from central supply become the forecast of demand for the factory master production schedule. Figure 11.11 shows the system schematically. The records shown are all for the same part number.

Example Problem

A company making lawnmowers has a central supply attached to its factory and two distribution centers. Distribution center A forecasts demand at 25, 30, 55, 50, and 30 units over the next 5 weeks and has 100 lawnmowers in transit that are due in week 2. The transit time is 2 weeks, the order quantity is 100 units, and there are 50 units on hand. Distribution center B forecasts demand at 95, 85, 100, 70, and 50 over the next 5 weeks. Transit time is 1 week, the order quantity is 200 units, and there are 100 units on hand. The central warehouse has a lead time of 2 weeks, the order quantity is 500 units, and there are 400 on hand. Calculate the gross requirements, projected available, and planned order releases for the two distribution centers, and the gross requirements, projected available, and planned order releases for the central warehouse.

ANSWER

Distribution Center A
Transit Time: 2 weeks
Order Quantity: 100 units

Week	1	2	3	4	5
Gross Requirements	25	30	55	50	30
In Transit		100			
Projected Available 50	25	95	40	90	60
Planned Order Release		100			

Distribution Center B
Transit Time: 1 week
Order Quantity: 200 units

Week	1	2	3	4	5
Gross Requirements	95	85	100	70	50
In Transit					
Projected Available 100	5	120	20	150	100
Planned Order Release	200		200		

Central Supply
Lead Time: 2 weeks
Order Quantity: 500 units

Week	1	2	3	4	5
Gross Requirements	200	100	200		
Scheduled Receipts					
Projected Available 400	200	100	400		
Planned Order Release	500				

SUMMARY

This chapter addresses the problem of when to order whereas Chapter 10 addressed the problem of how much to order. Systems for ordering should be simple to use, such as an order point system or a periodic review system. Ordering systems need to order in time to avoid running out of stock. Statistical applications allow a prediction of the demand during the critical lead time to establish safety stocks. The order point uses this safety stock plus anticipated demand during the lead time to ensure acceptable service to the customer. Distribution systems can take advantage of MRP-type logic to optimize order quantities all the way through the supply chain. Inventory and ordering systems are all affected by the lead time; discussion of techniques of shortening the lead time is a subject of most of the chapters in this book.

KEY TERMS

Average or mean 241

Centralized system 252

Decentralized system 252

Dispersion 242

Distribution requirements planning 252

Kanban system 248

Lead time 237

Normal curve or bell curve 241

Normal distribution 241

Order point 237

Permanent or static information 248

Perpetual inventory record 248

Safety factor 244

Safety lead time 239

Safety stock 239

Standard deviation 242

Target-level or maximum-level inventory 250

Two-bin system 248

Variable or dynamic information 249

QUESTIONS

1. What are independent demand items? What two basic ordering systems are used for these items? What are dependent demand items? What system should be used to order these items?

2. a. Using the order point system, when must an order be placed?
   b. Why is safety stock carried?
   c. What is the formula for the order point?
   d. On what two things does the order point depend?
   e. Why is the demand during the lead time important?

3. What are four characteristics of the order point system?

4. What are the five factors that can influence the amount of safety stock that should be carried? How does the length of the lead time affect the safety stock carried?

5. What is a normal distribution? What two characteristics define it? Why is it important in determining safety stock?

6. What is the standard deviation of demand during the lead time? If the standard deviation for the lead-time interval is 100 units, what percentage of the time would the actual demand be equal to ± 100 units? To ± 200 units? To ± 300 units?

7. What is service level?

8. What are the three categories of stockout costs? What do these costs depend upon in any company?

9. Why does the service level depend upon the number of orders per year?

10. If the lead time increases from 1 week to 4 weeks, will the standard deviation of demand during the lead time increase four times? If not, why not?

11. Describe the two-bin system.

12. What kinds of information are shown on a perpetual inventory record?

13. What are the differences between the order point system and the periodic review system regarding when orders are placed and the quantity ordered at any one time?

14. Define the target level used in the periodic review system.

15. Describe how changes in demand will affect the order quantity when using the period review system.

16. What are the objectives of distribution inventory management?

17. If a factory does not supply the customer directly, from where does demand on the factory come? Is it independent or dependent demand?

18. Describe and compare the pull and push systems of inventory management.

19. Describe distribution requirements planning.

20. Grocery stores are an example of well-controlled inventory and replenishment systems. Describe in your own words examples of safety stock, the two-bin system, and the periodic review system, including target level, review period, replenishment period, and order quantity.

21. Describe the advantages and disadvantages of a decentralized distribution system.

22. Describe how the pattern of continuous demand changes from a distribution center to central supply.

PROBLEMS

11.1. For a particular SKU, the lead time is 4 weeks, the average demand is 150 units per week, and safety stock is 100 units. What is the average inventory if 1600 units are ordered at one time? What is the order point?

Answer. Average inventory = 900 units

Order point = 700 units

11.2. For a particular SKU, the lead time is 6 weeks, the average demand is 90 units a week, and safety stock is 200 units. What is the average inventory if 10 weeks' supply is ordered at one time? What is the order point?

11.3. Given the following data, calculate the average x of the distribution and the standard deviation (σ).

Period	Actual Demand	Deviation	Deviation Squared
1	500		
2	600		
3	425		
4	450		
5	600		
6	575		
7	375		
8	475		
9	525		
10	475		
Total			

Answer. Average demand $\bar{x} = 500$ units

Sigma $= 71.59$ units

11.4. Given the following data, calculate the average demand and the standard deviation.

Period	Actual Demand	Deviation	Deviation Squared
1	1700		
2	2100		
3	1900		
4	2200		
5	2000		
6	1800		
7	2100		
8	2300		
9	2100		
10	1800		
Total			

11.5. If sigma is 150 units, and the demand during the lead time is 200 units, calculate the safety stock and order point for:

a. A 50% service level.

b. An 85% service level.

Use the table in Figure 11.5 to help you calculate your answer.

> *Answer.*   a. Safety stock = zero
>
> Order point = 200 units
>
> b. Safety stock = 156 units
>
> Order point = 356 units

11.6. The standard deviation of demand during the lead time is 100 units.

a. Calculate the safety stock required for the following service levels: 75%, 80%, 85%, 90%, 95%, 99.99%.

b. Calculate the *change* in safety stock required to increase the service levels from 75% to 80%, 80% to 85%, 85% to 90%, 90% to 95%, and 95% to 99.99%. What conclusion do you reach?

11.7. For an SKU, the standard deviation of demand during the lead time is 150 units, the annual demand is 10,000 units, and the order quantity is 750 units. Management says it will tolerate only one stockout per year. What safety stock should be carried? What is the average inventory? If the lead time is 2 weeks, what is the order point?

> *Answer.*   Safety stock 213 units
>
> Average inventory = 588 units
>
> Order point 598 units

11.8. A company stocks an SKU with a weekly demand of 225 units and a lead time of 3 weeks. Management will tolerate one stockout per year. If sigma for the lead time is 175 and the order quantity is 800 units, what is the safety stock, the average inventory, and the order point?

11.9. A company stocks an SKU with a weekly demand of 600 units and a lead time of 4 weeks. Management will tolerate one stockout per year. If sigma for the lead time is 100 and the order quantity is 2500 units, what is the safety stock, the average inventory, and the order point?

11.10. If the standard deviation is calculated from weekly demand data at 100 units, what is the equivalent sigma for a 3-week lead time?

Answer.   173 units

11.11. If the safety stock for an item is 200 units and the lead time is 3 weeks, what should the safety stock become if the lead time is extended to 5 weeks?

Answer.   258 units

11.12. If the weekly standard deviation is 180 units, what is it if the lead time is 3 weeks?

11.13. The safety stock on an SKU is set at 200 units. The supplier says it can reduce the lead time from 8 weeks to 6. What should be the new safety stock?

Answer.   173 units

11.14. The safety stock on an SKU is set at 500 units. The supplier says it has to increase the lead time from 4 weeks to 5 weeks. What should be the new safety stock?

11.15. Management has stated that it will tolerate one stockout per year. The forecast of annual demand for a particular SKU is 100,000 units, and it is ordered in quantities of 10,000 units. The lead time is 2 weeks. Sales history for the past 10 weeks follows. Calculate:

a. Sigma for the demand history time interval.

b. Sigma for the lead time interval.

c. The service level.

d. The safety stock required for this service level.

e. The order point.

Week	Actual Demand	Deviation	Deviation Squared
1	2100		
2	1700		
3	2600		
4	1400		
5	1800		
6	2300		
7	2200		
8	1600		
9	2100		
10	2200		
Total			

11.16. If in problem 11.15, management said that it is considering increasing the service level to one stockout every 2 years, what would the new safety stock be? If the cost of carrying inventory on this item is $10 per unit per year, what is the cost of increasing the inventory from one stockout per year to one every 2 years?

11.17. The annual demand for an item is 10,000 units, the order quantity is 250, and the service level is 90%. Calculate the probable number of stockouts per year.

Answer.   4 stockouts per year

11.18. A company that manufactures stoves has one plant and two distribution centers (DCs). Given the following information for the two DCs, calculate the gross requirements, projected available, and planned order releases for the two DCs and the gross requirements, projected available, and planned order releases for the central warehouse.

Distribution Center A
Transit Time: 2 weeks
Order Quantity: 100 units

Week	1	2	3	4	5
Gross Requirements	50	50	85	50	110
In Transit		100			
Projected Available 75					
Planned Order Release					

Distribution Center B
Transit Time: 1 week
Order Quantity: 200 units

Week	1	2	3	4	5
Gross Requirements	120	110	115	100	105
In Transit	200				
Projected Available 50					
Planned Order Release					

Central Supply
Lead Time: 2 weeks
Order Quantity: 500 units

Week	1	2	3	4	5
Gross Requirements					
Scheduled Receipts					
Projected Available 400					
Planned Order Release					

Answer.   Planned order release from central supply: 500 in week 2.

11.19. A company that manufactures snow shovels has one plant and two distribution centers (DCs). Given the following information for the two DCs, calculate the gross requirements, projected available, and planned order releases for the two DCs and the gross requirements, projected available, and planned order releases for the central warehouse.

Distribution Center A
Transit Time: 2 weeks
Order Quantity: 500 units

Week	1	2	3	4	5
Gross Requirements	300	200	150	275	300
In Transit	500				
Projected Available 200					
Planned Order Release					

Distribution Center B
Transit Time: 2 weeks
Order Quantity: 200 units

Week	1	2	3	4	5
Gross Requirements	50	75	100	125	150
In Transit					
Projected Available 150					
Planned Order Release					

Central Supply
Lead Time: 1 week
Order Quantity: 600 units

Week	1	2	3	4	5
Gross Requirements					
Scheduled Receipts					
Projected Available 400					
Planned Order Release					

11.20. A firm orders a number of items from a regional warehouse every 2 weeks. Delivery takes 1 week. Average demand is 200 units per week, and safety stock is held at 2 weeks' supply.

  a. Calculate the target level.

  b. If 600 units are on hand, how many should be ordered?

  Answer.   Target level = 1000 units

  Order quantity = 400 units

11.21. A regional warehouse orders items once a week from a central warehouse. The truck arrives 3 days after the order is placed. The warehouse operates 5 days a week. For a particular brand and size of chicken soup, the demand is fairly steady at 20 cases per day. Safety stock is set at 2 days' supply.

  a. What is the target level?

  b. If the quantity on hand is 90 cases, how many should be ordered?

11.22. A small hardware store uses a periodic review system to control inventory and calculate order quantities. Inventory is reviewed every 2 weeks and there is a 1-week lead time for delivery. Safety stock is set at 1 week's supply. The following table shows the products and the current on-hand inventory. Calculate the target level and order quantity for each of the items. Use 50 weeks per year for your calculations.

Item	Annual Demand	Target Level	On-Hand	Order Quantity
Nut – 6 mm	500		22	
Nut – 8 mm	750		54	
Bolt – 6 mm	200		0	
Bolt – 8 mm	100		6	
Screw #8 – 30 mm	250		12	
Screw #8 – 40 mm	200		8	
Washer – 8 mm	380		20	
Washer – 10 mm	100		5	
Pin – Split	400		40	

11.23. Using the data from problem 11.22, calculate the order quantities that would result if the store switched to a weekly review of inventory. What effect does more frequent ordering have on order quantities?

PHYSICAL INVENTORY AND WAREHOUSE MANAGEMENT

INTRODUCTION

Because inventory is stored in warehouses, the physical management of inventory and warehousing are intimately connected. In some cases, inventory may be stored for an extended time. In other situations, inventory is turned over rapidly, and the warehouse functions as a distribution center.

This chapter will deal with the physical management of inventory in a warehouse, including basic approaches to warehouse layout, the activities involved in handling goods, and the controls necessary to work efficiently while maintaining a desired level of customer service. Inventory accuracy is the responsibility of warehousing, and methods of determining the accuracy of stocks will be covered, along with a description of how to conduct an annual physical audit. The cycle counting method of auditing inventory will show the advantages of timely correction of errors, along with improved error prevention. **Bar coding** and **radio frequency identification (RFID)** will be introduced as a means to improve the speed and accuracy of gathering information.

In a factory, "stores" perform the same functions as warehouses and contain raw materials, work-in-process inventory, finished goods, supplies, and possibly repair parts. Since they perform the same functions, stores and warehouses are treated alike in this chapter.

WAREHOUSING MANAGEMENT

As with other elements in a distribution system, the objective of a warehouse is to minimize cost and maximize customer service. To do this, efficient warehouse operations perform the following:

- Provide timely customer service.
- Keep track of items so they can be found readily and correctly.
- Minimize the total physical effort and thus the cost of moving goods into and out of storage.
- Provide communication links with customers.

The costs of operating a warehouse can be broken down into capital and operating costs. Capital costs are dependent on the type of material to be stored and include those of building space, racking or shelving, tanks or containers, and materials handling equipment. The space needed depends on the peak quantities that must be stored, the methods of storage, and the need for ancillary space for aisles, docks, offices, and so on.

The major operating cost is labor, and the measure of labor productivity is the number of units (e.g., pallets) that an operator can move in a day. The labor cost depends on the type of material handling equipment used, the location and accessibility of stock, warehouse layout, stock location system, and the order-picking system used.

Warehouse Activities

Operating a warehouse involves several processing activities, and the efficient operation of the warehouse depends upon how well these are performed. These activities are as follows:

1. **Receive goods.** The warehouse accepts goods from outside transportation or an attached factory and accepts responsibility for them. This means the warehouse must:

   a. Check the goods against an order and the bill of lading.

   b. Check the quantities.

   c. Check for damage and fill out damage reports if necessary.

   d. Inspect goods if required.

2. **Identify the goods.** Items are identified with the appropriate stock-keeping unit (SKU) number (part number) and the quantity received is recorded.

3. **Dispatch goods to storage.** Goods are sorted and put away.

4. **Hold goods.** Goods are kept in storage and under proper protection until needed.

5. **Pick goods.** Items required from stock must be selected from storage and brought to a marshalling area.

6. **Marshal the shipment.** Goods making up a single order are brought together and checked for omissions or errors. Order records are updated.

7. **Dispatch the shipment.** Orders are packaged, shipping documents prepared, and goods loaded on the right vehicle.

8. **Operate an information system.** A record must be maintained for each item in stock showing the quantity on hand, quantity received, quantity issued, and location in the warehouse. The system can be very simple, depending on a minimum of written information and human memory, or it may be a sophisticated computer-based system.

In various ways, all these activities take place in any warehouse. The complexity depends on the number of SKUs handled, the quantities of each SKU, and the number of orders received and filled. To maximize productivity and minimize cost, warehouse management must work with the following:

1. **Maximum use of space.** Usually the largest capital cost is for space. This means not only floor space but cubic space as well since goods are stored in the space above the floor as well as on it.

2. **Effective use of labor and equipment.** Materials handling equipment represents the second-largest capital cost and labor the largest operating cost. There is a trade-off between the two in that labor costs can be reduced by using more materials handling equipment. Warehouse management will need to

   - Select the best mix of labor and equipment to maximize the overall productivity of the operation.
   - Provide ready access to all SKUs. The SKUs should be easy to identify and find. This requires a good stock identification system, stock location system, and layout.
   - Move goods efficiently. Most of the activity that goes on in a warehouse is materials handling: the movement of goods into and out of stock locations.

Several factors influence effective use of warehouses. Some are

   - Cube utilization and accessibility.
   - Stock location.
   - Order picking and assembly.
   - Packaging.

With the exception of packaging, these are discussed in the following sections.

Cube Utilization and Accessibility

Goods are stored not just on the floor, but in the cubic space of the warehouse. Although the size of a warehouse can be described as so many square feet, warehouse capacity depends on how high goods can be stored and the density of the storage.

Space is also required for aisles, receiving and shipping docks, offices, and order picking and assembly. In calculating the space needed for storage, some design figure for maximum inventory is needed. Suppose that a maximum of 90,000 cartons is to be inventoried and 30 cartons fit on a pallet. Space is needed for 3000 pallets. If pallets are stacked three high, 1000 pallet positions are required. A pallet is a platform usually measuring $48'' \times 40'' \times 4''$.

Pallet positions   Suppose a section of a warehouse is as shown in Figure 12.1. Since the storage area is 48″ deep, the 40″ side is placed along the wall. The pallets cannot be placed tight against one another; a 2″ clearance must be allowed between them so they can be moved. This then leaves room for $(120' \times 12'') \div 42'' = 34.3$, or 34, **pallet positions** along each side of the aisle. Since the pallets are stacked three high, there is room for $34 \times 3 \times 2 = 204$ pallets.

Example Problem

A company wants to store an SKU consisting of 13,000 cartons on pallets, each containing 30 cartons. How many pallet positions are needed if the pallets are stored three high?

ANSWER

Number of pallets required = $13,000 \div 30 = 433.33 \rightarrow 434$ pallets

Number of pallet positions = $434 \div 3 = 144.67 \rightarrow 145$ pallet positions

Notice one pallet position will contain only two pallets.

Accessibility   **Accessibility** means being able to get at the goods wanted with a minimum amount of work. For example, if no other goods had to be moved to reach an SKU, the SKU would be 100% accessible. As long as all pallets contain the same SKU, there is no problem with accessibility. The SKU can be reached without moving any other product. When several SKUs are stored in the area, each product should be accessible with a minimum of difficulty.

Cube utilization   Suppose items are stacked along a wall, as shown in Figure 12.2. There will be excellent accessibility for all items except item 9, but cube utilization is not maximized. **Cube utilization** is the use of space horizontally and vertically. There is room for 30 pallets, but only 21 spaces are being used for a cube utilization of 70%: $(21 \div 30) \times 100\%$. Some method must be devised to increase cube utilization and maintain accessibility. One way is to install tiers of racks so lower pallets can be removed without disturbing the upper ones. This represents a trade-off between the capital cost of the racking and the savings in the operating cost of extra handling. Whether the additional cost is worthwhile will depend on the amount of handling and the savings involved.

FIGURE 12.1 Cube utilization.

1	1	2	3	4					
1	1	2	3	4					10
1	1	2	3	4	5	6	7	8	9

FIGURE 12.2 Cube utilization versus accessibility.

Example Problem

A small warehouse stores five different SKUs in pallet loads. If pallets are stacked three high and there is to be 100% accessibility, how many pallet positions are needed? What is the cube utilization?

SKU A	4 pallets
SKU B	6 pallets
SKU C	14 pallets
SKU D	8 pallets
SKU E	5 pallets
Total	37 pallets

ANSWER

SKU	Pallet positions
A: 4 pallets	2
B: 6 pallets	2
C: 14 pallets	5
D: 8 pallets	3
E: 5 pallets	2
Total	14

In 14 pallet positions, there is room to store $14 \times 3 = 42$ pallets.

Number of pallets actually stored $= 37$

Cube utilization $= (37 \div 42) \times 100\% = 88\%$

Stock Location

Stock location, or warehouse layout, is concerned with the location of individual items in the warehouse. There is no single universal stock location system suitable for all occasions, but there are a number of basic systems that can be used. Which system, or mix of systems, is used depends on the type of goods stored, the type of storage facilities needed, the throughput, and the size of orders. Whatever the system, management must maintain enough inventory of safety and working stock to provide the required level of customer service, keep track of items so they can be found easily, and reduce the total effort required to receive goods, store them, and retrieve them for shipment.

The following are some basic systems of locating stock:

- **Group functionally related items together.** Group together items similar in their use (functionally related). For example, put all hardware items in the same area of the warehouse. If functionally related items are ordered together, order picking is easier. Warehouse personnel become familiar with the locations of items.

- **Group fast-moving items together.** If fast-moving items are placed close to the receiving and shipping area, the work of moving them in and out of storage is reduced. Slower-moving items can be placed in more remote areas of the warehouse.

- **Group physically similar items together.** Physically similar items often require their own particular storage facilities and handling equipment. Small packaged items may require shelving whereas heavy items, such as tires or drums, require different facilities and handling equipment. Frozen foods need freezer storage space.

- **Locate working stock and reserve stock separately.** Relatively small quantities of **working stock**—stock from which withdrawals are made—can be located close to the marshalling and shipping area whereas **reserve stock** used to replenish the working stock can be located more remotely. This allows order picking to occur in a compact area and replenishment of the working stock in bulk by pallet or container load. Warehouses with racking often use the floor level for order picking with reserve stock stored in the upper levels.

There are two basic systems for assigning specific locations to individual stock items: fixed location and floating location. Either system may be used with any of the location systems cited in the preceding paragraphs.

Fixed location In a **fixed-location system,** an SKU is assigned a permanent location or locations, and no other items are stored there. This system makes it possible to store and retrieve items with a minimum of record keeping. In some small, manual systems, no records are kept at all. It is like always keeping cornflakes on the same shelf in the kitchen cupboard at home. Everything is nice and simple so things are readily found. However, fixed-location systems usually have poor cube utilization. If demand is uniform, presumably the average inventory is half the order quantity, and enough space has to be allocated for a full-order quantity. On the average, only 50% of the cube space is utilized. Fixed-location systems are often used in small warehouses where space is not at a premium, where throughput is small, and where there are few SKUs.

Floating location In a **floating-location system,** goods are stored wherever there is appropriate space for them. The same SKU may be stored in several locations at the same time and different locations at different times. The advantage to this system is improved cube utilization. However, it requires accurate and up-to-date information on item location and the availability of empty storage space so items can be put away and retrieved efficiently. Modern warehouses using floating-location systems are usually computer based. The computer assigns free locations to incoming items, remembers what items are on hand and where they are located, and directs the order picker to the right location to find the item. Thus, cube utilization and warehouse efficiency are greatly improved.

Point-of-use storage Sometimes, particularly in repetitive manufacturing and in a JIT environment, inventory is stored close to where it will be used. There are several advantages to **point-of-use storage.**

- Materials are readily accessible to users.
- Material handling is reduced or eliminated.
- Central storage costs are reduced.
- Material is accessible at all times.

This method is excellent as long as inventory is kept low and operating personnel can keep control of inventory records. Sometimes C items are issued as "floor stock," where manufacturing is issued a large quantity, which is used as needed. Inventory records are adjusted when the stock is issued, not when it is used.

Central storage As opposed to point-of-use storage, **central storage** contains all inventory in one central location. There are several advantages:

- Ease of control.
- Inventory record accuracy is easier to maintain.
- Specialized storage can be used.
- Reduced safety stock, since users do not need to carry their own safety stock.

Order Picking and Assembly

Once an order is received, the items on the order must be retrieved from the warehouse, assembled, and prepared for shipment. All these activities involve labor and the movement of goods. The work should be organized to provide the level of customer service required and at least cost. There are several systems that can be used to organize the work, among which are the following:

1. **Area system.** The order picker circulates throughout the warehouse selecting the items on the order, much as a shopper would in a supermarket. The items are then taken to the shipping area for shipment. The order is self-marshalling in that when the order picker is finished, the order is complete. This system is generally used in small warehouses where goods are stored in fixed locations.

2. **Zone system.** The warehouse is divided into zones, and order pickers work only in their own area. An order is divided up by zone, and each order picker selects those items in their zone and sends them to the marshalling area, where the order is assembled for shipment. Each order is handled separately and leaves the zone before another is handled. If applied to the supermarket example above, one individual would go to say the fresh fruit department, another to the freezer section, and so on. They would then marshal the items from each department at the checkout.

    Zones are usually established by grouping together related parts. Parts may be related because of the type of storage needed for them (e.g., freezer storage) or because they are often ordered together.

    A variation of the zone system is to have the order move to the next zone rather than to the marshalling area. By the time it exits the last zone, it is assembled for shipment.

3. **Multi-order system.** This system is the same as the zone system except that, rather than handling individual orders, a number of orders are gathered together and all the items divided by zone. The pickers then circulate through their area, collecting all the items required for that group of orders. The items are then sent to the marshalling area where they are sorted to individual orders for shipment.

The area system is simple to manage and control, but as the warehouse throughput and size increases, it becomes unwieldy. The zone systems break down the order-filling process into a series of smaller areas that can be better managed individually. The multi-order system is probably most suited to the situation in which there are many items or many small orders with few items.

Working stock and reserve stock   In addition to the systems mentioned, reserve stock and working stock may be separated. This is appropriate when the pick unit for a customer's order may be a box or a case that is stored on pallets. A pallet can be moved into the working area by a lift truck and cartons or boxes picked from it. The working stock is located close to the shipping area so the work in picking is reduced. A separate workforce is used to replenish the working stock from the reserve stock.

PHYSICAL CONTROL AND SECURITY

Because inventory is tangible, items have a nasty habit of becoming lost, stray, or stolen, or of disappearing in the night. It is not that people are dishonest, rather that they are forgetful. What is needed is a system that makes it difficult for people to make mistakes or be dishonest. There are several elements that help:

- **A good-part numbering system.** Part numbering was discussed in Chapter 4, on material requirements planning. It must be clear and easy to use for the order pickers and materials handlers.

- **A simple, well-documented transaction system.** When goods are received, issued, or moved in any way, a transaction occurs. There are four steps in any transaction: identify the item, verify the quantity, record the transaction, and physically execute the transaction.

    1. **Identify the item.** Many errors occur because of incorrect identification. When receiving an item, the purchase order, part number, and quantity must be properly identified. When goods are stored, the location must be accurately specified. When issued, the quantity, location, and part number must be recorded.

2. **Verify quantity.** Quantity is verified by a physical count of the item by weighing or by measuring. Sometimes standard-sized containers are useful in counting.

3. **Record the transaction.** Before any transaction is physically carried out, all information about the transaction must be recorded.

4. **Physically execute the transaction.** Move the goods in, about, or out of the storage area.

Limited access   Inventory must be kept in a safe, secure place with **limited** general **access.** It should be locked except during normal working hours. This is less to prevent theft than to ensure people do not take things without completing the transaction steps. If people can wander into the stores area at any time and take something, the transaction system fails.

A well-trained workforce   Not only should the stores staff be well trained in handling and storing material and in recording transactions, but other personnel who interact with stores must be trained to ensure transactions are recorded properly.

INVENTORY RECORD ACCURACY

The usefulness of inventory is directly related to its accuracy. Based on the inventory record, a company determines net requirements for an item, releases orders based on material availability, and performs inventory analysis. If the records are not accurate, there will be shortages of material, disrupted schedules, late deliveries, lost sales, low productivity, and excess inventory (of the wrong things).

These three pieces of information must be accurate: part description (part number), quantity, and location. Accurate inventory records enable firms to:

- **Operate an effective materials management system.** If inventory records are inaccurate, gross-to-net calculations will be in error.
- **Maintain satisfactory customer service.** If records show an item is in inventory when it is not, any order promising that item will be in error.
- **Operate effectively and efficiently.** Planners can plan, confident that the parts will be available.
- **Analyze inventory.** Any analysis of inventory is only as good as the data it is based on.

Inaccurate inventory records will result in the following, with resulting costs to the company.

- Lost sales.
- Shortages and disrupted schedules.
- Excess inventory (of the wrong things).
- Low productivity.
- Poor delivery performance.
- Excessive expediting, since people will always be reacting to a bad situation rather than planning for the future.

Causes of Inventory Record Errors

Poor inventory record accuracy can be caused by many things, but they all result from poor record-keeping systems and poorly trained personnel. Some examples of causes of inventory record error follow:

- Unauthorized withdrawal of material. Employees will often take items from inventory due to problems or shortages in their department. This usually solves a problem for the department but the transactions are often not recorded.
- Unsecured stockroom. Secure stockrooms prevent unauthorized withdrawal, which may or may not be legitimate.

- Poorly trained personnel. Most employees do not realize the consequences of not properly recording transactions or picking the wrong items.

- Inaccurate transaction recording. Errors can occur because of inaccurate piece counts, unrecorded transactions, delay in recording transactions, inaccurate material location, and incorrectly identified parts.

- Poor transaction recording systems. Most systems today are computer based and can provide the means to record transactions properly. Errors, when they occur, are usually the fault of human input to the system. The documentation reporting system should be designed to reduce the likelihood of human error.

- Lack of audit capability. Some program of verifying the inventory counts and locations is necessary. The most popular one today is cycle counting, discussed in the next section.

Measuring Inventory Record Accuracy

Inventory accuracy ideally should be 100%. Banks and other financial institutions reach this level. Other companies can move toward this potential.

Figure 12.3 shows 10 inventory items, their physical count, and the quantity shown on their record. What is the inventory accuracy? The total of all items is the same, but only 2 of the 10 items are correct. Is the accuracy 100% or 20% or something else?

Tolerance   To judge inventory accuracy, a tolerance level for each part must be specified. For some items, this may mean no variance; for others, it may be very difficult or costly to measure and control to 100% accuracy. An example of the latter might be nuts or bolts ordered and used in the thousands. For these reasons, tolerances are set for each item. **Tolerance** is the amount of permissible variation between an inventory record and a physical count.

Tolerances are set on individual items based on value, critical nature of the item, availability, lead time, ability to stop production, safety problems, or the difficulty of getting precise measurement.

Part Number	Inventory Record	Shelf Count
1	100	105
2	100	100
3	100	98
4	100	97
5	100	102
6	100	103
7	100	99
8	100	100
9	100	97
10	100	99
Total	1000	1000

FIGURE 12.3 Inventory record accuracy.

Part Number	Inventory Record	Shelf Count	Tolerance	Within Tolerance	Outside Tolerance
1	100	105	5%	X	
2	100	100	±0%	X	
3	100	98	±3%	X	
4	100	97	±2%		X
5	100	102	±2%	X	
6	100	103	±2%		X
7	100	99	±3%	X	
8	100	100	±0	X	
9	100	97	±5%	X	
10	100	99	±5%	X	
Total	1000	1000			

FIGURE 12.4 Inventory accuracy with tolerance.

Figure 12.4 shows the same data as the previous figure but includes tolerances. This information tells us exactly what inventory accuracy is.

Example Problem

Determine which of the following items are within tolerance. Item A has a tolerance of ±5%; item B, ±2%; item C, ±3%; and item D, ±0%.

Part Number	Shelf Count	Inventory Record	Tolerance
A	1500	1550	±5%
B	120	125	±2%
C	225	230	±3%
D	155	155	±0%

ANSWER

Item A. With a tolerance of ±5%, variance can be up to ±75 units. Item A is within tolerance.

Item B. With a tolerance of ±2%, variance can be up to ±2 units. Item B is outside tolerance.

Item C. With a tolerance of ±3%, variance can be up to ±7 units. Item C is within tolerance.

Item D. With a tolerance of ±0%, variance can be up to ±0 units. Item D is within tolerance.

Auditing Inventory Records

Errors occur, and they must be detected so inventory accuracy is maintained. There are two basic methods of checking the accuracy of inventory records: periodic (usually annual) counts of all items and cyclic (usually daily) counts of specified items. It is important to audit record accuracy, but it is more important to audit the record system to find the causes of inaccuracies and eliminate them. Cycle counting does this; periodic audits tend not to.

Periodic (annual) inventory   The primary purpose of a **periodic (annual) inventory** is to satisfy the financial auditors that the inventory records represent the value of the inventory. To planners, the physical inventory represents an opportunity to correct any inaccuracies in the records. Whereas financial auditors are concerned with the total value of the inventory, planners are concerned with item detail.

The responsibility for taking the physical inventory usually rests with the materials manager, who should ensure that a good plan exists and it is followed. George Plossl once said that taking a physical inventory was like painting; the results depend on good preparation.[1] There are three factors in good preparation: housekeeping, identification, and training.

Housekeeping   Inventory must be sorted and the same parts collected together so they can easily be counted. Sometimes items can be precounted and put into sealed cartons.

Identification   Parts must be clearly identified and tagged with part numbers. This can, and should, be done before the inventory is taken. Personnel who are familiar with parts identification should be involved and all questions resolved before the physical inventory starts.

Training   Those who are going to do the inventory must be properly instructed and trained in taking inventory. Physical inventories are usually taken once a year, and the procedure is not always remembered from year to year.

Process   Taking a physical inventory consists of four steps:

1. Count items and record the count on a ticket left on the item.
2. Verify this count by recounting or by sampling.
3. When the verification is finished, collect the tickets and list the items in each department.
4. Reconcile the inventory records for differences between the physical count and inventory dollars. Financially, this step is the job of accountants, but materials personnel are involved in adjusting item records to reflect what is actually on hand. If major discrepancies exist, they should be checked immediately.

Taking a physical inventory is a time-honored practice in many companies mainly because it has been required for an "accurate" appraisal of inventory value for the annual financial statements. However, taking an annual physical inventory presents several problems. Usually the factory has to be shut down, thus losing production; labor and paperwork are expensive; the job is often done hurriedly and poorly since there is much pressure to get it done and the factory running again. In addition, the people doing the inventory are not used to the job and are prone to making errors. As a result, more errors often are introduced into the records than are eliminated.

Because of these problems, the idea of cycle counting has developed.

Cycle counting   **Cycle counting** is a system of counting inventory continually throughout the year. Physical inventory counts are scheduled so that each item is counted on a predetermined schedule. Depending on their importance, some items are counted

1. George W. Plossl, *Production and Inventory Control, Principles and Techniques*, 2nd ed., Appendix VI: Physical Inventory Techniques. Englewood Cliffs, NJ: Prentice Hall, 1985.

Classification	Number of Items	Count Frequency per Year	Number of Counts per Year	% of Total Counts	Counts per Day
A	1000	12	12,000	58.5	48
B	1500	4	6,000	29.3	24
C	2500	1	2,500	12.2	10
Total counts per year			20,500		
Workdays per year			250		
Counts per day			82		

FIGURE 12.5 Scheduling cycle counts.

frequently throughout the year whereas others are not. The idea is to count selected items each day.

The advantages to cycle counting are as follows:

- Timely detection and correction of problems. The purpose of the count is first to find the cause of error and then to correct the cause so the error is less likely to happen again.
- Complete or partial reduction of lost production. Cycle counting can usually be done without stopping production.
- Use of personnel trained and dedicated to cycle counting. This provides experienced inventory takers who will not make the errors "once-a-year" personnel do. Cycle counters are also trained to identify problems and to correct them.

Count frequency   The basic idea is to count some items each day so all items are counted a predetermined number of times each year. The number of times an item is counted in a year is called its **count frequency.** For an item, the count frequency should increase as the value of the item and number of transactions (chance of error) increase. Several methods can be used to determine the frequency. Three common ones are the ABC method, zone method, and location audit system.

- **ABC method.** This is a popular method. Inventories are classified according to the ABC system (refer to Chapter 9). Some rule is established for count frequency. For example, A items might be counted weekly or monthly; B items, bimonthly or quarterly; and C items, biannually or once a year. On this basis, a count schedule can be established. Figure 12.5 shows an example of a cycle count scheduled using the ABC system. Note that there should be 82 items counted each day, of which 58.5% should be A items or 48 counts per day. This will result in 250 days × 48 A items per day or 12,000 counts per year.

Example Problem

A company has classified its inventory into ABC items. It has decided that A items are to be counted once a month; B items, four times a year; and C items, twice a year. There are 2000 A items, 3000 B items, and 5000 C items in inventory. Develop a schedule of the counts for each class of item.

ANSWER

Classification	Number of Items	Count Frequency per Year	Number of Counts per Year	% of Total Counts	Counts per Day
A	2000	12	24,000	52.2	96
B	3000	4	12,000	26.1	48
C	5000	2	10,000	21.7	40
Total counts per year			46,000		
Workdays per year			250		
Counts per day			184		

- **Zone method.** Items are grouped by zones to make counting more efficient. The system is used when a fixed-location system is used, or when work-in-process or transit inventory is being counted.
- **Location audit system.** In a floating-location system, goods can be stored anywhere, and the system records where they are. Because of human error, these locations may not be 100% correct. If material is mislocated, normal cycle counting may not find it. In using location audits, a predetermined number of stock locations are checked each period. The item numbers of the material in each bin are checked against inventory records to verify stock point locations.

A cycle counting program may include all these methods. The zone method is ideal for fast-moving items. If a floating-location system is used, a combination of ABC and location audit is appropriate.

When to count   Cycle counts can be scheduled at regular intervals or on special occasions. Some selection criteria are as follows:

- **When an order is placed.** Items are counted just before an order is placed. This has the advantage of detecting errors before the order is placed and reducing the amount of work by counting at a time when stock is low. Items with high order frequency have more opportunities for transaction errors. This method counts fast moving items more often.
- **When an order is received.** Inventory is at its lowest level and easiest to count. Also, the effort of going to the stock location is already taking place.
- **When the inventory record reaches zero.** Again, this method has the advantage of reducing work.
- **When a specified number of transactions have occurred.** Errors occur when transactions occur. Fast-moving items have more transactions and are more prone to error.
- **When an error occurs.** A special count is appropriate when an obvious error is detected. This may be a negative balance on the stock record or when no items can be found although the record shows some in stock.

TECHNOLOGY APPLICATIONS

Most imbalances in inventory records are caused by human error. Reading stock codes and entering count quantities can be a source of many errors in any transaction, including during the audit itself. **Bar codes** can reduce this error as they are machine-readable symbols and are widely used to gather information at all levels of retailing, distribution, and manufacturing. The error rate for this method is extremely low compared to human error, which is estimated to be as high as 3% for repetitive entries. Bar codes are standardized by industry and are usually printed on a paper label or tag. Typically they only contain a unique identifier, such as part number, which can be referred to a database for further information, such as price or description, as required. The automotive industry requires labels designed to their specifications for layout and the type of code used. These labels will include, in addition to the product code, the manufacturer, package quantity, date of manufacture, and so forth.

Bar codes are read using a laser light, which picks up the reflection from the bars and spaces on the label and is usually read from a short distance, although range is improving with new designs. The use of bar codes improves the speed of data entry but, more importantly, improves the accuracy of the data retrieved.

Radio frequency identification (RFID) works in a way similar to bar codes, but rather than light it uses reflected radio waves from a small device or tag to receive its information. Unlike bar codes, RFID devices do not require a line of sight between the label and the reader and can accurately identify products that are within containers or otherwise hidden from view. This feature makes RFID suited for use as a security device or under conditions where labels are hard to read or access. Railroads in North America use RFID tags on all their rolling stock and locomotives. Trains are required to work in extreme conditions of dirt and weather and the passive RFID tags located on each side of all vehicles allows the accurate transfer of information such as owner, car number, type of equipment. RFID tags are more costly than printed bar codes, but the price is falling rapidly to only a few cents per tag, encouraging their use in wider applications. Major retailers such as Wal-Mart see the value in this method of gathering information and are demanding its use in many of their products, further reducing costs throughout the supply chain.

Similar to bar codes, most RFID tags only send information limited to an identification number. This identification number is used to reference databases, which have further information about the tagged item. In the railroad system a car's number can reference the car's contents, destination, and so forth, allowing delivery tracking and even safety/hazardous information access. Many organizations use RFID pass cards to access parking or secured areas. The user is identified by the RFID signal and is allowed access accordingly. Management can then easily exercise central control over these areas. When your season parking pass expires access is automatically restricted.

Supply chains are driven by information, and the ability to retrieve timely, accurate, and comprehensive information can lead to cost reductions. In previous chapters lead time was shown to affect inventories and customer service levels. Bar code and RFID technologies can reduce lead time allowing all members of a supply chain to reduce costs while at the same time drastically reducing the number of occurrences of out of stock.

SUMMARY

Previous chapters in this book have used theory and common sense to effectively manage inventories. This chapter looks at the physical handing and storage of inventory. Warehousing is changing from a place to simply store material to a strategic activity affecting a major investment to companies and a significant factor in improving customer service. The basic warehouse activities of receiving, identifying, storing, retrieving, and eventually shipping goods are all still required, but technology and the need for speed in the supply chain are changing the way we do things. "A place for everything and everything in its place" has given way to floating locations and point-of-use storage. As movements are being sped up there is an increasing need for control and security, and it is important that workers know and understand proper procedures and the consequences of errors. To provide high levels of customer service, inventory records must be accurate. Cycle counting improves record accuracy but, more importantly, finds errors in the inventory systems so that processes can be continually improved. Bar code and RFID technologies are widely used in any modern inventory and warehousing system, improving data accuracy and speeding the movement of product.

KEY TERMS

Accessibility 264	Limited access 268
Bar codes 273	Pallet positions 264
Bar coding 262	Periodic (annual) inventory 271
Central storage 266	Point-of-use storage 266
Count frequency 272	Radio frequency identification (RFID) 262
Cube utilization 264	Reserve stock 266
Cycle counting 271	Tolerance 269
Fixed-location system 266	Working stock 265
Floating-location system 266	

QUESTIONS

1. What are four objectives of warehouse operation?
2. Describe the eight warehouse activities as they would apply to a supermarket. Include in your description where each activity takes place and who performs the activity.
3. What are cube utilization and accessibility?
4. Why is stock location important in a warehouse? Name and describe four basic systems of stock location and give examples of each system from a retail setting.
5. Describe fixed and floating systems for assigning locations to SKUs.
6. Name and describe three order-picking systems.
7. What is the difference between working stock and reserve stock?
8. What are the four steps in any transaction?
9. What are some of the results of poor inventory accuracy?
10. Six causes of poor inventory accuracy are discussed in the text. Name and describe each.
11. How should inventory accuracy be measured? What is tolerance? Why is it necessary?
12. What is the basis for setting tolerance?
13. What are the two major purposes of auditing inventory accuracy?
14. In taking a physical inventory, what are the three factors in preparation? Why is good preparation essential?
15. What are the four steps in taking a physical inventory?
16. Describe cycle counting. On what basis can the count frequency be determined?
17. Why is cycle counting a better way to audit inventory records than an annual physical inventory?
18. When are some good times to count inventory?
19. What information is typically stored in a bar code or RFID tag?
20. Give three examples where RFID would be preferred over a bar code.
21. How do bar codes and RFID reduce costs in the supply chain?

PROBLEMS

12.1. A company wants to store an SKU consisting of 5000 cartons on pallets, each containing 30 cartons. They are to be stored three high in the warehouse. How many pallet positions are needed?

   Answer.   56 pallet positions

12.2. A company has 7000 cartons to store on pallets. Each pallet takes 30 cartons, and the cartons are stored four high. How many pallet positions are needed?

12.3. A company has an area for storing pallets as shown in the following diagram. How many pallets measuring 48″ × 40″ can be stored three high if there is a 2″ space between the pallets?

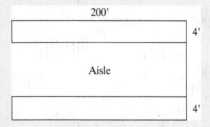

Answer.   342 pallets

12.4. A company has a warehouse with the dimensions shown in the following diagram. How many pallets measuring 48″ × 40″ can be stored three high if there is to be a 2″ space between the pallets?

12.5. A company wishes to store the following SKUs so there is 100% accessibility. The items are stored on pallets that can be stacked three high.

a. How many pallet positions are needed?

b. What is the cube utilization?

c. If the company bought racking for storing the pallets, how many pallet positions are needed to give 100% accessibility?

SKU	Number of Pallets	Pallet Positions Required
A	13	
B	4	
C	8	
D	10	
E	14	
Total		

Answer. a. Pallet positions needed = 19

b. Cube utilization = 86%

c. 17 pallet positions

12.6. A company wants to store the following seven SKUs so there is 100% accessibility. Items are stored on pallets that are stored four high.

a. How many pallet positions are needed?

b. What is the cube utilization?

c. If the company bought racking for storing the pallets, how many pallet positions are needed to give 100% accessibility?

SKU	Number of Pallets	Pallet Positions Required
A	14	
B	17	
C	40	
D	33	
E	55	
F	22	
G	34	
Total		

12.7. a. Which of the following items are within tolerance?

b. What is the percent accuracy by item?

Part Number	Shelf Count	Inventory Record	Difference	% Difference	Tolerance	Within Tolerance?
A	650	635			±3%	
B	1205	1205			±0%	
C	1350	1500			±5%	
D	77	80			±5%	
E	38	40			±3%	
Total						

Answer.   a. A, B, and D are within tolerance.

b. 60%

12.8. a. Which of the following items are within tolerance?

b. What is the percent accuracy by item?

Part Number	Shelf Count	Inventory Record	Difference	% Difference	Tolerance	Within Tolerance?
A	75	80			±3%	
B	120	120			±0%	
C	1400	1500			±5%	
D	75	76			±5%	
E	68	66			±2%	
Total						

12.9. A company does an ABC analysis of its inventory and calculates that out of 5000 items, 22% can be classified as A items, 33% as B items, and the remainder as C items. A decision is made that A items are to be cycle counted once a month, B items every 3 months, and C items twice a year. Calculate the total counts and the counts per day by classification. The company works 5 days per week and 50 weeks per year.

Classification	Number of Items	Count Frequency per Year	Number of Counts per Year	% of Total Counts	Counts per Day
A					
B					
C					
Total counts per year					
Work days per year					
Total counts per day					

Answer. Counts per day A = 53; B = 26; C = 18

12.10. A company does an ABC analysis of its inventory and calculates that out of 10,000 items, 19% can be classified as A items, 30% as B items, and the remainder as C items. A decision is made that A items are to be cycle counted twice a month, B items every 3 months, and C items once a year. Calculate the total counts and the counts per day by classification. There are 250 working days per year.

Classification	Number of Items	Count Frequency per Year	Number of Counts per Year	% of Total Counts	Counts per Day
A					
B					
C					
Total counts per year					
Work days per year					
Total counts per day					

CASE STYDY 12.1

CostMart Warehouse

Amy Gordon could not have been more pleased when she was first appointed as the new inventory management supervisor for the CostMart regional warehouse. She had previously worked part time as a clerk in the local CostMart Department Store while she finished her university degree. After she got the degree, she was named as the section head in charge of roughly one-fourth of the store. Now, a year later, she started to wonder about that old adage, "Be careful what you ask for—you just might get it."

Background

One constant problem Amy had complained about when she was head clerk was the difficulties she had with the warehouse replenishing supplies for her areas of responsibility. She was sure the problem was not hers. The store used point-of-sale terminals, in which the cash register doubled as a computer, instantly recognizing inventory movement. She also realized that shoplifting and other forms of loss were a constant problem in retail stores, so she instructed all her clerks to spot count inventory in their areas of responsibility whenever there was a "lull" in store traffic. The store computer had a built-in program to suggest replenishment orders when the stock reduced to a certain quantity. Amy had learned, of course, that these were only suggestions, since she knew that some items were "faddish" and would have to be ordered sooner or not reordered at all depending on how the fad was progressing. Some items were seasonal in nature, which needed to be accommodated, and she was also aware when an item would go on sale or have a special promotional campaign. These were announced well in advance during the monthly managerial meetings, and she had good estimates as to the projected impact on demand.

It was because she was so effective at managing the inventory in her area that she was so vocal about the problems at the warehouse. It seemed that almost everything she ordered for replenishment from the warehouse was a problem. Some items were late, occasionally by as many as six weeks. Other items were replenished in quantities far larger or smaller than what was ordered, even if they were occasionally delivered on time. It finally seemed to her that every warehouse delivery was a random event instead of the accurate filling of her orders. Her complaints to general management stemmed from the impact of the warehouse problems. Customers in her area were complaining more often and louder as stockouts of various items became a pattern. Several customers had vowed to never again shop at Cost-Mart because of their frustration. One customer even physically dragged Amy over to the sign above the entrance to the store—the one that proclaims "CostMart—Where Customer Service Is in Charge"—and suggested that she could be sued for false advertising.

In other cases, the quantity delivered was two to three times the amount she ordered. She would often have to hold special "unannounced sales" to avoid being burdened with the excessive inventory, especially since one of her performance metrics was inventory dollars. Of course, one of the major performance metrics was profitability, and both the stockouts and unannounced sales impacted that adversely. Finally, after one particularly frustrating day, she told the general manager, "Maybe you should put me in charge of the inventory over at the warehouse. I can control my own area here—I bet I could put that place back in shape pretty fast!" Two weeks later, she was notified she was "promoted" to inventory management supervisor for the warehouse.

The Current Situation

One of the first issues Amy faced was some not-so-subtle resentment from the warehouse general supervisor, Henry "Hank" Anderson. Hank had been a supervisor for over 10 years, having worked his way up from an entry-level handler position. The inventory supervisor position had been created specifically for Amy—Hank had previously had responsibility for the inventory. Their mutual boss had explained to Hank that the reduction in overall responsibility was not a demotion, in that growth in the warehouse made splitting the responsibilities a necessity. Although Hank outwardly acknowledged the explanation, everyone knew that in reality he felt the change was a "slap in the face." That would normally be enough to cause some potential resentment, but in addition, as Hank expressed in the lunchroom one day, "It's not enough that they take some of my job away, but then look who they give it to—a young, inexperienced college kid, and a female at that! Everyone knows you can't learn how to run a warehouse in some stupid college classroom—you have to live it and breathe it to really understand it."

Amy knew that the Hank situation was one she would have to work on, but in the meantime she had to understand how things were run, and specifically why the warehouse was causing all the problems she experienced at the store. Her first stop was to talk to Jane Dawson, who was responsible for processing orders from the store. Jane explained the situation from her perspective.

"I realize how much it must have bothered you to see how your store requests were processed here, but it frustrates me too. I tried to group orders to prioritize due dates and still have a full truckload to send to the store, but I was constantly having problems thrown back at me. Sometimes I was told the warehouse couldn't find the inventory. Other times I was told that the quantity you ordered was less than a full box, and they couldn't (or wouldn't) split the box up, so they were sending the full box. Then they would find something they couldn't find when it was ordered a long time ago, so now that they found it they were sending it. That order would, of course, take up so much room in the truck that something else had to be left behind to be shipped later. Those problems, in combination with true inventory shortages from supplier-missed shipments always seems to put us behind and never able to ship what we are supposed to. None of this seemed to bother Hank too much. Maybe you can do something to change the situation."

Amy's concern with what Jane told her was increased when she asked Jane if she knew the accuracy of their inventory records and was told that she wasn't sure, but the records were probably no more than 50% accurate. How can that be? Amy asked herself. She knew they had recently installed a new computer system to handle the inventory, they did cycle counting on a regular basis, and they used a "home base" storage system, where each SKU had its own designated space in the warehouse racks. She realized she needed to talk to one of the workers. She decided on Carl Carson, who had been with the company for about five years and had a reputation for being a dedicated and effective worker. Amy told Carl what she already knew and asked him if he could provide any additional information.

According to Carl, "What Jane told you is true, but what she didn't tell you is that a lot of it is her fault. If she would only give us some advanced warning about what she wants to send for the next shipment we could probably do a better job of finding the material and staging it. What happens, though, is that she gives us this shipment list out of the blue and expects us to find it all and get it ready in very little time. For one thing, she doesn't understand that it's very impractical to break boxes apart in order to ship just the quantity she wants. We don't have a good way to package the partial box, and an open box increases the chance for the remaining goods to be damaged or get dirty. Even if we had a way to partially package, the time it would take would increase the chance we wouldn't make the shipment on time.

"Then there's the problem of finding material. When supplier shipments come in, they are often for more goods of a given SKU than we have room for on the rack. We put the rest in an overflow area, but it's really hard to keep track of. Even if we locate it in the system correctly, someone will soon move it to get to something behind it. That person will usually forget to record the move in the heat of getting a shipment ready. Since the cycle counts don't find it in the designated rack, the cycle counters adjust the count so the system doesn't even know it exists anymore. You might think we should expand the space in the rack to hold the maximum amount of each SKU, but we would need a warehouse at least double this size to do that—and there's no way management would approve that. I guess the only good thing about the situation is that when we do find some lost material that was requested earlier, we ship it to make up for not shipping it earlier."

Amy was beginning to feel a tightening in her stomach as she realized the extent of the problem here. She almost had to force herself to talk to Crista Chávez, who worked for the purchasing department and was responsible for warehouse ordering. Crista was also considered to be experienced, capable, and dedicated to doing a good job for the company. Crista added the following perspective:

"We have good suppliers, but they're not miracle workers. Since we beat them up so badly on price most of the time, I can understand why they're not interested in doing more than they already are. The problem is we can't seem to get our own house in order to give them a good idea what we need and when we really need it. To do that, we would need to know what the warehouse needs and when, and also the existing inventory of the item. We seem to have no idea what we need, and the inventory records are a joke. I spend most of my day changing order dates, order quantities, or expediting orders to fill a shortage—and often the shortage isn't really a shortage at all. Our only hope has been to order early and increase our order quantities to ensure we have enough safety stock to cover the inventory accuracy problems. I've complained to Hank several times, but all he says is that it's my job to pull the suppliers in line, that the problem is obviously theirs."

At least by this point Amy had a better perspective about the problems. Unfortunately, it was now up to her to fix them. She wished she had never opened her mouth to complain about the problems. Too late for that—she now had to develop a strategy to deal with what she had been handed.

Case Analysis

1. Structure what you think the problems are. Be sure to separate the problems from the symptoms.

2. Assume Amy needs to build a data-based case to convince her boss and start to "win over" Hank. What data should she gather to help her build the case?

3. Develop a model of how you think the warehouse should work in this environment.

4. Develop a time-phased plan to move from the present situation to the model you developed in question 3.

PHYSICAL DISTRIBUTION

INTRODUCTION

Chapter 1 introduced the supply chain concept. It was pointed out that a supply chain is composed of a series of suppliers and customers linked together by a physical distribution system. Usually the supply chain consists of several companies linked in this way. This chapter will discuss the physical distribution aspect of supply chains. Channels of distribution cover the physical movement of goods as well as the change of ownership that occurs throughout the supply chain. The physical distribution system involves the transportation of goods through the various modes, the inventories that exist in transit and in distribution centers, the physical handling of goods, and the need for protective packaging. Multiple warehouse decisions involve the costs associated with adding more warehouses and the effect on customer service.

Physical distribution is the movement of materials from the producer to the consumer. It is the responsibility of the distribution department, which is part of an integrated materials management or logistics system. Figure 13.1 shows the relationship of the various functions in this type of system.

In Figure 13.1, the movement of materials is divided into two functions: physical supply and physical distribution. **Physical supply** is the movement and storage of goods from suppliers to manufacturing. Depending on the conditions of sale, the cost may be paid by either the supplier or the customer, but it is ultimately passed on to the customer. **Physical distribution**, on the other hand, is the movement and storage of finished goods from the end of production to the customer. The particular path in which the goods move—through distribution centers, wholesalers, and retailers—is called the channel of distribution.

Channels of Distribution

A channel of distribution is one or more companies or individuals who participate in the flow of goods and/or services from the producer to the final user or consumer. Sometimes a company delivers directly to its customers, but often it uses other companies or individuals

DOMINANT FLOW OF PRODUCTS AND SERVICES

DOMINANT FLOW OF DEMAND AND DESIGN INFORMATION

FIGURE 13.1 Supply chain (logistics system).

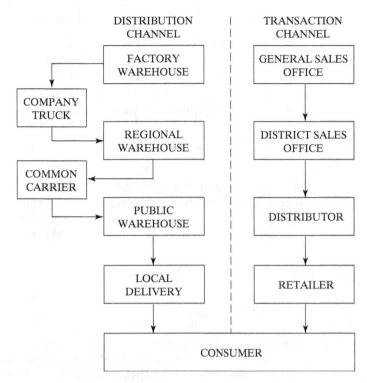

DISTRIBUTION CHANNEL

FACTORY WAREHOUSE

COMPANY TRUCK

REGIONAL WAREHOUSE

COMMON CARRIER

PUBLIC WAREHOUSE

LOCAL DELIVERY

TRANSACTION CHANNEL

GENERAL SALES OFFICE

DISTRICT SALES OFFICE

DISTRIBUTOR

RETAILER

CONSUMER

FIGURE 13.2 Separation of distribution and transaction channels.

to distribute some or all of its products to the final consumer. These companies or individuals are called intermediaries. Examples of intermediaries are wholesalers, agents, transportation companies, and warehousers.

There are really two related channels involved. The **transaction channel** is concerned with the transfer of ownership. Its function is to negotiate, sell, and contract. The **distribution channel** is concerned with the transfer or delivery of the goods or services. The same intermediary may perform both functions, but not necessarily.

Figure 13.2 shows an example of the separation of distribution and transaction channels. The example might be for a company distributing a major appliance such as a refrigerator or stove. In such a system the retailer usually carries only display models. When the customer orders an appliance, delivery is made from either the regional warehouse or the public warehouse.

In this text we are concerned with the distribution channel.

Although it can be argued that one firm's physical supply is another firm's physical distribution, frequently there are important differences, particularly as they relate to the bulk and physical condition of raw materials and finished goods. The logistics problems that occur in moving and storing iron ore are quite different from those that occur in moving sheet steel. These differences influence the design of a logistics system and are important in deciding the location of distribution centers and factories. This text refers to both physical distribution and physical supply as physical distribution, but the differences for any particular company should be remembered.

Physical distribution is vital in our lives. Usually, manufacturers, customers, and potential customers are widely dispersed geographically. If manufacturers serve only their local market, they restrict their potential for growth and profit. By extending its market, a firm can gain economies of scale in manufacturing, reduce the cost of purchases by volume discounts, and improve its profitability. However, to extend markets requires a well-run distribution system. Manufacturing adds form value to a product by taking the raw materials and creating something more useful. Bread is made from grain and is far more useful to humans than the grain itself. Distribution adds place value and time value by placing goods in markets where they are available to the consumer at the time the consumer wants them.

The specific way in which materials move depends upon many factors. For example:

- **The channels of distribution that the firm is using.** For example, producer to wholesaler to retailer to consumer.
- **The types of markets served.** Market characteristics such as the geographic dispersion of the market, the number of customers, and the size of orders.
- **The characteristics of the product.** For example, weight, density, fragility, and perishability.
- **The type of transportation available to move the material.** For example, trains, ships, planes, and trucks.

All are closely related. For instance, florists selling a perishable product to a local market will sell directly and probably use their own trucks. However, a national canning company selling a nonperishable product to a national market through a distribution channel composed of wholesalers and retailers may use trucks and rail transport.

Reverse Logistics

Increasingly, companies must deal with the flow of goods coming back from the final customer or other companies in the distribution channel. This reverse flow of goods is due to the increased quality demands of customers in the goods they purchase and to financial pressures on distributors to reduce slow-moving or unwanted inventories. The twelfth edition of the *APICS Dictionary* defines *reverse logistics* as a complete supply chain dedicated to the reverse flow of products and materials for the purpose of returns, repair, remanufacture, and/or recycling.

In some distribution channels reverse logistics can represent major costs, which are growing partly due to the increased use of the Internet. Sales through the Internet tend to be to a wider geographic area and have a higher-than-normal frequency of returns. The total costs associated with reverse logistics are estimated to exceed $50 billion per year in the United States alone. The amount of goods returned in the publishing industry can be as high as 50% of the original shipments as magazines go out of date, or 90% in the automotive parts industry for the rebuilding of starter motors and alternators. In addition to this, companies are being forced to take responsibility for the return of packaging. There are two main categories of reverse logistics: asset recovery, which is the return of actual products, and green reverse logistics, which represents the responsibility of the supplier to dispose of packaging materials or environmentally sensitive materials such as heavy metals and other restricted materials.

The costs of green reverse logistics are reduced through the use of reusable packaging, such as bins or racks rather than corrugated containers, or an overall reduction in the amount of packaging. Environmentally sensitive materials can be sorted and either reused in manufacturing or disposed of in the most cost-effective method possible, hopefully avoiding landfills. Refillable beverage containers reduce the need for landfill space but impose a cost on the producer for sorting and handling.

Reducing costs associated with asset recovery involves coordinating the handling of the materials, perhaps with the outbound flow of new goods. Information on the returned materials is necessary to ensure proper reuse or disposal of the materials. If the return will generate a credit to the sender, then this will also require information. An example of this working quite well occurs with the replacement of a starter motor in a car. The installer orders a starter motor and installs it. The old starter motor, which should be the same size and model as the replacement, is placed in the original carton and sent back to the supplier for a credit. The carton will have all the information describing the motor and can be used for identification as it travels back to the rebuilder. To reduce costs, distributors will coordinate the outbound shipments of new motors with the return of old motors for rebuilding.

Goods are returned for many reasons, which can include the following:

- Quality demands by final customers (both real and perceived).
- Damaged or defective products.

- Inventories that result from over-forecast demand.
- Seasonal inventories.
- Out-of-date inventories.
- Remanufacturing and refurbishment of products.

Returned goods can be

- Returned to inventory.
- Refurbished for resale.
- Sold into alternate markets.
- Broken down into reusable components.
- Sorted to recover valuable materials (further reducing disposal costs).

If the distribution channel is very simple, as in the return of starter motors example, organizations can reduce reverse logistics costs by coordinating outbound and inbound shipments. Should the distribution channel, however, be very complex, third-party logistics companies (3PLs), discussed later in this chapter, can be used to centralize the handling and disposition of the returned goods. The 3PLs are also very good at providing the information to track the flow of the goods. Companies that take a strategic approach to reverse logistics can recover significant costs and provide better inventory levels throughout the supply chain. These companies will also build reputations as good corporate citizens.

PHYSICAL DISTRIBUTION SYSTEM

Physical distribution is responsible for delivering to the customer what is wanted on time and at minimum cost. The objective of distribution management is to design and operate a distribution system that attains the required level of customer service and does so at least cost. To reach this objective, all activities involved in the movement and storage of goods must be organized into an integrated system.

Activities in the Physical Distribution System

A system is a set of components or activities that interact with each other. A car engine is a system; if any part malfunctions, the performance of the whole engine suffers. In a distribution system, six interrelated activities affect customer service and the cost of providing it:

1. **Transportation.** Transportation involves the various methods of moving goods outside the firm's buildings. For most firms, transportation is the single highest cost in distribution, usually accounting for 30% to 60% of distribution costs. Transportation adds place value to the product.
2. **Distribution inventory.** Distribution inventory includes all finished goods inventory at any point in the distribution system. In cost terms, it is the second most important item in distribution, accounting for about 25% to 30% of the cost of distribution. Inventories create time value by placing the product close to the customer.
3. **Warehouses (distribution centers).** Warehouses are used to store inventory. The management of warehouses makes decisions on site selection; number of distribution centers in the system; layout; and methods of receiving, storing, and retrieving goods.
4. **Materials handling.** Materials handling is the movement and storage of goods inside the distribution center. The type of materials handling equipment used affects the efficiency and cost of operating the distribution center. Materials handling represents a capital cost, and a trade-off exists between this capital cost and the operating costs of the distribution center.
5. **Protective packaging.** Goods moving in a distribution system must be contained, protected, and identified. In addition, goods are moved and stored in packages and must fit into the dimension of the storage spaces and the transportation vehicles.

6. **Order processing and communication.** Order processing includes all activities needed to fill customer orders. Order processing represents a time element in delivery and is an important part of customer service. Many intermediaries are involved in the movement of goods, and good communication is essential to a successful distribution system.

Total-Cost Concept

The objective of distribution management is to provide the required level of customer service at the *least total system cost*. This does not mean that transportation costs or inventory costs or any one activity cost should be a minimum but that the total of all costs should be a minimum. What happens to one activity has an effect on other activities, total system cost, and the service level. Management must treat the system as a whole and understand the relationships among the activities.

Example Problem

A company normally ships a product by rail. Transport by rail costs $200, and the transit time is 10 days. However, the goods can be moved by air at a cost of $1000 and will take 1 day to deliver. The cost of inventory in transit for a particular shipment is $100 per day. What are the costs involved in their decision?

ANSWER

	Rail	Air
Transportation Cost	$ 200	$1000
In-Transit Inventory-Carrying Cost	1000	100
Total	$1200	$1100

There are two related principles illustrated here:

1. **Cost trade-off.** The cost of transportation increased with the use of air transport, but the cost of carrying inventory decreased. There was a cost trade-off between the two.

2. **Total cost.** By considering all of the costs and not just any one cost, the total system cost is reduced. Note also that even though no cost is attributed to it, customer service is improved by reducing the transit time. The total cost should also reflect the effect of the decision on other departments, such as production and marketing.

The preceding example does not mean that using faster transport always results in savings. For example, if the goods being moved are of low value and inventory-carrying cost is only $10 per day, rail will be cheaper. In addition, other costs may have to be considered.

Most of the decisions in distribution, and indeed much of what is done in business and in our own lives, involve trade-offs and an appreciation of the total costs involved. In this section, the emphasis is on the costs and trade-offs incurred and on improvement in customer service. Generally, but not always, an increase in customer service requires an increase in cost, which is one of the major trade-offs.

Global Distribution

Global distribution is the movement of goods to and from locations around the world. Organizations are moving toward the global sourcing and selling of goods due to lower manufacturing costs in other nations and the ability of both foreign and domestic manufacturers to supply a global market. Global distribution of goods is similar to movement within North America since information is needed to control inventories, customer needs must be satisfied, and carriers depend on communications to reach their destinations. Some differences, however, must be taken into consideration when dealing with organizations around the world: distance, language, culture, currency, and measurement.

The longer the distance that goods must travel, the greater the time to reach markets. Such distances may require conducting business across different time zones. As the goods cross borders, the languages spoken may differ for the manufacturer, warehouse agencies, and carriers. Cultural differences can include the methods of conducting business, the occurrence of religious holidays, and the local work ethic. Currency exchange and international fund transfers are becoming increasingly easy; however, fluctuations in currencies can change costs dramatically and must be taken into account when assessing the risks involved in deciding where to source goods. Measurement systems will differ around the world, and a good example of this is weight. A ton is 2000 pounds, a long ton is 2240 pounds, and a metric tonne is 2205 pounds. The units of measure for weight can depend on the country that is handling the goods. Overall, global distribution can be very complicated for individuals and companies facing this challenge.

Fortunately, technologies and systems in place now can alleviate some of these problems. Time is less of an issue. The Internet allows companies to conduct business at all hours of the day. With written Internet transactions, fewer misinterpretations of order information such as sizes, quantities, and descriptions occur. International standards help solve many distribution issues The International Organization for Standardization (ISO) (discussed in Chapter 16), for example, has established standards for ocean shipping containers that allow the seamless handling of goods from ship, to rail, to truck across virtually all nations. Some standards have a long history. As early as 1936, Incoterms were developed by the Paris-based International Chamber of Commerce to provide internationally accepted regulations for trade terms such as export packing costs, customs clearance, inland and ocean transportation costs, and damage insurance. Incoterms are explained later in this chapter.

Global distribution will continue to grow, become easier, and increasingly allow companies to manufacture goods at competitive rates and to sell their products in a global market. As global distribution becomes essential, people working in distribution will need to expand their knowledge of global-based supply systems and international business practices to remain effective.

3PLs: Third Party Logistics Providers

Buyers and suppliers of goods often work with a third party who is in a position to offer physical distribution services at less cost than the buyer or seller would incur performing these services themselves. Beyond providing delivery services, a 3PL supplies services such as warehousing, electronic data interchange (EDI), packaging, warehousing, freight forwarding, and delivery. They can provide these services at an economical rate since they already have the infrastructure in place and combine one company's distribution needs with those of their other clients. FedEx is an example of this, providing customers over geographically dispersed markets with local warehousing, inventory management, labeling requirements, and more.

3PLs allow businesses to concentrate on their core competencies and leave the problems associated with delivering or servicing their products to someone else. They also react well to problems of scale where the volumes shipped or the number of customers either increase or decrease. 3PLs are especially effective in emerging markets where a supplier needs the capabilities of a local warehouse but does not have the resources or volumes to justify their own facility.

INTERFACES

By taking the goods produced by manufacturing and delivering them to the customer, physical distribution provides a bridge between marketing and production. As such, there are several important interfaces among physical distribution and production and marketing.

Marketing

Although physical distribution interacts with all departments in a business, its closest relationship is probably with marketing. Indeed, physical distribution is often thought of as a marketing subject, not as part of materials management or logistics.

The "marketing mix" is made up of product, promotion, price, and place, and the latter is created by physical distribution. Marketing is responsible for transferring ownership.

This is accomplished by such methods as personal selling, advertising, sales promotion, merchandising, and pricing. Physical distribution is responsible for giving the customer possession of the goods and does so by operating distribution centers, transportation systems, inventories, and order processing systems. It has the responsibility of meeting the customer service levels established by marketing and the senior management of the firm.

Physical distribution contributes to creating demand. Prompt delivery, product availability, and accurate order filling are important competitive tools in promoting a firm's products. The distribution system is a cost, so its efficiency and effectiveness influence the company's ability to price competitively. All of these affect company profits.

Production

Physical supply establishes the flow of material into the production process. The service level must usually be very high because the cost of interrupted production schedules caused by raw material shortages is usually enormous.

There are many factors involved in selecting a site for a factory, but an important one is the cost and availability of transportation for raw materials to the factory and the movement of finished goods to the marketplace. Sometimes the location of factories is decided largely by the sources and transportation links of raw materials. This is particularly true where the raw materials are bulky and of relatively low value compared to the finished product. The location of steel mills on the Great Lakes is a good example. The basic raw material, iron ore, is bulky, heavy, and of low unit value. Transportation costs must be kept low to make a steel mill profitable. Iron ore from mines in either northern Quebec or Minnesota is transported to the mills by boat, the least costly mode of transportation. In other cases, the availability of low-cost transportation makes it possible to locate in areas remote from markets, but where labor is inexpensive.

Unless a firm is delivering finished goods directly to a customer, demand on the factory is created by the distribution center orders and not directly by the final customer. As noted in Chapter 11, this can have severe implications on the demand pattern at the factory. Although the demand from customers may be relatively uniform, the factory reacts to the demand from the distribution centers for replenishment stock. If the distribution centers are using an order point system, the demand on the factory will not be uniform and will be dependent rather than independent. The distribution system is the factory's customer, and the way that the distribution system interfaces with the factory will influence the efficiency of factory operations.

TRANSPORTATION

Transportation is an essential ingredient in the economic development of any area. It brings together raw materials for production of marketable commodities and distributes the products of industry to the marketplace. As such, it is a major contributor to the economic and social fabric of a society and aids economic development of regional areas.

The carriers of transportation can be divided into five basic modes:

1. Rail.
2. Road, including trucks, buses, and automobiles.
3. Air.
4. Water, including oceangoing, inland, and coastal ships.
5. Pipeline.

Each mode has different cost and service characteristics. These determine which method is appropriate for the types of goods to be moved. Certain types of traffic are simply more logically moved within one mode than they are in another. For example, trucks are best suited to moving small quantities to widely dispersed markets, but trains are best suited to moving large quantities of bulky cargo, such as grain.

Costs of Carriage

To provide transportation service, any carrier, whatever mode, must have certain basic physical elements. These elements are ways, terminals, and vehicles. Each results in a cost to the carrier and, depending on the mode and the carrier, may be either capital (fixed) or operating (variable) costs. **Fixed costs** are costs that do not change with the volume of goods carried. The purchase cost of a truck owned by the carrier is a fixed cost. No matter how much it is used, the cost of the vehicle does not change. However, many costs of operation, such as fuel, maintenance, and driver's wages, depend on the use made of the truck. These are **variable costs**.

Ways are the paths over which the carrier operates. They include the right-of-way (land area being used), plus any roadbed, tracks, or other physical facilities needed on the right-of-way. The nature of the way and how it is paid for vary with the mode. Ways may be owned and operated by the government or by the carrier or provided by nature.

Terminals are places where carriers load and unload goods to and from vehicles and make connections between local pickup and delivery service and line-haul service. Other functions performed at terminals are weighing; connecting with other routes and carriers; vehicle routing, dispatching, and maintenance; and administration and paperwork. The nature, size, and complexity of the terminal varies with the mode and size of the firm and the types of goods carried. Terminals are generally owned and operated by the carrier but, in some special circumstances, may be publicly owned and operated.

Vehicles of various types are used in all modes except pipelines. They serve as carrying and power units to move the goods over the ways. The carrier usually owns or leases the vehicles, although sometimes the shipper owns or leases them.

Besides ways, terminals, and vehicles, a carrier will have other costs such as maintenance, labor, fuel, and administration. These are generally part of operating costs and may be fixed or variable.

Rail

Railways provide their own ways, terminals, and vehicles, all of which represent a large capital investment. This means that most of the total cost of operating a railway is fixed. Thus, railways must have a high volume of traffic to absorb the fixed costs. They will not want to install and operate rail lines unless there is a large enough volume of traffic. Trains move goods by trainloads composed of perhaps a hundred cars each with a carrying capacity in the order of 160,000 pounds.

Therefore, railways are best able to move large volumes of bulky goods over long distances. Their frequency of departure will be less than trucks, which can move when one truck is loaded. Rail speed is good over long distances, the service is generally reliable, and trains are flexible about the goods they can carry. Train service is cheaper than road service for large quantities of bulky commodities, such as coal, grain, potash, and containers moved over long distances.

Road

Trucks do not provide their own ways (roads and highways) but pay a fee to the government as license, gasoline, and other taxes and tolls for the use of roads. Terminals are usually owned and operated by the carrier but may be either privately owned or owned by the government. Vehicles are owned, or leased, and operated by the carrier. If owned, they are a major capital expense. However, in comparison to other modes, the cost of a vehicle is small. This means that for road carriers most of their costs are operating (variable) in nature.

Trucks can provide door-to-door service as long as there is a suitable surface on which to drive. In the United States and Canada, the road network is superb. The unit of movement is a truckload, which can be up to about 100,000 pounds. These two factors—the excellent road system and the relatively small unit of movement—mean that trucks can provide fast flexible service almost anywhere in North America. Trucks are particularly suited to distribution of relatively small-volume goods to a dispersed market.

Air

Air transport does not have ways in the sense of fixed physical roadbeds, but it does require an airway system that includes air traffic control and navigation systems. These systems are usually provided by the government. Carriers pay a user charge that is a variable cost to them. Terminals include all of the airport facilities, most of which are provided by the government. However, carriers are usually responsible for providing their own cargo terminals and maintenance facilities, either by owning or renting the space. The carrier provides the aircraft through either ownership or leasing. The aircraft are expensive and are the single most important cost element for the airline. Since operating costs are high, airlines' costs are mainly variable.

The main advantage of air transport is speed of service, especially over long distances. Most cargo travels in passenger aircraft, and thus many delivery schedules are tied to those of passenger service. The service is flexible about destination provided there is a suitable landing strip. Transportation cost for air cargo is higher than for other modes. For these reasons, air transport is most often suitable for high-value, low-weight cargo or for emergency items.

Water

Waterways are provided by nature or by nature with the assistance of the government. The St. Lawrence Seaway system is an example of this. The carrier thus has no capital cost in providing the ways but may have to pay a fee for using the waterway.

Terminals may be provided by the government but are increasingly privately owned. In either case, the carrier will pay a fee to use them. Thus, terminals are mainly a variable cost. Vehicles (ships) are either owned or leased by the carrier and represent the major capital or fixed cost to the carrier.

The main advantage of water transport is cost. Operating costs are low, and since the ships have a relatively large capacity, the fixed costs can be absorbed over large volumes. Ships are slow and operate door to door only if the shipper and the consignee are on a waterway. Therefore, water transportation is most useful for moving low-value, bulky cargo over relatively long distances where waterways are available.

Pipelines

Pipelines are unique among the modes of transportation in that they move only gas, oil, and refined products on a widespread basis. As such, they are of little interest to most users of transportation. Capital costs for ways and pipelines are high and are borne by the carrier, but operating costs are very low.

LEGAL TYPES OF CARRIAGE

Carriers are legally classified as public (for hire) or private (not for hire). In the latter, individuals or firms own or lease their vehicles and use them to move their own goods. Public transport, on the other hand, is in the business of hauling for others for pay. All modes of transport have public and for-hire carriers.

For-hire carriers are subject to economic regulation by federal, state, or municipal governments. Depending on the jurisdiction, economic regulation may be more or less severe, and in recent years, there has been a strong move by government to reduce regulations. Economic regulation has centered on three areas:

1. Regulation of rates.
2. Control of routes and service levels.
3. Control of market entry and exit.

Private carriers are not subject to economic regulation but, like public carriers, are regulated in such matters as public safety, license fees, and taxes.

For Hire

A for-hire carrier may carry goods for the public as a common carrier or under contract to a specified shipper.

Common carriers make a standing offer to serve the public. This means that whatever products they offer to carry will be carried for anyone wanting their service. With some minor exceptions, they can carry only those commodities they are licensed to carry. For instance, a household mover cannot carry gravel or fresh vegetables. Common carriers provide the following:

- Service available to the public.
- Service to designated points or in designated areas.
- Scheduled service.
- Service of a given class of movement or commodity.

Contract carriers haul only for those with whom they have a specific formal contract of service, not the general public. Contract carriers offer a service according to a contractual agreement signed with a specific shipper. The contract specifies the character of the service, performance, and charges.

Private

Private carriers own or lease their equipment and operate it themselves. This means investment in equipment, insurance, and maintenance expense. A company normally considers operating its own fleet only if the volume of transport is high enough to justify the capital expense.

Service Capability

Service capability depends on the availability of transportation service, which in turn depends on the control that the shipper has over the transportation agency. The shipper must go to the marketplace to hire a common carrier and is subject to the schedules and regulations of that carrier. Least control is exercised over common carriers. Shippers can exercise most control over their own vehicles and have the highest service capability with private carriage.

Other Transportation Agencies

There are several transportation agencies that use the various modes or combinations of the modes. Some of these are the post office, freight forwarders, couriers, and shippers. They all provide a transportation service, usually as a common carrier. They may own the vehicles, or they may contract with carriers to move their goods. Usually, they consolidate small shipments into large shipments to make economic loads.

TRANSPORTATION COST ELEMENTS

There are four basic cost elements in transportation. Knowledge of these costs enables a shipper to get a better price by selecting the right shipping mode. The four basic costs are as follows:

1. Line haul.
2. Pickup and delivery.
3. Terminal handling.
4. Billing and collecting.

We will use motor transport as an example, but the principles are the same for all modes.

FIGURE 13.3 Shipping patterns.

Goods move either directly from the shipper to the consignee or through a terminal. In the latter, they are picked up in some vehicle suitable for short-haul local travel. They are then delivered to a terminal where they are sorted according to destination and loaded onto highway vehicles for travel to a destination terminal. There, they are again sorted, loaded on local delivery trucks, and taken to the consignee. Figure 13.3 shows this pattern schematically.

Line-Haul Costs

When goods are shipped, they are sent in a moving container that has a weight and volume capacity. The carrier, private or for hire, has basic costs to move this container, which exist whether the container is full or not. For a truck, these include such items as the driver's wages and depreciation due to usage. These costs vary with the distance traveled, not the weight carried. The carrier has essentially the same basic costs whether the truck moves full or empty. If it is half full, the basic costs must be spread over only those goods in the truck.

Therefore, total line-haul costs vary directly with the distance shipped, not on the weight shipped. For example, if for a given commodity the line-haul cost is $3 per mile and the distance is 100 miles, the total line-haul cost is $300. If the shipper sends 50,000 pounds, the total line-haul cost is the same as if 10,000 pounds is sent. However, the line-haul costs (LHC) per hundredweight (cwt.) is different.

$$\text{LHC/cwt.} = \frac{300}{500}$$

$$= \$0.60 \text{ per cwt. } [\text{for } 50{,}000 \text{ lbs. } (500 \text{ cwt.})]$$

$$\text{LHC/cwt.} = \frac{300}{100}$$

$$= \$3 \text{ per cwt. } [\text{for } 10{,}000 \text{ lbs. } (100 \text{ cwt.})]$$

Thus, the **total line-haul cost** varies with (a) the cost per mile and (b) the distance moved. However, the **line-haul cost per hundredweight** varies with (a) the cost per mile, (b) the distance moved, and (c) the weight moved.

Example Problem

For a particular commodity, the line-haul cost is $2.50 per mile. For a trip of 500 miles and a shipment of 600 cwt., what is the cost of shipping per cwt.? If the shipment is increased to 1000 cwt., what is the saving in cost per cwt.?

ANSWER

$$\text{Total line} - \text{haul cost} = \$2.5 \times 500 = \$1250$$

$$\text{Cost per cwt.} = \$1250 \div 600 = \$2.083$$

If 1000 cwt. is shipped:

$$\text{Cost per cwt.} = \$1250 \div 1000 = \$1.25$$

$$\text{Saving per cwt.} = \$2.08 - \$1.25 = \$0.83$$

The carrier has two limitations or capacity restrictions on how much can be moved on any one trip: the weight limitation and the cubic volume limitation of the vehicle. With some commodities, their density is such that the volume limitation is reached before the weight limitation. If the shipper wants to ship more, a method of increasing the density of the goods must be found. This is one reason that some lightweight products are made so they nest (e.g., disposable cups) and bicycles and wheelbarrows are shipped in an unassembled state. This is not to frustrate us poor mortals who try to assemble them but to increase the density of the product so more weight can be shipped in a given vehicle. The same principle applies to goods stored in distribution centers. The more compact they are, the more can be stored in a given space. Therefore, if shippers want to reduce transportation cost, they should (a) increase the weight shipped and (b) maximize density.

Example Problem

A company ships barbecues fully assembled. The average line-haul cost per shipment is $12.50 per mile, and the truck carries 100 assembled barbecues. The company decides to ship the barbecues unassembled and figures it can ship 500 barbecues in a truck. Calculate the line-haul cost per barbecue assembled and unassembled. If the average trip is 300 miles, calculate the saving per barbecue.

Answer

Line-haul cost assembled = $12.50 ÷ 100 = $0.125 per barbecue per mile

Line-haul cost unassembled = $12.50 ÷ 500 = $0.025 per barbecue per mile

Physical Distribution

Saving per mile = $0.125 − 0.025 = $0.10

Trip saving = 300 × $0.10 = $30.00 per barbecue

Pickup and Delivery Costs

Pickup and delivery costs are similar to line-haul costs except that the cost depends more on the time spent than on the distance traveled. The carrier will charge for each pickup and the weight picked up. If a shipper is making several shipments, it will be less expensive if they are consolidated and picked up on one trip.

Terminal Handling

Terminal-handling costs depend on the number of times a shipment must be loaded, handled, and unloaded. If full truckloads are shipped, the goods do not need to be handled in the terminal but can go directly to the consignee. If part loads are shipped, they must be taken to the terminal, unloaded, sorted, and loaded onto a highway vehicle. At the destination, the goods must be unloaded, sorted, and loaded onto a local delivery vehicle.

Each individual parcel must be handled. A shipper who has many customers, each ordering small quantities, will expect the terminal-handling costs to be high because there will be a handling charge for each package.

The basic rule for reducing terminal-handling costs is to reduce handling effort by consolidating shipments into fewer parcels.

Billing and Collecting

Every time a shipment is made, paperwork must be done and an invoice made out. **Billing and collecting costs** can be reduced by consolidating shipments and reducing the pickup frequency.

Total Transportation Costs

The total cost of transportation consists of line-haul, pickup and delivery, terminal-handling, and billing and collecting costs. To reduce shipping costs, the shipper needs to do the following:

- Decrease line-haul costs by increasing the weight shipped.
- Decrease pickup and delivery cost by reducing the number of pickups. This can be done by consolidating and increasing the weight per pickup.

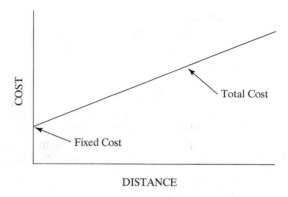

FIGURE 13.4 Distance versus cost of carriage.

- Decrease terminal-handling costs by decreasing the number of parcels by consolidating shipments.
- Decrease billing and collecting costs by consolidating shipments.

For any given shipment, the line-haul costs vary with the distance shipped. However, the pickup and delivery, terminal-handling, and billing costs are fixed. The total cost for any given shipment thus has a fixed cost and a variable cost associated with it. This relationship is shown in Figure 13.4. The carrier will consider this relationship and either charge a fixed cost plus so much per mile or offer a tapered rate. In the latter, the cost per mile for short distances far exceeds that for longer distances.

The rate charged by a carrier will also vary with the commodity shipped and will depend upon the following:

- **Value.** A carrier's liability for damage will be greater the more valuable the item.
- **Density.** The more dense the item, the greater the weight that can be carried in a given vehicle.
- **Perishability.** Perishable goods often require special equipment and methods of handling.
- **Packaging.** The method of packaging influences the risk of damage and breakage.

In addition, carriers have two rate structures, one based on full loads called truckload (TL) or carload (CL) and one based on less than truckload (LTL) and less than carload (LCL). For any given commodity, the LTL rates can be up to 100% higher than the TL rates. The basic reason for this differential lies in the extra pickup and delivery, terminal-handling and billing, and collection costs. Truckers, airlines, and water carriers accept less than full loads, but usually the railways do not accept LCL shipments.

Transportation Terms

The transporters of goods in North America have for many years used terminology to specify who pays the cost of transportation and who owns the goods in-transit. The four basic terms in common use are based on the term *FOB, freight on board*, which specifies who is responsible for the goods and pays the insurance against risk for the goods. It is interesting that many of the terms come from a long history of marine shipments. We "ship" things to people who receive them on a "dock." A collection of docks is called a shipping "bay."

The four FOB terms used allow astute buyers and sellers to take advantage of their own area of expertise to keep costs as low as possible. A small company with a low shipping volume often pays higher transportation fees than a large supplier. In the case of a small buyer, it is often better to get the shipper to pay for transportation and bill the buyer at a lower total cost. A company with their own fleet of trucks would want to take responsibility for the freight charges.

FOB shipping point, freight collect. The seller makes the goods available at their dock and all risk and costs of transportation are assumed at this point by the buyer.

FOB shipping point, freight pre-paid. The seller delivers the goods to the buyer but the buyer has the risk of the goods while in-transit and pays the insurance.

FOB destination, freight pre-paid.   The seller is responsible for all costs of risk and transportation to the buyer's location.

FOB destination, freight collect.   The seller is responsible for the risk to the buyer's location but the buyer is responsible for the freight.

The term *FOB* indicates the point of transfer of ownership for North American shipments only and is contrary to the international standards set out in Incoterms, which is discussed in the next section. Using the North American FOB interpretation of shipping terms outside of North America can lead to serious costs and risks for any shipper.

Incoterms

International Commercial Terminology (Incoterms) was developed by the International Chamber of Commerce in 1936 to establish standards governing the responsibilities between buyers and sellers when transporting goods within and across international boundaries. The terms have been subsequently updated; the following definitions are based on Incoterms 2000. In-transit goods represent a major investment to buyer and seller and run many risks of damage or loss. It is essential that a clear understanding exists as to who actually owns the goods at a given time or location in the supply chain and who will pay the expenses incurred to transport the goods. Another risk when transporting hazardous goods is the potential for accidents or spills and the potential environmental cleanup costs.

There are three responsibilities to be addressed:

- Cost of transportation of the goods.
- Ownership or insurance against risk of the goods.
- Preparation of customs documentation for the movement of the goods.

Incoterms are divided into four groups, which progressively increase the sellers' responsibility for costs and risks.

Group E: Departure

EXW (named place): Ex Works.   The seller makes the goods available at their premises. The buyer is responsible for all charges to transport and insure the goods. including customs documentation.

Group F: Main carriage unpaid

FCA (named carrier): Free carrier.   The seller is responsible for preparing the export documentation and delivering the goods to the transporter named after the Incoterm. The buyer then takes responsibility for all subsequent costs.

FAS (named ship): Free alongside ship.   This term is strictly used for maritime transportation where the seller is responsible for export documentation and the transportation of the goods to the point of shiploading at the port of export.

FOB (named ship): Free on board.   This term is strictly used for maritime transportation where the seller is responsible for export documentation and delivery of the goods on to the named vessel or "past the ship's rail."

Note that this term is not the same as the term *FOB* introduced earlier for North American freight. As we continue to trade goods internationally the use of Incoterms will become more widely used to correctly identify costs, risks, and ownership of goods in-transit.

Group C: Main Carriage Paid

CFR (named destination port): Cost and freight.   The seller is responsible for export documentation and pays for the freight to the port of destination. However, when the goods "pass the ship's rail" in the port of shipment the buyer assumes the risk for the goods. This term is used in maritime transportation only.

CIF (named destination port): Cost, insurance, and freight.   This maritime-use-only term is the same as CFR except the seller is also responsible for the insurance (or risk) associated with the goods to the named destination port.

CPT (named destination port): Carriage paid to.   This term is used for air, truck, and multi-modal transportation such as containers where a "ship's rail" has no significance. The seller is responsible for export documentation and pays the freight to the named destination. However, the risk passes to the buyer when they are handed over to the first carrier.

CIP (named destination): Carriage and insurance paid to.   This term is used for air, truck, and multi-modal shipments and is similar to the maritime term *CIF*. The seller pays the costs of transportation to the destination and prepares the export documentation. Risk transfers to the buyer when the goods are handed over to the first carrier.

Group D: Arrival

DAF (named place): Delivered at frontier.   This term is used for shipping goods between adjoining countries where the seller prepares the export documentation and transportation cost to deliver the goods to the border entry. Risk and costs of transportation are then paid from the point of entry to their factory by the buyer.

DES (named ship and port): Delivered ex ship.   This maritime-use term holds the seller to provide documentation to get the goods off the ship at the named port and the costs of shipping up to that point. The seller assumes risk and pays for the unloading of the ship and any further customs documentation. This term is most often used in shipping bulk commodities where the seller either owns or charters their own vessel.

DEQ (named destination): Delivered ex quay.   This term is similar to DES; however, the transfer of risk does not occur until the goods have been unloaded from the ship.

DDU (named destination): Delivered duty unpaid.   This term can be used for any mode of transportation. The seller is responsible for all risks and costs of transportation to the named destination; however, the buyer is responsible for all duties and taxes.

DDP (named destination): Delivered duty paid.   This term, which can be used for any mode of transportation, has the seller paying all the costs of shipping, export documentation, and any duties to the named destination, which is typically the buyer.

WAREHOUSING

Chapter 12 discussed the management of warehouses. This section is concerned with the role of warehouses in a physical distribution system.

Warehouses include plant warehouses, regional warehouses, and local warehouses. They may be owned and operated by the supplier or intermediaries such as wholesalers, or they may be public warehouses. The latter offer a general service to their public, which includes providing storage space and warehouse services. Some warehouses specialize in the kinds of services they offer and the goods they store. A freezer storage is an example. The service functions that warehouses perform can be classified into two kinds:

1. The **general warehouse** is where goods are stored for long periods and where the prime purpose is to protect goods until they are needed. There is minimal handling, movement, and relationship to transportation. Furniture storage or a depository for documents are examples of this type of storage. It is also the type used for inventories accumulated in anticipation of seasonal sales.

2. The **distribution warehouse** has a dynamic purpose of movement and mixing. Goods are received in large-volume uniform lots, stored briefly, and then broken down into small individual orders of different items required by the customer in the marketplace. The emphasis is on movement and handling rather than on storage. This type of warehouse is widely used in distribution systems. The size of the warehouse is not so much its physical size as it is the throughput, or volume of traffic handled.

As discussed in the previous chapter, warehouses or distribution centers are places where raw materials, semi-finished, or finished goods are stored. They represent an interruption in the flow of material and thus add cost to the system. Items should be warehoused only if there is an offsetting benefit gained from storing them.

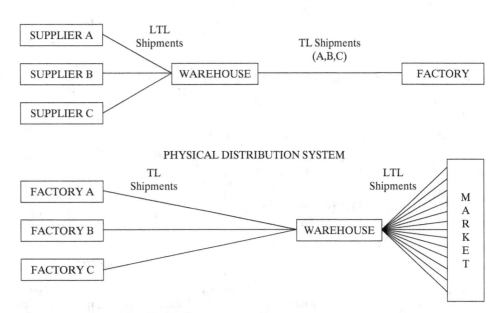

FIGURE 13.5 Transportation consolidation.

Role of Warehouses

Warehouses serve three important roles: transportation consolidation, product mixing, and service.

Transportation consolidation   As shown in the preceding section, transportation costs can be reduced by using warehouses. This is accomplished by consolidating small (LTL) shipments into large (TL) shipments.

Consolidation can occur in both the supply and distribution systems. In physical supply, LTL shipments from several suppliers can be consolidated at a warehouse before being shipped as TL to the factory. In physical distribution, TL shipments can be made to a distant warehouse and LTL shipments made to local users. Figure 13.5 shows the two situations graphically. Transportation consolidation in physical distribution is sometimes called **break-bulk**, which means the bulk (TL) shipments from factories to distribution centers are divided into small shipments going to local markets.

Product mixing   Although transportation consolidation is concerned with reduction of transportation costs, product mixing deals with the grouping of different items into an order and the economies that warehouses can provide in doing this. When customers place orders, they often want a mix of products that are produced in different locations.

Without a distribution center, customers would have to order from each source and pay for LTL transport from each source. Using a distribution center, orders can be placed and delivered from a central location. Figure 13.6 illustrates the concept.

Service   Distribution centers improve customer service by providing place utility. Goods are positioned close to markets so the markets can be served more quickly.

Warehousing and Transportation Costs

Any distribution system should try to provide the highest service level (the number of orders delivered in a specified time) at the lowest possible cost. The particular shipping pattern will depend largely upon the following:

- Number of customers.
- Geographic distribution of the customers.

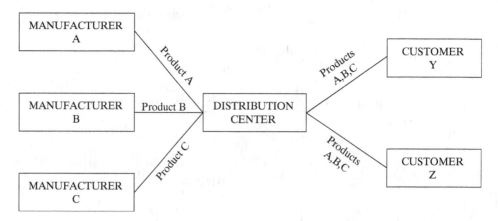

FIGURE 13.6 Product mixing.

- Customer order size.
- Number and location of plants and distribution centers.

Suppliers have little or no control over the first three but do have some control over the last. They can establish local distribution centers in their markets. With respect to transportation, it then becomes a question of the cost of serving customers direct from the central distribution center or from the regional distribution center. If truckload shipments are made, the cost is less from the central distribution center, but if LTL shipments are made, it may be cheaper to serve the customer from the local distribution center.

Example Problem

Suppose a company with a plant located in Toronto is serving a market in the northeastern United States with many customers located in Boston. If the company ships direct to customers from the Toronto plant, most shipments will be less than truckload. However, if it locates a distribution center in Boston, it can ship truckload to Boston and distribute by local cartage (LTL) to customers in that area. Whether this is economical or not depends on the total cost of shipping direct compared with shipping via the distribution center. Assume the following figures represent the average shipments to the Boston area:

Plant to customer LTL: $100/cwt.

Plant to distribution center TL: $50/cwt.
Inventory-carrying cost (distribution center): $10/cwt.
Distribution center to customer LTL: $20/cwt.

Is it more economical to establish the distribution center in Boston? If the annual shipped volume is 10,000 cwt., what will be the annual saving?

Answer

Costs if a distribution center is used:

TL Toronto to Boston = $50 per cwt.
Distribution center costs = $10 per cwt.
LTL in Boston area = $20 per cwt.
Total cost = $80 per cwt.
Saving per cwt. = $100 − $80 = $20
Annual saving = $20 × 10,000 = $200,000

Market Boundaries

Continuing with the previous example problem, the company can now supply customers in other locations directly from the factory in Toronto or through the distribution center in Boston. The question is to decide which locations should be supplied from each source. The answer, of course, is the source that can service the location at least cost.

FIGURE 13.7 Market boundary.

Laid-down cost (LDC) is the delivered cost of a product to a particular geographic point. The delivered cost includes all costs of moving the goods from A to B. In the previous example problem, the laid-down cost of delivering from Toronto would be the transportation cost per mile times the miles to a particular destination. The LDC from Boston would include all costs of getting the goods to Boston, inventory costs in the Boston distribution center, and the transportation costs in getting to a particular destination.

$$LDC = P + TX$$

where

P = Product costs

T = transportation costs per mile

X = distance

The product cost includes all costs in getting the product to the supply location and storing it there. In the previous example, the product cost at Boston includes the TL cost of delivery to Boston and the inventory cost at Boston.

Example Problem

Syracuse is 300 miles from Toronto. The product cost for an item is $10 per cwt., and the transportation cost per mile per cwt. is $0.20. What is the laid-down cost per cwt.?

ANSWER

LDC = Product cost + (transportation cost per mile)(distance)

= $10 + ($0.20 × 300) = $70 per cwt.

Market boundary   The **market boundary** is the line between two or more supply sources where the laid-down cost is the same. Consider Figure 13.7. There are two sources of supply: A and B. The market boundary occurs at Y where the LDC from A is the same as B.

In the example shown in Figure 13.7, the distance between A and B is 100 miles. If we let the distance from A to Y be X miles, then the distance from B to Y is $(100 - X)$ miles. Assume supply A is the factory and supply B is a distribution center. Assume the product cost at A is $100 and product cost from B is $100 plus TL transportation from A to B and inventory costs at B. For this example, assume the TL transportation and inventory-carrying costs are $10 per unit so the product cost from B is $110. Transportation costs from either A or B are $0.40 per unit per mile.

Point Y occurs where

$$LCD_A = LDC_B$$
$$100 + 0.40X = 110 + 0.40(100 - X)$$
$$X = 62.5$$

Thus a point Y, 62.5 miles from A, marks the market boundary between A and B.

Example Problem

The distance between Toronto and Boston is about 500 miles. Given the cost structure in the previous example problems and an LTL transportation cost of $0.20 per cwt. per mile, calculate the location of the market boundary between Toronto and Boston. Assume the product cost at Toronto is $10 per cwt.

ANSWER

The product cost at Boston is the sum of the product cost at Toronto, plus the cost of TL shipment from Toronto to Boston, plus the handling costs at Boston.

Product cost at Boston = product cost at A + TL transporation + handling costs

$$= \$10 + \$50 + \$10$$

$$= \$70$$

The market boundary occurs where

$$LDC_T = LDC_B$$

$$\$10 + \$0.20X = \$70 + \$0.20(500 - X)$$

$$0.4X = 160$$

$$X = 400$$

The market boundary is 400 miles from Toronto or 100 miles from Boston.

Effect on Transportation Costs of Adding More Warehouses

We have seen from the previous example that establishing a distribution center in Boston reduces total transportation costs. Similarly, if a second distribution center is established, perhaps in Cleveland, we expect total transportation costs to be reduced further.

Generally, as more distribution centers are added to the system, we can expect the following:

- The cost of truckload (and carload) shipments to the distribution centers to increase.
- The cost of LTL shipments to customers to decrease.
- The total cost of transportation to decrease.

As expected, the major savings is from the addition of the first few distribution centers. Eventually, as more distribution centers are added, the savings decrease. The first distribution center added to the system is located to serve the largest market; the second distribution center, the second largest market, and so on. The number of customers served by additional distribution centers decreases, and the volume that can be shipped TL to the additional distribution centers is less than to the first distribution centers. Figure 13.8 shows the relationship that exists between transportation costs and the number of distribution centers in a system.

FIGURE 13.8 Transportation cost versus number of warehouses.

PACKAGING

The basic role of packaging in any industrial organization is to carry the goods safely through a distribution system to the customer. The package must do the following:

- Identify the product.
- Contain and protect the product.
- Contribute to physical distribution efficiency.

For consumer products, the package may also be an important part of the marketing program.

Physical distribution must not only move and store products but also identify them. The package serves as a means of identifying the product in a way not possible from its outward appearance. When shoes are offered in 10 sizes, the package becomes an important identifier.

Packaging must contain and protect the product, often against a wide range of hazards such as shock, compression, vibration, moisture, heat, solar radiation, oxidation, and infestation by animals, insects, birds, mold, or bacteria. Packages are subject to distribution hazards in loading and off-loading, in movement, in transportation, and in warehousing and storage. The package must be robust enough to protect and contain the product through all phases of distribution.

Packaging is a pure cost that must be offset by the increased physical distribution efficiency that the package can provide.

There are usually at least three levels of packaging required in a distribution system. First is a primary package that holds the product, for example, a box of cornflakes. Next, for small packages, a shipping container such as a corrugated box is needed. Finally, there is a third level of packaging, where several primary or secondary packages are assembled into a unit load.

Unitization

Unitization is the consolidation of several units into large units, called **unit loads**, so there is less handling. A unit load is a load made up of a number of items, or bulky material, arranged or constrained so the mass can be picked up or moved as a single unit too large for manual handling. Material handling costs decrease as the size of the unit load increases. It is more economical to move the product by cartons rather than individually and still more economical to move several cartons in one unit load.

This principle is used when we go shopping and put a number of articles into bags and then put the bags into the trunk of the car. In industry, unit loads are used instead of shopping bags.

There are a number of unit-load devices such as sheets, racks, and containers. One of the most common is the **pallet**.

As noted in Chapter 12, the pallet is a platform usually measuring 48" × 40" × 4" and designed so that it can be lifted and moved by a forklift industrial truck. Packages are arranged on it so that several packages may be moved at one time. Loaded with packages, it forms a cube that is a unit load.

Unitization can be successive. Shippers place their products into primary packages, the packages into shipping cartons, the cartons onto pallets, and the pallets into warehouses, trucks, or other vehicles.

To use the capacity of pallets, trucks (or other vehicles), and warehouses, there should be some relationship between the dimensions of the product, the primary package, the shipping cartons, the pallet, the truck, and the warehouse space. The packages should be designed so space on the pallet is fully utilized and so the cartons interlock to form a stable load. Figure 13.9 shows two unit loads, each using the total space of the pallet. However, load B does not interlock and is not stable.

Pallets fit into trucks and railway cars. The standard dimensions are selected so pallets would fit into nominal 50' railway cars and 40' truck trailers with a minimum of lost space. Figure 13.10 shows the layout in railcars and trailers.

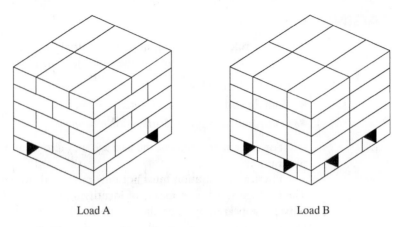

Load A   Load B

FIGURE 13.9 Stable and unstable pallet loads.

FIGURE 13.10 Railcar and trailer pallet position plan.

Thus, to get the highest cube utilization, consideration must be given to the dimensions of the product, the carton, the pallet, the vehicle, and the warehouse.

MATERIALS HANDLING

Materials handling is the short-distance movement that takes place in or around a building such as a plant or distribution center. For a distribution center, this means the unloading and loading of transport vehicles and the dispatch and recall of goods to and from storage. In addition, the racking systems used in distribution centers are usually considered to be part of materials handling.

Some objectives of materials handling are as follows:

1. To increase cube utilization by using the height of the building and by reducing the need for aisle space as much as possible.
2. To improve operating efficiency by reducing handling. Increasing the load per move will result in fewer moves.
3. To improve the service level by increasing the speed of response to customer needs.

There are many types of materials handling equipment. For convenience, they can be grouped into three categories: conveyors, industrial trucks, and cranes and hoists.

Conveyors are devices that move material (or people) horizontally or vertically between two fixed points. They are expensive, create a fixed route, and occupy space continuously. As a result, they are used only where there is sufficient throughput between fixed points to justify their cost.

Industrial trucks are vehicles powered by hand, electricity, or propane. Diesel and gasoline are not used indoors because they are noxious and lethal. Industrial trucks are more flexible than conveyors in that they can move anywhere there is a suitable surface and no obstructions. They do not occupy space continuously. For these reasons, they are the most often-used form of materials handling in distribution centers and in manufacturing.

Cranes and hoists can move materials vertically and horizontally to any point within their area of operation. They use overhead space and are used to move heavy or large items. Within their area of operation, they are very flexible.

MULTI-WAREHOUSE SYSTEMS

This section will look at the result of adding more distribution centers to the system. As might be expected, there is an effect on the cost of warehousing, materials handling, inventories, packaging, and transportation. Our purpose will be to look at how all of these costs and the total system cost behave. We also want to know what happens to the service level as more distribution centers are added to the system. To make valid comparisons, we must freeze the sales volume. We can then compare costs as we add distribution centers to the system.

Transportation Costs

In the section on transportation, we saw that if shipments to customers are in less-than-full vehicle lots, the total transportation cost is reduced by establishing a distribution center in a market area. This is because more weight can be shipped for greater distances by truck or carload and the LTL shipments can be made over relatively short distances. Generally, then, as more distribution centers are added to a system, we expect the following:

- The cost of TL shipments increases.
- The cost of LTL shipments decreases.
- The total cost of transportation decreases.

The major savings are made with the addition of the first distribution centers. Eventually, as more distribution centers are added, the marginal savings decrease.

Inventory-Carrying Cost

The average inventory carried depends on the order quantity and the safety stock. The average order quantity inventory in the system should remain the same since it depends on demand, the cost of ordering, and the cost of carrying inventory.

The total safety stock will be affected by the number of warehouses in the system. Safety stock is carried to protect against fluctuations in demand during the lead time and depends, in part, on the number of units sold. In Chapter 11, it was shown that the standard deviation varies as the square root of the ratio of the forecast and lead-time intervals. Similarly, for the same SKU, the standard deviation varies approximately as the square root of the ratio of the different annual demands. Suppose that the average demand is 1000 units and, for a service level of 90%, the safety stock is 100 units. If the 1000 units is divided between two distribution centers each having a demand of 500 units, the safety stock in each is:

$$SS = 100\sqrt{\frac{500}{1000}} = 71 \text{ units (in each warehouse)}$$

With two distribution centers and the same total sales, the total safety stock increases to 142 from 100. Thus, with a constant sales volume, as the number of distribution centers increases, the demand on each decreases but there is an increase in the total safety stock in all distribution centers.

Warehousing Costs

The fixed costs associated with distribution centers are space and materials handling. The space needed depends on the amount of inventory carried. As we have seen, as more distribution centers are added to the system, more inventory has to be carried, which requires more space.

In addition, there will be some duplication of nonstorage space such as washrooms and offices. So as the number of distribution centers increases, there will be a gradual increase in distribution center space costs.

Operating costs also increase as the number of distribution centers increases. Operating costs depend largely on the number of units handled. Since there is no increase in sales, the total number of units handled remains the same, as does the cost of handling. However, the nondirect supervision and clerical costs increase.

Materials Handling Costs

Materials handling costs depend upon the number of units handled. Since the sales volume remains constant, the number of units handled should also remain constant. There will be little change in materials handling costs as long as the firm can ship unit loads to the distribution center. However, if the number of distribution centers increases to the point that some nonunitized loads are shipped, materials handling costs increase.

Packaging Costs

Per-unit packaging costs will remain the same, but since there will be more inventory in the multi-warehouse system, total packaging costs will rise with inventory.

Total System Cost

We have assumed that total system sales remain the same. Figure 13.11 shows graphically how the costs of transportation, warehousing, materials handling inventory, and packaging behave as distribution centers are added to the system. Up to a point, total costs decrease and then start to increase. It is the objective of logistics to determine this least-cost point.

System Service Capability

The service capability of the system must also be evaluated. One way of assessing this is by estimating the percentage of the market served within a given period. Figure 13.12 represents such an estimate.

As expected, the service level increases as the number of distribution centers increases. It increases rapidly from one to two distribution centers and much less rapidly as the number is further increased. The first distribution center is built to serve the best market, the next to serve the second-best market, and so on. Let us assume that a study has been made of a system of 1 to 10 distribution centers and the costs are as shown in Figure 13.13.

FIGURE 13.11 Total system cost.

Number of Warehouses	Percentage of Market Reached in 1 Day
1	30
2	70
3	87
10	95

FIGURE 13.12 Estimate of market reached versus number of warehouses.

Cost ($1000)	Number of Locations			
	1	2	3	10
Transportation	$8000	$6000	$5000	$4500
Warehousing	500	600	700	900
Materials Handling	1000	1000	1100	1400
Inventory	400	425	460	700
Packaging	100	100	100	100
Total Cost	$10,000	$8125	$7360	$7600

FIGURE 13.13 Cost versus number of warehouses.

A three-distribution-center system would provide the least total cost. Figure 13.13 shows that by moving from 3 to 10 distribution centers, the 1-day service level increases by 8%. Management must decide which system to select. The decision must be based on adequate analysis of the choices available and a comparison of the increase in costs and service level.

SUMMARY

Physical distribution is the movement of goods into and out of a company and is changing in both the global economy and in the individual delivery of goods to Internet customers. The majority of goods are still shipped in large economical units through distribution channels. Third party logistics providers are applying their area of specialization to help companies drive down costs while improving customer service. Sound packaging design is critical to a company not only because it affects the efficient handling of product all the way through the supply chain but also because it can have a high environmental cost. Reverse logistics along with a change in the distribution channel to Internet customers is another reason for the growth of 3PLs. Warehouses strategically placed through the supply chain can help provide improved customer service and reduce costs.

The global sourcing and distribution of goods across international boundaries has increased the need for accurate, comprehensive documentation to determine things such as who pays the freight? who prepares the documentation? who owns the goods and may be responsible for any environmental problems? Incoterms, standard terms accepted around the world, address most of these concerns and are a requirement of any freight movement in or out of North America.

KEY TERMS

Billing and collecting costs 293

Break-bulk 297

Common carriers 291

Contract carriers 291

Conveyors 303

Cost trade-off 286

Cranes and hoists 303

Density 294

Distribution channel 283

Distribution inventory 285

Distribution warehouse 296

Fixed costs 289

Freight on board (FOB) 294

General warehouse 296

Green reverse logistics 284

Incoterms 287

Industrial trucks 303

Laid-down cost (LDC) 299

Line-haul cost per hundred weight 292

Market boundary 299

Materials handling 285

Order processing and communication 286

Packaging 294

Pallet 301

Perishability 294

Physical distribution 282

Physical supply 282

Pickup and delivery costs 293

Private carriers 290

Protective packaging 285

Reverse logistics 284

Terminal-handling costs 293

Terminals 289

Third Party Logistics (3PLs) 285

Total cost 286

Total line-haul cost 292

Transaction channel 283

Transportation 285

Transportation terms 294

Unit loads 301

Unitization 301

Value 294

Variable costs 289

Vehicles 289

Warehouses (distribution centers) 285

Ways 289

QUESTIONS

1. Name and describe the three functions in the flow of materials from supplier to consumer. What are the differences between physical supply and physical distribution?

2. What is the primary function of the transaction channel and the distribution channel?

3. The particular way that goods move depends in part on four factors. What are they?

4. Describe the reverse logistics system of a beverage company, including the movement of goods and the flow of payment. What steps does the company take to reduce their costs?

5. Why are the total costs associated with reverse logistics increasing? Will this trend continue into the future?

6. What are the objectives of a physical distribution system?

7. Name and describe each of the six system activities in a physical distribution system.

8. What are the cost trade-off and total cost concepts? Why are they important?

9. Describe the relationship between marketing and physical distribution. How does physical distribution contribute to creating demand?

10. Why is the demand placed on a central distribution center or a factory by distribution centers considered dependent?

11. What are the five basic modes of transportation?

12. What are the three physical elements in a transportation system? For each of the five modes, describe who provides them and how they are funded.

13. Describe why train service is cheaper than road transport for large quantities of bulky commodities moving over long distances.

14. Why can trucks provide a fast, flexible service for the distribution of small volumes of goods to a dispersed market?

15. What are the major characteristics of water and air transport?

16. What are the major legal types of carriage? What are the three areas of economic regulation? To which legal type of carriage do they apply?

17. Compare common and contract carriage. How do they differ from private carriage? Which will give the highest level of service?

18. On what do total line-haul costs and line-haul costs per hundredweight depend? What two ways can shippers reduce line-haul costs?

19. Describe how a shipper can reduce the following:
    a. Pickup and delivery costs.
    b. Terminal-handling costs.
    c. Billing and collecting costs.

20. The rates charged by a shipper vary with the commodity shipped. Name and describe four factors that affect the rates.

21. Why are LTL rates more expensive than TL rates?

22. Name and describe the two basic types of warehouses.

23. Name and describe the three important roles warehouses serve.

24. Name four factors that affect shipping patterns. Which can a supplier control?

25. What is the laid-down cost? What is a market boundary? Why are laid-down costs important in determining market boundaries?

26. As more distribution centers are added to a system, what happens to the cost of truckload, less than truckload, and total transportation costs?

27. What are the three roles of packaging in a distribution system? Describe why each is important.

28. What is unitization? Why is it important in physical distribution? Why is it successive?

29. What are three prime objectives of materials handling? Describe the characteristics of conveyors, industrial trucks, cranes, and hoists.

30. As more warehouses are added to the system, what would we expect to happen to the following:
    a. Transportation costs.
    b. Inventory costs.
    c. Materials handling costs.
    d. Packaging costs.
    e. Total system costs.
    f. System service capability.

31. How does the use of the transportation term *FOB* for domestic shipments in North America differ from the use of the term in international shipments?

32. Which North American shipping term has the minimum risk for
    a. the buyer?
    b. the seller?

33. A buyer in England would like to import a Harley-Davidson motorcycle directly from a dealer in the United States. Which Incoterm would minimize the buyer's efforts? Would arranging the shipment themselves save money for the buyer?

34. What is meant by the term *green reverse logistics*?

35. Describe how a 3PL would benefit a company that sells their product to individuals through the Internet.

36. Describe how reverse logistics would apply to your school bookstore.

PROBLEMS

13.1. A company normally ships to a customer by rail at a cost of $500 per load. The transit time is 14 days. The goods can be shipped by truck for $700 per load and a transit time of 4 days. If transit inventory cost is $35 per day, what does it cost to ship each way?

Answer.   Rail, $990; truck, $840

13.2. A company manufactures component parts for machine tools in North America and ships them to Southeast Asia for assembly and sale in the local market. The components are shipped by sea, transit time averages 6 weeks, and the shipping costs $1000 per shipment. The company is considering moving the parts by air at an estimated cost of $7500; the shipment taking 2 days to get there. If inventory in transit for the shipment costs $150 per day, should they ship by air?

In Chapter 8, it was said that forecasts are more accurate for nearer periods of time. Should this be considered? What activities are affected by the shorter lead time?

13.3. For a given commodity, the line-haul cost is $13 per mile. For a trip of 200 miles and a shipment of 300 cwt., what is the cost per hundredweight? If the shipment is increased to 500 cwt., what is the saving in cost per hundredweight?

Answer. $3.47 per cwt.

13.4. A company ships a particular product to a market located 1500 miles from the plant at a cost of $4 per mile. Normally it ships 500 units at a time. What is the line-haul cost per unit?

13.5. In problem 13.4, if the company can ship the units unassembled, it can ship 800 units in a truck. What is the line-haul cost per unit now?

Answer.   Line-haul cost per unit = $7.50.

13.6. A company processes feathers and ships them loose in a covered truck. The line-haul cost for an average shipment is $400, and the truck carries 2000 pounds of feathers. A bright new graduate has just been hired and has suggested that they should bale the feathers into 500-pound bales. This would make them easier to handle and also allow them to be compressed into about one-tenth of the space they now occupy. How many pounds of feathers can the truck now carry? What is the present line-haul cost per pound? What will it be if the proposal is adopted?

13.7. A company in Calgary serves a market in the northwestern United States. Now it ships LTL at an average cost of $30 per unit. If the company establishes a distribution center in the market, it estimates the TL cost will be $15 per unit, inventory-carrying costs will be $7 per unit, and the local LTL cost will average $6 per unit. If the company forecasts annual demand at 200,000 units, how much will they save annually?

Answer.   Annual saving = $400,000

13.8. A company ships LTL to customers in a market in the Midwest at an average cost of $40 per cwt. It proposes establishing a distribution center in this market. If TL shipment costs $20 per cwt., the estimated inventory-carrying costs are $5 per cwt., and the local cartage (LTL) cost is estimated at $6 per cwt. If the annual shipped volume is 100,000 cwt., what will the annual savings be by establishing the distribution center?

13.9. A company has a central supply facility and a distribution center located 400 miles away. The central supply product cost is $75, TL transportation rates from central supply to the DC are $60 per unit, and handling costs at the DC are $4 per unit. Calculate the market boundary location and the laid-down cost at the market boundary. LTL rates are $2 per unit per mile.

Answer. Market boundary is 216 miles from central supply. LDC = $507

13.10. Suppose the company in problem 13.8 had another market area located between the parent plant and the proposed distribution center. The LTL costs from the plant to that market are $35 per cwt. The company estimates that LTL shipments from the distribution center will cost $4 per cwt. Should it supply this market from the distribution center or central supply?

13.11. A company can ship LTL direct to customers in city A or use a public warehouse located in city B. It has determined the following data.

Cost per cwt. for shipping LTL to city A is $0.70 + $0.30 per mile.

Cost per cwt. for shipping TL to warehouse is $0.40 + $0.15 per mile.

Warehouse handling costs are $0.30 per cwt.

Distances: Plant to city A = 115 miles

Plant to city B = 135 miles

From city B to city A = 30 miles

a. What is the total cost per cwt. to ship from the plant direct to customers in city A?

b. What is the total cost per cwt. to ship via the warehouse in city B?

c. In this problem, the cost per cwt. has a fixed and a variable component. Why?

CASE STYDY 13.1

Metal Specialties, Inc.

Metal Specialties is a wholesaler of specialty metals such as stainless steels and tool steels. The company purchases its stainless steel from a mill located some 200 miles away. At present the company operates its own truck. However, the truck is in need of repairs estimated at $20,000. Annual operating costs are $30,000 and the line-haul costs are $2.20 per mile. Janet Jones (JJ), the traffic manager, wants to reduce the cost of bringing in the stainless steel, and because of the impending repair expense, she feels now is a good time to look at alternatives. She has solicited a number of proposals and has narrowed her choices down to a motor carrier and a rail carrier.

Heavy Metal Transport (HMT), a contract motor carrier, has an excellent reputation for service and reliability. It has submitted an incremental rate, $4.00/cwt. for shipments weighting less than 150 cwt., $3.80 for shipments between 150 and 200 cwt., $3.60 for shipments between 200 and 250 cwt., and $3.40 for shipments over 250 cwt. up to a maximum of 400 cwt.

Midland Continental Railway has submitted a piggyback rate of $3.25 per cwt. with a minimum load of 200 cwt. The piggyback rate includes pickup by truck at the steel mill, line haul by trailer on flat car, and delivery by truck to Metal Specialities' warehouse. They are considered to be a reliable carrier as well.

The finance department estimates that Metal Specialities' annual inventory-carrying cost is 20%, the cost of inventory in transit is 10%, and the cost of capital is 8%. The cost of placing an order for stainless steel is estimated to be $40 per order. Stainless steel presently costs $300 per cwt.

Case Analysis

1. JJ has to make a decision soon. Given the information provided, what would you advise her to do?

PRODUCTS AND PROCESSES

INTRODUCTION

The effect and the efficiency of operations management, just-in-time manufacturing, and total quality management all depend on the way products are designed and the processes selected. The way products are designed determines the processes that are available to make them. The product design and the process determine the quality and cost of the product. Quality and cost determine the profitability of the company. This chapter studies the relationship between product design and process design and the costs associated with different types of processes. Finally, the chapter looks at the improvement of existing processes.

NEED FOR NEW PRODUCTS

Products, like people, have a limited life span. A product passes through several stages, known as the product life cycle, beginning with its introduction and ending with its disappearance from the marketplace. Figure 14.1 gives a simplified view of the profit and volume relationships in each phase of the cycle. No time scale is implied. The life cycle may take months or years to complete depending on the products and the market.

Introduction phase   This phase is the most expensive and risky stage. To get customer acceptance of the product the firm will usually spend heavily on advertising and sales promotion, hoping these costs will be recovered in future sales. If the introduction fails the firm loses money, a fact that underlines the importance of thoroughly researching a new product before introducing it.

Growth phase   In this phase, sales of a successful product increase at a rapid rate. Production increases and the unit cost of the product drops. The increased sales volume and the lower unit cost cause profits to increase rapidly. However, the success of the product usually attracts the attention of competitors. Their entrance into the market forces prices down, possibly reducing the firm's sales. At this point profits are squeezed.

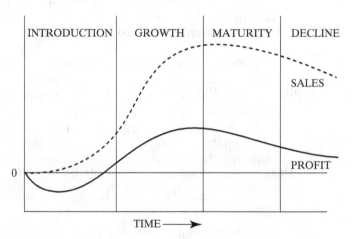

FIGURE 14.1 Life cycle of a product.

Maturity or saturation phase   Nearly everyone interested in the product has sampled or owns the product and sales begin to level off. The market is saturated. Price competition is often severe and profits start to decline.

Decline phase   Sales drop as customers begin to lose interest in the product or to buy improved versions from competitors. As profits decline still further, companies will look for ways to maintain profitability. Generally, there are three ways in which this can be done:

- Introduce new products.
- Improve existing products.
- Improve the methods of production.

Depending on the firm's resources it may do these things through its own research and development, by copying competitors' products, or by relying on customers or suppliers to do the research and development work. We will concern ourselves with the firm that does its own research, development, and engineering.

PRODUCT DEVELOPMENT PRINCIPLES

A few organizations supply a single product, but most supply a range of similar or related products. There are two conflicting factors to be considered in establishing the range of products to supply.

- If the product line is too narrow, customers may be lost.
- If the product line is too wide, customers may be satisfied, but operating costs will increase because of the lack of specialization.

Sales organizations are responsible for increasing sales and revenue. They want to offer product variety to consumers. Often this means the organization must offer a variety of products, many of which sell in small volumes.

Operations, on the other hand, would like to produce as few products as possible and make them in long runs. In this way it could reduce the number of setups (and cost) and probably lower run costs by using special machinery. It would fulfill its mandate to produce at the lowest cost.

Somehow the needs of sales and the economics of production must be balanced. Usually this balance can be obtained with good programs of:

- Product simplification.
- Product standardization.
- Product specialization.

Simplification

Simplification is the process of making something easier to do or make. It seeks to cut out waste by getting rid of needless product varieties, sizes, and types. The emphasis is not in cutting out products simply to reduce variety but to remove unnecessary products and variations.

As well as reducing the variety of parts, product design can often be simplified to reduce operations and material costs. For example, the use of a snap-on plastic cap instead of a screw cap reduces the cost of both materials and labor.

Standardization

In product design, a **standard** is a carefully established specification covering the product's material, configuration, measurements, and so on. Thus, all products made to a given specification will be alike and interchangeable. Light bulbs are a good example of standardization: the sockets and wattage are standardized and the light bulbs are interchangeable.

A range of standard specifications can be established so it covers most uses for the item. Men's shirts are made in a range of standard collar sizes and sleeve lengths so nearly everyone can be fitted. Most shirt manufacturers also use the same standards so the consumer can get the same size shirt from any manufacturer and expect it to fit.

Because product standardization allows parts to be interchangeable, as long as the range of standard specifications has been well chosen, a smaller variety of components is needed. Using the example of light bulbs, the wattages are standardized at 40, 60, and 100 watts. This range allows users to pick wattages that satisfy their needs and manufacturers to reduce the number of different bulbs, thus reducing inventory.

Another aspect of standardization is the way parts fit together. If the designs of assemblies are standardized so various models or products are assembled in the same way, then mass production is possible. The automotive industry designs automobiles so many different models can be assembled on the same assembly line. For example, several different engines can be mounted in a chassis because the engines are mounted in the same way and designed so they will all fit into the engine compartment.

Modularization Modularization uses standardized parts for flexibility and variety. Standardization does not necessarily reduce the range of choice for the customer. By standardizing on *component parts*, a manufacturer can make a variety of finished goods, one of which will probably satisfy the customer. Automobile manufacturing is a prime example of this. Cars are usually made from a few standard components and a series of standard options so the consumer has a selection from which to choose. For example, the Mazda Miata contains 80% parts standard to other Mazda cars, which enables Mazda to produce the car quickly and at low cost, thus making a profit even though sales are comparatively small. Chrysler uses one platform—the basic frame of the vehicle—for all models of its minivan. Thus, the company has only one set of frame costs for all minivans.

Modularization also permits the practice of postponement as introduced in Chapter 1 where the components to manufacture the final product for the customer are made ahead of time. The final product is then configured to customer specifications once the order is placed. This reduces the lead time to the customer without the need for final product inventory.

Specialization

Specialization is concentration of effort in a particular area or occupation. Electricians, doctors, and lawyers specialize in their chosen fields. In product specialization, a firm may produce and market only one or a limited range of similar products. This leads to process and labor specialization, which increases productivity and decreases costs.

With a limited range of products, productivity can be increased and costs reduced by

- Allowing the development of machinery and equipment specially designed to make the limited range of products quickly and cheaply.
- Reducing the number of setups because of fewer task changes.
- Allowing labor to develop speed and dexterity because of fewer task changes.

Specialization is sometimes called focus and can be based either on product and market or on process.

Product and market focus Product and market focus can be based on characteristics such as customer grouping (serving similar customers), demand characteristics (volume), or degree of customization. For example, one company may specialize in a limited range of high-volume products, whereas another may specialize in providing a wider range of low-volume products with a high level of customization.

Process focus Process focus is based on the similarity of process. For example, automobile manufacturers specialize in assembling automobiles. Other factories and companies supply the assemblers with components and the assembler specializes in assembly operations.

Focused factory Currently there is a trend toward more specialization in manufacturing whereby a factory specializes in a narrow product mix for a niche market. Generally **focused factories** are thought to produce more effectively and economically than more complex factories, the reason being that repetition and concentration in one area allow the workforce and management to gain the advantages of specialization. The focused factory may be a "factory within a factory," an area in an existing factory set aside to specialize in a narrow product mix.

Specialization has the disadvantage of inflexibility. Often it is difficult to use highly specialized labor and equipment for tasks other than those for which they were trained or built.

In summary, the three ideas of simplification, standardization, and specialization are different but interrelated. Simplification is the elimination of the superfluous and is the first step toward standardization. Standardization is establishing a range of standards and standard components that will meet most needs. Finally, specialization would not be possible without standardization. Specialization is concentration in a particular area and therefore implies repetition, which cannot be arrived at without standard products or procedures.

A program of product simplification, standardization, and specialization allows a firm to concentrate on the things it does best, provides the customers with what they want, and allows operations to perform with a high level of productivity. Reducing part variety will create savings in raw material, work-in-process, and finished goods inventory. It will also allow longer production runs, improve quality because there are fewer parts, and improve opportunities for automation and mechanization. Such a program contributes significantly to reducing cost.

PRODUCT SPECIFICATION AND DESIGN

Product design is responsible for producing a set of specifications that manufacturing can use to make the product. Products should be designed to be

- Functional.
- Capable of low-cost processing.
- Environmentally sensitive.

Functional   The product will be designed to perform as specified in the marketplace. The marketing department produces a market specification laying down the expected performance, sales volume, selling price, and appearance values of the product. Product design engineers design the product to meet the market specifications. Engineers establish the dimensions, configurations, and specifications so the item, if properly manufactured, will perform as expected in the marketplace.

Low-cost processing   The product must be designed so it can be made at least cost. The product designer specifies materials, tolerances, basic shapes, methods of joining parts, and so on and, through these specifications, sets the minimum product cost. Usually, many different designs will satisfy functional and appearance specifications. The job then is to pick the design that will minimize manufacturing cost.

Poor design can add cost to processing in several ways:

- The product and its components may not be designed to be made using the most economical methods impossible.
- Parts may be designed so excessive material has to be removed.
- Parts may be designed so operations are difficult.
- Lack of standardized components may mean batches of work have to be small. Using standard parts across a range of products reduces the number of parts in inventory, tooling, and operator training and permits the use of special-purpose machinery. All this reduces product cost.
- Finally, product design can influence indirect costs such as production planning, purchasing, inventory management, and inspection. For example, one design may call for 20 different nonstandard parts, whereas another uses 15 standard parts. The effort required to plan and control the flow of materials and the operations will be greater, and more costly, in the first case than the second.

Low cost has to be designed into the product.

Environmental or "green" sensitivity   There are several issues that should be included or considered. One of these issues concerns the materials and processes used. Specifically, consideration should be given as to whether materials are recyclable or

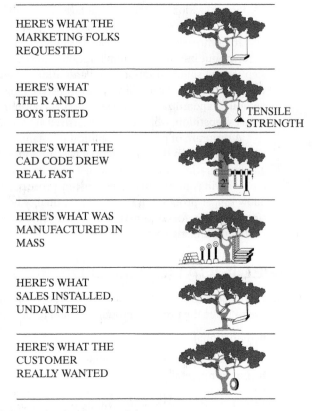

HERE'S WHAT THE
MARKETING FOLKS
REQUESTED

HERE'S WHAT
THE R AND D
BOYS TESTED
TENSILE STRENGTH

HERE'S WHAT THE
CAD CODE DREW
REAL FAST

HERE'S WHAT WAS
MANUFACTURED IN
MASS

HERE'S WHAT
SALES INSTALLED,
UNDAUNTED

HERE'S WHAT THE
CUSTOMER
REALLY WANTED

FIGURE 14.2 Communication is essential.

renewable. If not, one should question if they are harmful to the environment or not. In addition, some consideration should be made as to how easy it is to recycle or reuse the materials. Many of these environmental concerns can be listed under the overall term **sustainability**. Sustainability also can include issues of being a responsible community "citizen" and being ethical in your approach to business.

Simultaneous Engineering

To design products for low-cost manufacture requires close coordination between product design and process design, which is called **simultaneous engineering**. If the two groups can work together, they have a better chance of designing a product that will function well in the marketplace and can be manufactured at least cost. This relationship between product design and process design can spell the success or failure of a product. If a product cannot be produced at a cost that will allow a profit to be made, then it is a failure for the firm.

The traditional approach to product and process design has been a little like a relay race. When product design finished, it would pass the work to process design and let that department figure out how to make it. This system has proved time consuming and expensive. Figure 14.2 shows, with some humor, what can happen without strong communication and interaction between all parties in the product development cycle.

Today, many organizations concurrently develop the design for the product and the process. Often a team is made up of people from product design, process design, quality assurance, production planning and inventory control, purchasing, marketing, field service, and others who contribute to, or are affected by, the delivery of the product to the customer. This group works together to develop the product design so it meets the needs of the customer and can be made and delivered to the customer at low cost in a process called **concurrent engineering**.

There are several advantages to this approach:

■ **Time to market is reduced.** The organization that gets its products to market before the competition gains a strong competitive advantage.

- **Cost is reduced.** Involving all stakeholders early in the process means less need for costly design changes later.
- **Better quality.** Because the product is designed for ease of manufacture and ease of maintaining quality in manufacture, the number of rejects will be reduced. Because quality is improved, the need for after-sales service is reduced.
- **Lower total system cost.** Because all groups affected by the product design are consulted, all concerns are addressed. For example, field service might need a product that is designed so it is easy to service in the field, thus reducing servicing costs.

PROCESS DESIGN

Operations management is responsible for producing the products and services the customer wants, when wanted, with the required quality, at minimum cost and maximum effectiveness and productivity. **Processes** are the means by which operations management reaches these objectives.

A process is a method of doing something, generally involving a number of steps or operations. Process design is the developing and designing of the steps.

Everything we do involves a process of some description. When we go to the bank to deposit or withdraw money, prepare a meal, or go on a trip we are involved in a process. Sometimes, as consumers, we are personally involved in the process. Most of us have waited at a checkout counter in a store and wondered why management has not devised a better process for serving customers.

Nesting Another way of looking at the hierarchy of processes is the concept of **nesting**. Small processes are linked to form a larger process. Consider Figure 14.3. Level zero shows a series of steps, each of which may have its own series of steps. One of the operations on level zero is expanded into its component parts and shown on level one. The nesting can continue to further levels of detail.

Mass customization Recent changes in process flexibility have allowed for the development of a concept called **mass customization**. If the operation is designed to be flexible and efficient enough, it will allow the production of customized products (specific to customer demand) at virtually the same cost as mass-produced product.

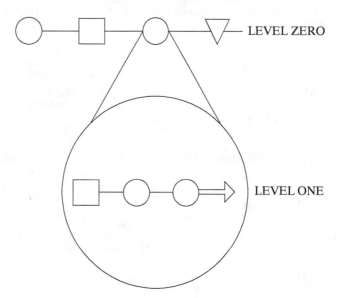

FIGURE 14.3 Nesting concept.

FACTORS INFLUENCING PROCESS DESIGN

Six basic factors must be considered when designing a process.

Product design and quality level   The product's design determines the basic processes needed to convert the raw materials and components into the finished product. For example, if a steak is to be barbecued, then the process must include a barbecue operation. The process designer can usually select from a variety of different machines or operations to do the job. The type of machine or operation selected will depend upon the quantity to be produced, the available equipment, and the quality level needed.

The desired quality level affects the process design, because the process must be capable of achieving that quality level and doing it repeatedly. If the process cannot do that, operations will not be able to produce what is wanted except with expensive inspection and rework. The process designer must be aware of the capabilities of machines and processes and select those that will meet the quality level at least cost.

Demand patterns and flexibility needed   If there is variation in demand for a product, the process must be flexible enough to respond to these changes quickly. For example, if a full-service restaurant sells a variety of foods, the process must be flexible enough to switch from broiling hamburgers to making pizzas. Conversely, if a pizza parlor sells nothing but pizzas, the process need not be designed to cook any other type of food. Flexible processes require flexible equipment and personnel capable of doing a number of different jobs.

Quantity/capacity considerations   Product design, the quantity to produce, and process design are closely related. Both product and process design depend on the quantity needed. For example, if only one of an item is to be made, the design and the process used will be different than if the volume is 100,000 units. The quantity needed and the process design determine the capacity needed. Figure 14.4 shows this relationship. Note that all three are directly connected to the customer.

Customer involvement   Chapter 1 discussed four manufacturing strategies—engineer-to-order, make-to-order, assemble-to-order, and make-to-stock—and the extent of customer involvement in each. Process design will depend on which strategy is chosen.

Environmental concerns   The process design should have minimal impact on the environment, if at all possible. In addition concern should be taken to minimize the amount of energy utilized. This consideration also directly impacts the cost of running the process. Painting often involves the use of solvents and other chemicals that are harmful to the environment and workers. Water-based paints have been developed which reduce

FIGURE 14.4 Product design, process design, and capacity are closely related.

emissions and clean-up. The paint and the equipment used to apply it is often expensive but the company saves in cleanup and worker protection costs.

Make or buy decision   A manufacturer has the alternative of making parts in-house or of buying them from an outside supplier. Few companies make everything or buy everything they need. Indeed, on the average, North American manufacturers purchase more than 50% of the cost of goods manufactured. A decision has to be made about which items to make and which to buy. Although cost is the main determinant, other factors such as the following are usually considered:

Reasons to Make In-house
- Can produce for less cost than a supplier.
- To utilize existing equipment to fullest extent.
- To keep confidential processes within control of the firm.
- To maintain quality.
- To maintain workforce.

Reasons to Buy Out
- Requires less capital investment.
- Uses specialized expertise of suppliers.
- Allows the firm to concentrate on its own area of specialization.
- Provides known and competitive prices.
- Can accommodate large changes in volume.

The decision to make or buy is clear for many items such as nuts and bolts, motors, or components that the firm does not normally manufacture. For other items that are in the firm's specialty area, a specific decision will have to be made.

As supply chains are becoming more tightly linked and sources of supply are becoming more global, the issue to buy (outsource) becomes more complex. For example, exchange rates, transit inventory levels, impact of transit time on lead time, and government controls are all becoming issues that need to be considered in making the decision to make or buy.

PROCESSING EQUIPMENT

Processing equipment can be classified in several ways, but for our purposes one of the most convenient is the degree of specialization of machinery and equipment.

General-purpose machinery   General-purpose machinery can be used for a variety of operations or can do work on a variety of products within its machine classification. For example, a home sewing machine can sew a variety of materials, stitches, and patterns within its basic capability. Different auxiliary tools can be used to create other stitches or for particular sewing operations.

Special-purpose machinery   Special-purpose machinery is designed to perform specific operations on one work piece or a small number of similar work pieces. For example, a sewing machine built or equipped to sew shirt collars would be a special-purpose machine capable of sewing collars on any size shirt of any color but not capable of performing other sewing operations unless it was modified extensively.

General-purpose machinery is generally less costly than special-purpose machinery. However, its runtime is slow, and because it is operated by humans, the quality level tends to be lower than when using special-purpose machinery. One exception is robotic machines, which automate the human aspect and tend to produce high quality, but the cost is much higher. Special-purpose machinery is less flexible but parts can be produced with it much quicker than with general-purpose machinery.

PROCESS SYSTEMS

Depending on the product design, volume, and available equipment, the process engineer must design the system to make the product. Based on material flow, processes can be organized in three ways:

- Flow.
- Intermittent.
- Project (fixed position).

The system used will depend on the demand for the item, range of products, and the ease or difficulty of moving material. All three systems can be used to make discrete units such as automobiles or textbooks, or to make nondiscrete products such as gasoline, paint, or fertilizer.

Flow Processes

Workstations needed to make the product, or family of similar products, are grouped together in one department and are laid out in the sequence needed to make the product. Examples are assembly lines, cafeterias, oil refineries, and steel rolling mills. In **flow processing**, work flows from one workstation to another at a nearly constant rate and with no delays. There is some form of mechanical method of moving goods between workstations. If the units are discrete, such as automobiles, flow manufacturing is called *repetitive manufacturing*. If not, for example gasoline, it is called *continuous manufacturing*. The typical flow pattern is shown in Figure 14.5. Flow process layout is sometimes called **product layout** because the system is set up for a limited range of similar products.

Flow systems produce only a limited range of similar products. For example, an assembly line that produces a certain type of refrigerator cannot be used to assemble washing machines. The operations used to make one are different and in a different sequence than those used for making the other. Demand for the family of products has to be large enough to justify setting up the line economically. If sufficient demand exists, flow systems are extremely efficient, for several reasons:

- Workstations are designed to produce a limited range of similar products, so machinery and tooling can be specialized.
- Because material flows from one workstation to the next, there is very little buildup of work-in-process inventory.
- Because of the flow system and the low work-in-process inventory, lead times are short.
- In most cases, flow systems substitute capital for labor and standardize what labor there is into routine tasks.

Because it is so cost effective, this system of processing should be used wherever and to whatever extent it can be.

Intermittent Processes

In **intermittent manufacturing**, goods are not made continuously as in a flow system but are made at intervals in lots or batches. Workstations must be capable of processing many different parts. Thus, it is necessary to use general-purpose workstations and machinery that can perform a variety of tasks.

WORKSTATIONS

FIGURE 14.5 Material flow: flow process.

WORKSTATIONS

FIGURE 14.6 Material flow: intermittent process.

General-purpose workstations do not produce goods as quickly as special purpose workstations used in flow manufacturing. Usually, workstations are organized into departments based on similar types of skills or equipment. For example, all welding and fabrication operations are located in one department, machine tools in another, and assembly in yet another department. Work moves only to those workstations needed to make the product and skips the rest. This results in the jumbled flow pattern shown in Figure 14.6.

Intermittent processes are flexible. They can change from one part or task to another more quickly than can flow processes. This is because they use general-purpose machinery and skilled flexible labor that can perform the variety of operations needed.

Control of work flow is managed through individual work orders for each lot or batch being made. Because of this and the jumbled pattern of work flow, manufacturing planning and control problems are severe. Often, many work orders exist, each of which can be processed in different ways.

Provided the volume of work exists to justify it, flow manufacturing is less costly than intermittent manufacturing. There are several reasons for this:

- Setup costs are low. Once the line is established, changeovers are needed infrequently to run another product.
- Since work centers are designed for specific products, run costs are low.
- Because products move continuously from one workstation to the next, work-in-process inventory will be low.
- Costs associated with controlling production are low because work flows through the process in a fixed sequence.

But the volume of specific parts must be enough to use the capacity of the line and justify the capital cost.

Project (Fixed Position) Processes

Project or fixed position manufacturing is mostly used for large, complex projects such as locomotives, ships, or buildings. The product may remain in one location for its full assembly period, as with a ship, or it may move from location to location after considerable work and time are spent on it. Large aircraft are made this way. Project manufacturing has little advantage except it avoids the very high costs of moving the product from one workstation to another.

There are many variations and combinations of these three basic types of processes. Companies will try to find the best combination to make their particular products. In any one company it is not unusual to see examples of all three being used.

SELECTING THE PROCESS

Generally, the larger the volume (quantity) to be produced, the greater the opportunity to use special-purpose processes. The more special purpose an operation, the faster it will produce. Often the capital cost for such machinery or for special tools or fixtures is high. Capital costs are called fixed costs and the production, or run, costs are called variable costs.

Fixed costs These are costs that do not vary with the volume being produced. Purchase costs of machinery and tools and setup costs are considered fixed costs. No matter what volume is produced, these costs remain the same. Suppose it costs $200 to set up a process; this cost will not change no matter how much is produced.

Variable costs These are costs that vary with the quantity produced. Direct labor (labor used directly in the making of the product) and direct material (material used directly in the product) are the major variable costs. If the runtime for a product is 12 minutes per unit, the labor cost $10 per hour, and the material cost $5 per unit, then:

$$\text{Variable cost} = \frac{12}{60} \times \$10.00 + \$5.00 = \$7.00 \text{ per unit}$$

Let:

FC = Fixed cost
VC = Variable cost per unit
x = Number of units to be produced
TC = Total cost
UC = Unit (average) cost per unit
Total cost = Fixed cost + (Variable cost per unit)(number of units produced)

Then:

$$TC = FC + VCx$$

$$\text{Unit cost} = \frac{\text{Total cost}}{\text{number of units produced}} = \frac{TC}{x}$$

Example

A process designer has a choice of two methods for making an item. Method A has a fixed cost of $2000 for tooling and jigs and a variable cost of $3 per unit. Method B requires a special machine costing $20,000 and the variable costs are $1 per piece. Let x be the number of units produced.

	Method A	Method B
Fixed cost	$2000.00	$20,000.00
Variable unit cost	$3.00	$1.00
Total cost	$2000.00 + 3x$	$20,000.00 + 1x$
Unit (average) cost	$\dfrac{\$2000.00 + 3x}{x}$	$\dfrac{\$2000.00 + 1x}{x}$

Table 14.1 shows what happens to the total cost as quantities produced are increased. The total cost data in this table are shown graphically in Figure 14.7. From Table 14.1 and Figure 14.7, we can see that initially the total cost and unit cost of method A are less than method B. This is because the fixed cost for method B is greater and has to be absorbed over a small number of units. Although the total cost for both methods increases as more units are produced, the total cost for method A increases faster until, at some quantity between 8000 and 10,000 units, the total cost for method B becomes less than for method A.

Volume	Total Cost (Dollars)		Unit Cost (Dollars)	
(Units)	Method A	Method B	Method A	Method B
2000	$8000	$22,000	$4.00	$11.00
4000	14000	24000	3.5	6
6000	20000	26000	3.33	4.33
8000	26000	28000	3.25	3.5
10000	32000	30000	3.2	3
12000	38000	32000	3.17	2.67
14000	44000	34000	3.14	2.43
16000	50000	36000	3.13	2.25

TABLE 14.1   Total and average cost versus quantity produced.

FIGURE 14.7 Total cost versus quantity produced.

Similarly, the unit cost for both methods decreases as more units are produced. However, the unit cost for method B decreases at a faster rate until, at some quantity between 8000 and 10,000 units, unit costs for both methods are equal.

Cost Equalization Point

Knowing the quantity beyond which the cost of using method B becomes less than for method A enables us to decide easily which process to use to minimize the total cost (and the unit cost).

This quantity is called the **cost equalization point (CEP)** and is the volume for which the total cost (and unit cost) of using one method is the same as another. For our example, the total cost calculations are as follows.

$$TC_A = TC_B$$
$$FC_A + VC_Ax = FC_B + VC_Bx$$
$$\$2000 + \$3x = \$20,000 + \$1x$$
$$3x - 1x = 20,000 - 2000$$
$$2x = 18,000$$
$$x = 9000 \text{ units}$$

The CEP is 9000 units. At this quantity the total cost of using method A will be the same as for method B.

$$TC_A = FC_A + VC_Ax - 2000 + (3 \times 9000) = \$29,000$$
$$TC_B = FC_B + VC_Bx = 20,000 + (1 \times 9000) = \$29,000$$

We can get the same results by using unit costs instead of total costs.
From the preceding calculations we can say

- If the volume (quantity to produce) is less than the CEP, the method with the lower fixed cost will cost less.
- If the volume is greater than the CEP, the method with the greater fixed cost will cost less.

For example, if the volume were 5000 units, method A would cost less, and if the volume were 10,000 units, method B would cost less.

Variable costs, mostly direct labor and material, can be reduced by substituting machinery and equipment (capital) for direct labor. This increases the fixed costs and decreases the variable costs. But to justify this economically the volume must be high enough to reduce the total or unit cost of production.

Increasing Volume

The obvious way to increase volume is to increase sales. However, a finished product is made up of several purchased or manufactured components. If the volume of these components can be increased, then the unit cost of the components, and the final product, will be reduced.

The volume of components can be increased without increasing sales by a program of simplification and standardization, discussed previously in this chapter.

If a subassembly or component part can be standardized for use in more than one final product, then the volume of the subassembly or part is increased without an increase in the total sales volume. Thus more specialized and faster-running processes can be justified and the cost of operations reduced.

Standardization of parts is a major characteristic of modern mass production. At the turn of the 20th century, Henry Ford revolutionized manufacturing by standardizing the finished product—one model of car. The joke often heard then was that you could have any color you wanted as long as it was black. Today a vast range of models are made, but if each model was exploded into its subassemblies and component parts, we would find specific components common to a great number of models. In this way, modern manufacturers can provide the consumer with a wide choice of finished products made from standard parts and components.

CONTINUOUS PROCESS IMPROVEMENT

People have always been concerned with how best to do a job and the time it should take to do it. Process improvement is concerned with improving the effective use of human and other resources. *Continuous* implies an ongoing activity; *improvement* implies an increase in the productivity or value of quality or condition. Hence the name continuous process improvement (CPI).

Continuous process improvement consists of a logical set of steps and techniques used to analyze processes and to improve them.

Improving productivity Productivity can be improved by spending money (capital) on better and faster machines and equipment. However, with any given amount of capital, a method must be designed to use the machinery and equipment most productively. A workstation might consist of highly sophisticated machinery and equipment worth $1 million or more. Its productivity and return on investment depend on how the equipment is used and how the operator manages it. CPI determines how equipment is used and managed.

Continuous process improvement is a low-cost method of designing or improving work methods to maximize productivity. The aim is to increase productivity by better use of existing resources. Continuous process improvement is concerned with removing work content, not with spending money on better and faster machines.

Peter Drucker has said, "Efficiency is doing things right; effectiveness is doing the right things." CPI aims to do the right things and to do them efficiently.

People involvement Today management recognizes the need to maximize the potential of flexible, motivated workers. People are capable of thinking, learning, problem solving, and contributing to productivity. With existing processes and equipment, people are the primary source of improvement because they are the experts in the things they do.

Process improvement is not solely the responsibility of industrial engineers. Everyone in the workforce must be given the opportunity to improve the processes they work with. Techniques that help to analyze and improve work are not complicated and can be learned. Indeed, the idea of continuous improvement is based on the participation of operators and improvement in methods requiring relatively little capital.

Workers have two jobs:

- Their "as defined" job.
- To improve their "as defined" job.

Teams One of the features of CPI is team involvement. A team is a group of people working together to achieve common goals and objectives. The members of the team should be all those who are involved with the process. Teams are successful because of the emphasis placed on people. Not all problems can be solved by teams, nor are all people suited to teams. However, they are often effective. Often problems cross functional lines and thus multifunctional teams are common.

Continuous process improvement can still be effectively carried out by the individuals.

The Six Steps in Continuous Process Improvement

The CPI system is based on the *scientific method*. This general method is used to solve many kinds of problems. The six steps are as follows:

1. Select the process to be studied.
2. Record the existing method to collect the necessary data in a useful form.
3. Analyze the recorded data to generate alternative improved methods.
4. Develop the best method of doing the work by evaluating the alternatives.
5. Install the method as standard practice by training the operator.
6. Maintain the new method.

Select the Process

The first step is to decide what to study. This depends on the ability to recognize situations that have good potential for improvement. Observation of existing methods comes first.

Observe The important feature in observation is a questioning attitude. Questions such as why, when, and how must be asked whenever we observe something. This attitude needs development because we tend to assume that the familiar method is the only one. Often we hear, "We have always done it this way!" "This way" is not necessarily the only, most productive, or most effective way.

Any situation can be improved but some have better potential than others. Indicators that show areas most needing improvement include:

- High scrap, reprocessing, rework, and repair costs.
- Backtracking of material flow caused by poor plant layout.
- Bottlenecks.
- Excessive overtime.
- Excessive manual handling of materials, both from workplace to workplace and at the workplace.
- Use of environmentally hazardous materials
- Employee grievances without true assignable causes.

Select   The purpose of continuous process improvement is to improve productivity to reduce operating, product, or service costs. In selecting jobs or operations for method improvement, there are two major considerations: economic and human.

Economic considerations   The cost of the improvement must be justified. The cost of making the study and installing the improvement must be recovered from the savings in a reasonable time. One to two years is a commonly used period.

   The job size must justify the study. Almost anything can be improved, but the improvement must be worthwhile. Suppose a method improvement saves 1 hour on a job taking 5 hours, performed once a month or 12 times a year. The reduction in time is 20% and the total time saved in a year is 12 hours. Another method improvement saves 1 minute on a job taking 10 minutes, performed 200 times per week. The time saved in this case is only 10% but will be ($1 \times 200 \times 52 \div 60 = 173.3$) hours per year, a much higher rate of return on the investment made in the study.

The human factor   The human factor governs the success of method improvement. The resistance to change, by both management and worker, must always be remembered. Working situations characterized by high fatigue, accident hazards, absenteeism, and dirty and unpleasant conditions should be identified and improved. Sometimes it is difficult to give specific economic justification for such improvements, but the intangible benefits are extensive and should weigh heavily in selecting studies.

Pareto diagrams   Pareto analysis can be used to select problems with the greatest economic impact. The theory of Pareto analysis is the same as that used in the ABC analysis discussed in Chapter 9. This theory says that a few items (usually about 20%) account for most of the cost or problems. It separates the "vital few" from the "trivial many." Examples of the "vital few" are

- A few processes account for the bulk of scrap.
- A few suppliers account for most rejected parts.
- A few problems account for most process downtime.

   The steps in making a **Pareto analysis** are as follows:

1. Determine the method of classifying the data: by problem, cause, nonconformity, and so forth.
2. Select the unit of measure. This is usually dollars but may be the frequency of occurrence.
3. Collect data for an appropriate time interval, usually long enough to include all likely conditions.
4. Summarize the data by ranking the items in descending order according to the selected unit of measure.
5. Calculate the total cost.
6. Calculate the percentage for each item.
7. Construct a bar graph showing the percentage for each item and a line graph of the cumulative percentage.

Example Problem

A product has failed in the field a number of times. Data are collected according to the type of failure with the following results: Type A—11, type B—8, type C—5, type D—60, type E—100, type F—4, other—12. Construct a table summarizing the data in descending order of magnitude. From this table, construct a Pareto diagram.

ANSWER

Type of Failure	Number of Failures	Percent	Cumulative Percentage
E	100	50.0	50.0
D	60	30.0	80.0
A	11	5.5	85.5
B	8	4.0	89.5
C	5	2.5	92.0
F	4	2.0	94.0
O (Other)	12	6.0	100.0
Total	200	100.0	

Note that Pareto analysis does not report what the problems are, only where they seem to occur. In the previous example, further investigation into the causes of failure types E and D will give the best return for the effort spent. It is important to select the categories carefully. For example, in the previous problem, if the location of failures were recorded rather than the type of failure, the results would be quite different and perhaps not significant.

Cause-and-effect diagram   Sometimes called a fishbone or an Ishikawa diagram, the **cause-and-effect diagram** is a very useful tool for identifying root causes. Figure 14.8 shows such a diagram.

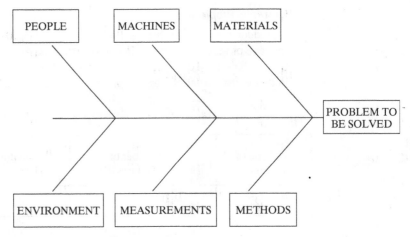

FIGURE 14.8 Cause-and-effect diagram.

The fishbone diagram is best used by a group or team working together. It can be constructed by discussion and brainstorming. The steps in developing a fishbone diagram are as follows:

1. Identify the problem to be studied and state it in a few words. For example, the reject rate on machine A is 20%.

2. Generate some ideas about the main causes of the problem. Usually all probable root causes can be classified into six categories.

   - **Materials.** For example, from consistent to inconsistent raw materials.
   - **Machines.** For example, a well-maintained machine versus a poorly maintained one.
   - **People.** For example, a poorly trained operator instead of a well-trained one.
   - **Methods.** For example, changing the speed on a machine.
   - **Measurement.** For example, measuring parts with an inaccurate gauge.
   - **Environment.** For example, increased dust or humidity.

3. Brainstorm all possible causes for each of the main causes.

4. Once all the causes have been listed, try to identify the most likely root causes and work on these.

Record

The next step is to record all the facts relating to the existing process. To be able to understand what to record, it is necessary to define the process being studied. Recording defines the process. The following must be determined to properly define the process.

- **The process boundaries.** All processes, big or small, begin and end somewhere. Starting and ending points form the boundaries of the process. For example, the starting point in the process of getting to work in the morning might be getting out of bed. The ending point might be arrival at the desk or classroom.
- **Process flow.** This is a description of what happens between the starting and ending points. Usually this is a listing of the steps taken between the start and finish of the process. There are several recording techniques to help perform this step. Some of these will be discussed later in this chapter.
- **Process inputs and outputs.** All processes change something. The things that are changed are called inputs and they may be physical, such as raw materials, or informational, such as data. Outputs are the result of what goes on in the process. For example, raw materials are converted into something more useful or data are manipulated to produce reports.
- **Components.** Components are the resources used in changing inputs to outputs. They are composed of people, methods, and equipment. Unlike process inputs, components do not become part of the output but are part of the process. For example, in producing a report, the word processor, graphics program, computer, and printer are all components.

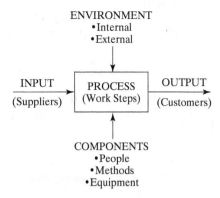

FIGURE 14.9 Schematic of a process.

- **Customer.** Processes exist to serve customers and customers ultimately define what a process is supposed to do. If customer needs are not considered, there is a risk of improving things that do not matter to the users of the output.
- **Suppliers.** Suppliers are those who provide the inputs. They may be internal to the organization or external.
- Business **Environment.** The process is controlled or regulated by external and internal factors. The external factors are beyond control and include customers' acceptance of the process output, competitors, and government regulation. Internal factors are in the organization and can be controlled.

Figure 14.9 shows a schematic of the system.

The next step is to record all facts relating to the existing method. A record is necessary because it is difficult to record and maintain a large mass of detail in our heads for the duration of the analysis. Recording helps us consider all elements of the problem in a logical sequence and makes sure we do consider all the steps in the process. The record of the present method also provides the basis for both the critical examination and the development of an improved method.

Classes of activity Before discussing some of the charts used, we should look at the kinds of activities recorded. All activity can generally be classified into one of six types. As a method of shorthand, there are six universally used symbols for these activities. The activities and symbols are shown in Figure 14.10. One of the activities shown, decision, may not always be used. If not, a decision is usually considered an operation.

Following are descriptions of some of the various charting techniques.

Operations process charts Operations process charts record in sequence only the main operation and inspections. They are useful for preliminary investigation and give a bird's-eye view of the process. Figure 14.11 shows such a chart.

The description, and sometimes the times, for each operation is also shown. An operations process chart would be used to record product movement.

Process flow diagram A **process flow diagram** shows graphically and sequentially the various steps, events, and operations that make up a process. It provides a picture, in the form of a diagram, of what actually happens when a product is made or a service performed. In addition to the six symbols shown in Figure 14.10, others may be used to show such things as rework and documentation. Figure 14.12 shows an example of a process flow diagram. In this example, the process starts when the goods are received and ends when a check is sent to the supplier.

Analyze

Examination and analysis are the key steps in continuous process improvement. Although all the other steps are significant, they either lead up to, or result from, the critical analysis. This step involves analyzing every aspect of the present method and evaluating all proposed possible methods.

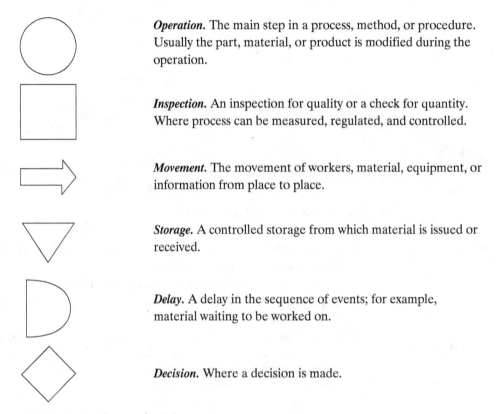

Operation. The main step in a process, method, or procedure. Usually the part, material, or product is modified during the operation.

Inspection. An inspection for quality or a check for quantity. Where process can be measured, regulated, and controlled.

Movement. The movement of workers, material, equipment, or information from place to place.

Storage. A controlled storage from which material is issued or received.

Delay. A delay in the sequence of events; for example, material waiting to be worked on.

Decision. Where a decision is made.

FIGURE 14.10 Classes of activity.

FIGURE 14.11 Operations process chart.

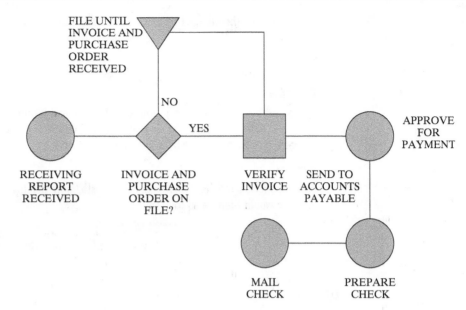

FIGURE 14.12 Process flow diagram.

Find the root cause Frequently it is difficult to separate symptoms from the root causes of problems. Often symptoms are what we see and it is difficult to trace back to the root cause. To find root causes you must have a questioning attitude. For the analyst, "why" is the most important word. Every aspect of the existing method should be questioned. In "The Elephant's Child," from *The Just-So Stories*, Rudyard Kipling wrote:

> *I keep six honest serving-men*
> *(They taught me all I know);*
> *Their names are What and Why and When*
> *And How and Where and Who.*

Kipling personifies six words normally used as questions; they are also the "serving men" of the methods analyst.

A rule of thumb common to many problem-solving methods says it is necessary to ask (and answer) the "why" question up to five times before one reaches the root cause of a problem.

Three approaches can help in examining:

- **A questioning attitude.** This implies an open mind, examining the facts as they are, not as they seem, avoiding preconceived ideas, and avoiding hasty judgments.
- **Examining the total process to define what is accomplished, how, and why.** The answers to these questions will determine the effectiveness of the total process. The results may show that the process is not even needed.
- **Examining the parts of the process.** Activities can be divided into two major categories: those in which something is happening to the product (worked on, inspected, or moved) and those in which nothing constructive is happening to the product (delay or storage, for example). In the first category, value is added only when the part is being worked on. Setup, put away, and move, while necessary, add cost to the product but do not increase its value. They must be minimized. Value will be added when the product is being worked on but, again, the goal is to maximize the productivity of these operations.
- **Analysis of the relationship between production rate, item throughput, and process inventory.** For processes that have the rate of material input equal to the rate of output, there is a basic relationship between the amount of inventory in the process and the time it takes for a single item to be processed through the process (often called throughput time). If the processing rate of the process is called R, the inventory is

called *I*, and the throughput time is called *T* then the relationship (called **Little's Law**) is given as

$$I = RT$$

Example

A process has the ability to produce two items every minute. The process currently has 100 of the items being processed. If another item were introduced into the process, how long would it take until the new item?

ANSWER

The production rate is two items per minute, and the inventory is 100 units. The solution would then be as follows:

$$I = RT$$
$$100 \text{ units} = (2 \text{ units/minute}) \times T$$
$$T = 50 \text{ minutes}$$

Develop

When developing possible solutions, there are four approaches to take to help develop a better method.

- *Eliminate* all unnecessary work. Question why the work is being done in the first place and if it can be eliminated.
- *Combine* operations wherever possible. Thus material handling will be reduced, space saved, and the throughput time reduced. This is a major thrust of just-in-time manufacturing.
- *Rearrange the sequence* of operations for more effective results. This is an extension of the previous approach. If sequences are changed, then possibly they can be combined.
- *Simplify* wherever possible by making the necessary operations less complex. If the questioning attitude is used, then complexity should be reduced. Usually the best solutions are the simple ones.

Principles of motion economy   There are several principles of motion economy, among which are the following:

1. Locate materials, tools, and workplace within normal working areas and pre-position tools and materials.

2. Locate the work done most frequently in the normal working areas and everything else within the maximum grasp areas.

3. Arrange work so motions of hands, arms, legs, and so on are balanced by being made simultaneously, in opposite directions, and over symmetrical paths. Both hands should be working together and should start and finish at the same time. The end of one cycle should be located near the start of the next cycle.

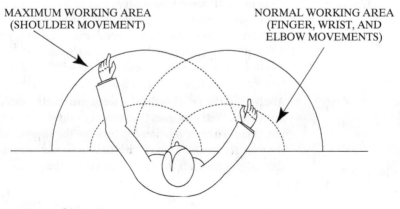

MAXIMUM WORKING AREA
(SHOULDER MOVEMENT)

NORMAL WORKING AREA
(FINGER, WRIST, AND
ELBOW MOVEMENTS)

FIGURE 14.13 Working areas.

4. Conditions contributing to operator fatigue must be reduced to a minimum. Provide good lighting, keep tools and materials within maximum working areas (see Figure 14.13), provide for alternate sitting and standing at work, and design workplaces of proper height to eliminate stooping.

Human and environmental factors   In addition to the principles of motion economy, other important matters that influence human and environmental conditions must be considered. These include safety, comfort, cleanliness, and personal care; so provision must be made for lighting, ventilation and heating, noise reduction, seating, and stimulation.

Of these, stimulation may be less obvious. In highly repetitive work, workers may become bored and dissatisfied, which may lead to emotional problems. A pleasant environment created by attractive color schemes in plants or offices, location of windows, and music during working hours can do much to reduce stress and absenteeism.

Methods improvement is based on the concepts of scientific management. It concentrates on the task and ways of removing work content (waste) from tasks. It gives little consideration to the human being and higher-level needs, such as self-esteem and self-fulfillment, and work can become repetitive and boring. **Job design** is an attempt to provide more satisfying meaningful jobs and to use the worker's mental and interpersonal skills. These improvements include the following.

Job enlargement expands a worker's job by clustering similar or related tasks into one job. For example, a job might be expanded to include a sequence of activities instead of only one activity. This is called *horizontal enlargement.*

Job enrichment adds more meaningful, satisfying, and fulfilling tasks. The job not only includes production operations but many setup, scheduling, maintenance, and control responsibilities.

Job rotation trains workers to do several jobs so they can be moved from one job to another. This is called cross-training.

All these factors help to produce a more motivated and flexible workforce. In modern manufacturing, where quick response to customers' needs is essential, these characteristics can mean the difference between business success and failure.

Employee empowerment and self-directed teams assume the workers have more knowledge and responsibility for understanding and performing the work. Empowering the workers to take more responsibility can lead to self-directed teams, where there is typically no supervisor. The workers themselves will understand what is to be done and will manage their own activities to accomplish the required work efficiently and effectively with little or no supervision.

Install

So far, the work done by the analyst has been planning. Now the plans must be put into action by installing the new method.

In planning the installation, consideration must be given to the best time to install, the method of installing, and the people involved. Then the analyst needs to be sure that equipment, tooling, information, and the people are all available. At installation time, a dry run will show whether all equipment and tooling are working properly.

Training the operator is the most important part of the installation. If the operator has been involved in designing the method change, this should not be difficult. The worker will be familiar and comfortable with the change and will probably feel some sense of ownership.

Learning curve   Over time, as the operator does the tasks repetitively, speed will increase and errors decrease. This process is known as the learning curve and is illustrated in Figure 14.14. Note there is no time scale shown. Depending on the task, a worker may progress through the learning curve in a few minutes or, for high-skill jobs, several months or years.

Maintain

Maintaining is a follow-up activity that has two parts. The first is to be sure that the new method is being done as it should be. This is most critical for the first few days, and close supervision may be necessary. The second is to evaluate the change to be sure that the planned benefits are accomplished. If not, the method must be changed.

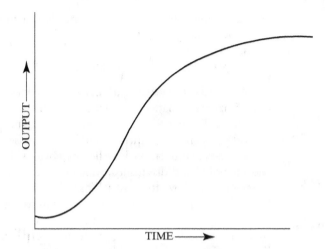

FIGURE 14.14 Learning curve.

SUMMARY

Products and the processes used to make them are continually being redesigned to create products more appealing to customers, to improve productivity or to make the products and their associated processes friendlier to the environment. Producers follow well established principles of product development. The 3 S's: simplification, standardization and specialization are very powerful principles which can help to improve productivity and make products more reliable. With information easy to share in today's environment product design and process design can work simultaneously to bring better quality products to market faster and with reduced costs. As the design of the product is being established the process is also being designed based on: the quality level desired, the ability of the process to react quickly to changes in customer demand (flexibility), the overall volume of demand and how much the customer wants to be involved in the production of the product. Depending on the volume the decision may be made to buy the product rather than make it, or, to use one process rather than another. This is best determined with the cost equalization point CEP which determines a volume below which we use the low fixed cost high variable cost alternative and above which we invest in the high fixed cost and low variable cost alternative.

Continuous Process Improvement CPI applies to all processes to make them more cost effective and competitive. It is done on an ongoing basis not just when new products are introduced. CPI uses the traditional tools of the scientific methods in six steps: select, record, analyze, develop, install and maintain. All the steps have one thing in common and that is the involvement of people.

With improvements to product and process design goods tend to flow quickly and smoothly resulting in lower costs and improved profits. Continuous improvement leads to the next chapter in this text on just in time and lean production.

KEY TERMS

Cause-and-effect diagram 325

Continuous Process Improvement 322

Concurrent engineering 314

Cost equalization point (CEP) 322

Employee empowerment and self-directed teams 331

Flow processing 318

Focused factories 312

General-purpose machinery 317

Intermittent manufacturing 318

Job design 331

Job enlargement 331

Job enrichment 331

Job rotation 331

Little's Law 329

Mass customization 315

Modularization 312

Nesting 315

Operations process charts 327

Pareto analysis 325

Process flow diagram 327

Process focus 312

Processes 315

Product and market focus 312

Product layout 318

Project or fixed position manufacturing 319

Simplification 322

Simultaneous engineering 314

Specialization 312

Special-purpose machinery 317

Standard 311

QUESTIONS

1. Describe simplification, standardization, and specialization. Why are they important and why are they interrelated?
2. What are the advantages and disadvantages of standardization?
3. What are the advantages and disadvantages of specialization?
4. What are product focus and process focus based on? What is a focused factory?
5. What is the advantage to modular design?
6. How are production costs affected by
   a. Standard sizes?
   b. Universal fit parts?
7. What are the two criteria for designing a product?
8. Why is product design important to operations costs?
9. Why is product design important to quality?
10. What is simultaneous engineering, and what are some of its advantages?
11. What is a process? What is process nesting?
12. What are the five basic factors that must be considered when designing a process?
13. Why are product design, quantity to produce, and process design intimately related?
14. Give four reasons why companies will make a product in-house and why they will outsource.
15. Describe general-purpose and special-purpose machinery. Compare each for flexibility of use, operator involvement, run time per piece, setup time, quality, capital cost, and application.
16. What is flow processing, and what are its advantages and disadvantages?
17. What is intermittent processing and when is it used? Contrast it with flow processing.
18. When is project (fixed position) processing used?
19. Define fixed and variable costs and give examples of each in manufacturing. What is total cost, and what is the equation for it?
20. What is the cost equalization point?
21. How can the variable cost be reduced? What does this do to the fixed costs, and what is needed to economically justify this course of action?
22. What are the six steps in continuous process improvement?
23. Name and describe the two considerations in selecting a job to be studied.
24. What is a Pareto diagram, and why is it useful?
25. What is a cause-and-effect diagram, and why is it useful?
26. Why is it necessary to record?
27. Describe each of the following as it relates to recording:
   a. Process boundaries.
   b. Process flow.
   c. Process inputs and outputs.

    d. Process components.

    e. Suppliers.

    f. Environment.

28. What are the six symbols used in method analysis? Are there other symbols that can be used?

29. Describe each of the following:

    a. Operations process chart.

    b. Process flow diagram.

30. What is the purpose of the analysis step in continuous process improvement? What is the basic question?

31. What are the four approaches that should be taken when developing a better method?

32. What are the four principles of motion economy?

33. Describe job design.

34. What is the learning curve?

35. What might be some of the advantages and disadvantages of self-directed work teams?

36. How might the learning curve impact standard production times used for planning? How would you possibly deal with this impact?

37. How might an application of Little's Law prove useful?

38. What is meant by the term "business environment"?

39. Select a product with which you are familiar. How do you think it might be redesigned to make it easier to manufacture and possibly more useful to the user?

PROBLEMS

14.1. Given the following fixed and variable costs and the volumes, calculate the total and unit costs.

Fixed cost	Variable cost	Volume (units)	Total cost	Unit cost
$200.00	$10.00	100		
$200.00	$7.00	1000		
$50.00	$15.00	20		
$1,000.00	$1.00	2000		
$500.00	$20.00	500		

14.2. A process costs $200 to set up. The run time is 5 minutes per piece and the run cost is $30 per hour. Determine the following:

    a. The fixed cost.

    b. The variable cost.

    c. The total cost and unit cost for a lot of 600.

    d. The total cost and unit cost for a lot of 1200.

        Answer. a. Fixed cost = $200.00

                b. Variable cost = $2.50

                c. Total cost = $1450.00

                   Unit cost = $2.90

                d. Total cost = $2700.00

                   Unit cost = $2.70

14.3. A manufacturer has a choice of purchasing and installing a heat-treating oven or having the heat treating done by an outside supplier. The manufacturer has developed the following cost estimates:

	Heat Treat In-house	Purchase Services
Fixed cost	$28,000.00	$0.00
Variable cost	$10.00	$17.00

a. What is the cost equalization point?

b. Should the company have the heat treating done outside if the annual volume is 3000 units? 5000 units?

c. What would be the unit (average) cost for the selected process for each of the volumes in b above?

Answer. a. CEP = 4000 units

b. Volume 3000 units purchase services;
Volume 5000 units heat treat in-house

c. Unit cost for 3000 units is $17.00; for 5000 units is $15.60

14.4. Bananas are on sale at the Cross Towne store for 79¢ per pound. They normally sell for 99¢ per pound at your corner store. If round-trip bus fare costs $3.60 to the Cross Towne store, is it worth going? Discuss other ways of taking advantage of this bargain.

14.5. Given the following costs, which process should be used for an order of 400 pieces of a given part? What will be the unit cost for the process selected?

	Buy	Process A	Process B
Setup		$40.00	$180.00
Tooling		$10.00	$20.00
Labor/unit		$4.10	$3.80
Material/unit		$2.00	$2.00
Purchase cost	$6.10		

14.6. The Light Company is planning on producing a new type of light shade, the parts for which may be made or bought. If purchased, they will cost $2 per unit. Making the parts on a semiautomatic machine will involve a $5000 fixed cost for tooling and $1.30 per unit variable cost. The alternative is to make the parts on an automatic machine. The tooling costs are $15,000, but the variable cost is reduced to 60¢ per unit.

a. Calculate the cost equalization point between buying and the semiautomatic machine.

b. Calculate the cost equalization point between the semiautomatic and automatic machines.

c. Which method should be used for expected sales of the following?
  i. 5000 units
  ii. 6000 units
  iii. 8000 units
  iv. 10,000 units
  v. 25,000 units

d. What is the unit cost for the selected process for each of the sales in c above?

Answer. i. Unit cost = $2.00
  ii. Unit cost = $2.00
  iii. Unit cost = $1.925
  iv. Unit cost = $1.80
  v. Unit cost = $1.20

14.7. A major mail order house collected data on the reasons for return shipments over a 3-month period with the following results: wrong selection 62,000; wrong size 50,000; order canceled 15,000; wrong address 3000; other 15,000. Construct a Pareto diagram.

Reason	Number	Percent	Cumulative Percent
Total			

14.8. A firm experienced abnormal scrap and collected data to see which parts were causing the problem, with the following results: part A—$5720, part B—$10,500, Part C—$890, Part D—$1130, Part F—$700. Complete the following table, listing the errors in descending order of importance. Construct a Pareto diagram.

Part	Number	Percent	Cumulative Percent
Total			

14.9. A process has a production rate of 30 units per hour. If it takes 40 minutes for a single unit to be completed in the process, what is the inventory of units in the process?

14.10. Draw an operations process chart for the assembly of a ballpoint pen. The pen is made from three subassemblies (see figure):

1. upper barrel
2. cartridge
3. lower barrel

Operation 1 attach clip to upper barrel
2 insert button into upper barrel
3 insert rotor into upper barrel
4 press ball into tip of cartridge
5 insert tip into cartridge
6 fill cartridge with ink

Inspection 1 test cartridge

Operation 7 insert cartridge into upper barrel
8 slip spring over cartridge
9 screw lower barrel and upper barrel together

Inspection 2 test operation of pen
3 final inspection

14.12. Draw a process flow diagram for your activities from the time you wake up until you arrive at work. Can you think of ways to improve the process?

14.13. A process can produce a final product at the rate of 2 products per minute. If an individual product takes 30 minutes to pass through the process, what is the inventory of products in the process at any time?

14.14. A university registration process can register a person every 4 minutes. If there are an average of 10 people in line for the registration, how long will each person have to wait in line?

CASE STYDY 14.1

Cheryl Franklin, Production Manager

Cheryl Franklin had been production manager at Cooper Toy Company for only a week when she started to wonder if her promotion had really been a good thing. Her boss was concerned that production was falling behind on one of their newest toys. The company had spent a lot to advertise the toy and the demand that had been created was not being met by production.

Cheryl decided to try to investigate to discover the problem and try to get the production volume back on track. Unfortunately, she found that almost everyone involved was blaming someone else.

The toy in question was one of those plastic water guns popular at beaches and swimming pools. Water is held in a reservoir and then air is pumped into the gun, allowing a fairly large stream of water to be shot about 10 meters.

Cheryl knew that the slowest part of the production line that she was using to produce the toy should be able to produce one every 3 minutes, and she also knew that the demand averaged only about one toy every 5 minutes. When she started her investigation at the assembly area, however, she found that assembly was averaging only one toy every 10 minutes. The assembly supervisor had a good explanation, however. He said that they didn't have enough inventory to work on. They were getting the water tanks being released from inspection on average only one every 8 minutes, so they were assembling the toys as fast as they could.

When Cheryl went to the inspection area, she discovered that there were lots of tanks waiting there to be inspected. The inspector assigned to the tanks appeared to be working hard, but obviously that was the problem.

Cheryl talked to the quality manager and got quite a bit more information. To quote the quality manager, "Look, we need to put those tanks through some important testing. If a child pumps too much air into the tank they are designed to let some of the air out through a relief valve. Unfortunately, a lot of the tanks have improperly glued seams. If one of those bad tanks gets on a toy then the tank is liable to rupture before the relief value activates. That rupture could send pieces of plastic flying. The last thing we need is to have some child get injured with flying plastic. We find that we have to inspect every tank since the reject rate on the gluing of the seams has been running close to 20 percent!"

Cheryl continued her investigation and discovered the following:

- The supervisor of the production area where the glue was applied claims the machine used to spread the glue will often clog, and even when it works the glue will often be applied unevenly.
- The maintenance people in charge of the glue machine claim the machine doesn't work well because the glue fixture is not correct for the application and the glue itself is too thick for the type of application.
- The engineers in charge of the design and installation of the glue fixture claim that the toy was rushed into production so quickly that they did not have time to design a proper fixture so they were forced to use an old one that was originally designed for a different application.
- The purchasing agent responsible for buying the glue claims that they were not given good specifications for the glue and therefore relied on the recommendation from the supplier as to which glue to use.
- The marketing people claimed that the toy market is so competitive that they need to get a toy to market quickly, especially given that the life cycle of the average toy is very short.
- Cheryl needs your help. Specifically, develop answers to the following:
  1. What are the underlying problems here? Try to be as specific as possible.
  2. What is the best solution for these problems? Again, try to be specific.
  3. Suggest how continuous process improvement techniques could be applied to the problems.

LEAN PRODUCTION

INTRODUCTION

In the past several years manufacturing has become much more competitive and the global economy is now a forceful reality. Producers in many countries can produce goods of consistently superior quality and deliver them to North American markets at a competitive price and schedule. They have responded to changing market needs and often have detected those needs before the consumer. Because of such competition, North America has lost the edge in the manufacture of such goods as radios, televisions, cameras, and ships.

How have some of these companies been able to do this? It is not necessarily only because of their culture, geography, government assistance, new equipment, or cheap labor, but because many of them practice lean production. **Lean production** is a philosophy that relates to the way a manufacturing company organizes and operates its business. It includes both the approach to organizing the business and the practice of **just-in-time** production (JIT). These are not magic formulas or a set of new techniques that suddenly makes a manufacturer more productive. Rather, they are the very skillful and coordinated application of existing industrial and manufacturing engineering principles. Several Japanese companies in particular have forced us to examine some of our basic assumptions and approach manufacturing with a different philosophy.

Another philosophical approach to production developed originally by Eliyahu M Goldratt in his book *The Goal* was adding yet another perspective to those assumptions about how we approach production. This approach is generally called the Theory of Constraints (TOC). TOC was introduced and discussed in Chapter 6, describing the general concepts as well as the TOC scheduling approach often called drum-buffer-rope.

This chapter will introduce the concepts of lean production and JIT. It will also elaborate more about TOC and discuss some of the environments where each of these concepts can best be applied.

LEAN PRODUCTION

Lean production is a concept that has evolved from JIT concepts over the past several years. There were many less-than-successful implementations of JIT worldwide during the 1980s, in spite of the well-documented advantages and benefits resulting from JIT. There is strong evidence that many manufacturers, eager to take advantage of the documented advantages, attempted to implement JIT without first understanding the fully integrated approach and impacts of such a highly integrated system. This condition led to many disappointing implementations or outright failures of JIT implementations during that period. Part of the misunderstanding can be attributed to confusion between the higher level JIT "philosophy" (the fundamental changes in business practices) and the more specific JIT production, which in its simplest form can be interpreted as delivering material to a production process "just in time" for its need.

As is often the case when fundamental concepts are not fully understood, the JIT concepts were viewed by many manufacturers as invalid or inappropriate for their particular production environment. In the meantime, the development of highly integrated production systems was rapidly evolving. Material requirements planning was recognized to be an effective engine to drive an integrated enterprise-wide information system that is today called Enterprise Resource Planning (ERP). Purchasing and logistics activities were similarly being integrated with fundamental internal materials management principles into an enterprise-wide approach, today called supply chain management. Similarly, the fundamental concepts of the higher level JIT approaches evolved to an enterprise-wide perspective called lean production, and the JIT term has come to be reserved for the specific concept of JIT production, which often implies a pull production system..

What was originally called JIT is still called JIT in the lean production approach, for it implies the pull system used to deliver just what is needed just in time for the need. **Lean production**, on the other hand, implies understanding and correctly implementing the major enterprise-wide changes required to truly eliminate or significantly reduce waste in the system. It is the system-wide philosophical approach used to integrate the system toward an ultimate goal of maximized customer service with minimal system waste.

Lean production can be defined in many ways, but the most popular is the *elimination of all waste and continuous improvement of productivity*. Waste means anything other than the minimum amount of equipment, parts, space, material, production time and workers' time absolutely necessary to add value to the product. This means the ideal approach is that there should be no surplus, there should be no safety stocks, and lead times should be minimal: "If you can't use it now, don't make it now."

The long-term result of eliminating waste is a cost-efficient, quality-oriented, fast-response organization that is responsive to customer needs. Such an organization has the potential to acquire a huge competitive advantage in the marketplace. While the fundamental objective focused on waste reduction, the waste reduction approaches that were developed also led to rapid responses to market demand through reduction of lead times, increased levels of quality, and lower production costs.

A principal result of the lean production approach is that removal or reduction of excessive (waste) inventory or capacity between activities in a process, regardless of the reason that inventory or capacity existed, serves to force a tighter coupling of the activities in the system. In other words, the organization must be managed as a *system* instead of a set of relatively disjointed activities. This is an important point, in that organizations can sometime produce failed implementations as they may focus on only certain aspects of lean production rather than recognizing that it is really an integrated system.

Adding Value

What constitutes value to the user? It is having the right parts and quantities at the right time and place. It is having a product or service that does what the customer wants, does it well and consistently, and is available when the customer wants it. Value satisfies the actual and perceived needs of the customer and does it at a price the customer can afford and considers reasonable. Another word for this is *quality*. Quality is meeting and exceeding customers' expectations.

Value starts in the marketplace when marketing must decide what the customer wants. Design engineering must design the product so it will provide the required value to the customer. Manufacturing engineering must first design a process to make the product and then build the product according to certain specifications. The loop is complete when the product is delivered to the customer. Figure 15.1 shows this loop schematically. If any part of the chain does not add value for the customer, there is waste.

FIGURE 15.1 Product development cycle.

Adding value to a product does not mean adding cost. Users are not concerned with the manufacturer's cost but only with the price they must pay and the value they receive. Many activities increase cost without adding value and, as much as possible, these activities should be eliminated.

WASTE

Anything in the product development cycle that does not add value to the product is **waste**. This section will look at the causes of waste in each element of the product cycle.

Waste Caused by Poor Product Specification and Design

Waste making starts with the policies set by management in responding to the needs of the marketplace. Management is responsible for establishing policies for the market segments the company wishes to serve and for deciding how broad or specialized the product line is to be. These policies affect the costs of manufacturing. For example, if the range and variety of product are large, production runs will be short and then machines must be changed over frequently. There will be little opportunity to use specialized machinery and fixtures. On the other hand, a company with a limited product range can probably produce goods on an assembly-line basis and take advantage of special-purpose machinery. In addition, the greater the diversity of products, the more complex the manufacturing process becomes, and the more difficult it is to plan and control.

Component standardization   As stated in Chapter 14, companies can specialize in the products they make and still offer customers a wide range of options. If companies standardize on the component parts used in the different models they make, they can supply customers with a variety of models and options made from standard components. Parts standardization has many advantages in manufacturing. It creates larger quantities of specific components that allow longer production runs. This, in turn, makes it more economical to use more specialized machinery, fixtures, and assembly methods. Standardization reduces the planning and control effort needed, the number of items required, and the inventory that has to be carried.

The "ideal" product is one that meets or exceeds customer expectations, makes the best use of material, and can be manufactured with a minimum of waste (at least cost). As well as satisfying the customer, the product's design determines both the basic manufacturing processes that have to be used and the cost and quality of the product. The product should be designed so it can be made by the most productive process with the smallest number of operations, motions, and parts and includes all of the features that are important to the customer.

Chapter 14 discussed the principles of product design in more detail.

Waste Caused in Manufacturing

Manufacturing takes the design and specifications of the product and, using the manufacturing resources, converts them into useful products. First, however, manufacturing engineering must design a system capable of making the product. They do so by selecting the manufacturing steps, machinery, and equipment and by designing the plant layout and work methods. Manufacturing must then plan and control the operation to produce the goods. This involves manufacturing planning and control, quality management, maintenance, and labor relations.

As part of their lean production program, Toyota has identified seven important sources of waste in manufacturing. The first four relate to the design of the manufacturing system and the last three to the operation and management of the system:

1. **The process.** The best process is one that has the capability to consistently make the product with an absolute minimum of scrap, in the quantities needed, and with the least cost added. Waste, or cost, is added to the process if the wrong type or size of machine is used, if the process is not being operated correctly, or if the wrong tools and fixtures are used.

2. **Methods.** Waste is added if the methods of performing tasks by the operators cause wasted movement, time, or effort. Activities that do not add value to the product should be eliminated. Searching for tools, walking, or unnecessary motions are all examples of waste.

3. **Movement.** Moving and storing components adds cost but not value. For example, goods received may be stored and then issued to production. This requires labor to put away, find, and deliver to production. Records must be kept and a storage system maintained. Poorly planned layouts may make it necessary to move products over long distances, thus increasing the movement cost and possibly storage and record-keeping costs.

4. **Product defects.** Defects interrupt the smooth flow of work. If the scrap is not identified, the next workstation receiving it will waste time trying to use the defective parts or waiting for good material. Schedules must be adjusted. If the next step is the customer, then the cost will be even higher. Sorting out or reworking defects are also waste.

5. **Waiting time.** There are two kinds of waiting time: that of the operator and that of material. If the operator has no productive work to do or there are delays in getting material or instructions, there will be waste. Ideally, material passes from one work center to the next and is processed without waiting in queue.

6. **Overproduction.** Overproduction is producing products beyond those needed for immediate use. When this occurs, raw materials and labor are consumed for parts not needed, resulting in unnecessary inventories. Considering the costs of carrying inventory, this can be very expensive. Overproduction causes extra handling of material, extra planning and control effort, and quality problems. Because of the extra inventory and work-in-process, overproduction adds confusion, tends to bury problems in inventory, and often leads to producing components that are not needed instead of those that are. Overproduction is not necessary as long as market demand is met. Machines and operators do not always need to be fully utilized.

7. **Inventory.** As we saw in Chapter 9, inventory costs money to carry, and excess inventory adds extra cost to the product. However, there are other costs in carrying excess inventory.

To remain competitive, a manufacturing organization must produce better products at lower cost while responding quickly to the marketplace. Let us look at the role inventory plays in each of these steps.

A better product suggests one that has features and quality superior to others. The ability to take advantage of product improvement opportunities depends on the speed with which engineering changes and improvements can be implemented. If there are large quantities of inventory to work through the system, it takes longer and is more costly before the engineering changes reach the marketplace. Lower inventories improve quality. Suppose that a component is made in batches of 1000 and that a defect occurs on the first operation. Eventually, the defect will be caught, very often after several more operations have been completed. Thus, all 1000 pieces have to be inspected. Because much time has elapsed since the first operation when the defect occurred, it is also difficult to pinpoint the cause of the problem. If the batch size had been 100 instead of 1000, it would have moved through the system more quickly and been detected earlier—and there would only be 100 to inspect.

Companies can offer better prices if their costs are low. Lower inventories reduce cost. Also, if work-in-process inventory is reduced, less space is needed in manufacturing, resulting in cost savings.

Responsiveness to the marketplace depends on being able to provide shorter lead times and better due-date performance. In Chapter 6, we saw that manufacturing lead time depends on queue, and queue depends on the number and the batch size of the orders in process. If batch size is reduced, the queue and lead time will be reduced. Chapter 8 noted that forecasts were more accurate for nearer periods of time. Reducing lead time improves forecast accuracy and provides better order promising and due-date performance.

Poka-Yoke (Fail Safe)

Poka-yoke was introduced by Shigeo Shingo of Japan. It implies the concept of removing faults at the first instance and making a process or product "foolproof." Shingo argued that statistical quality control does not prevent defects. He differentiated between errors and defects; errors will always be made, but defects can be prevented. Errors are primarily related to the process while defects primarily are associated with the product. Process errors are not always directly related to the creation of a defect, but usually imply the need for focused inspection at least until process improvement can be made. Corrective action should take place immediately after a mistake is made, which implies 100% inspection as soon as an action occurs. This inspection can take one of three forms: successive check, self-check, and source inspection. *Successive check* inspection is done by the next person in the process who passes the information back to the worker who just performed the operation who can then make any needed repair. *Self-check* is done by the worker and can be used on all items where a sensory perception is sufficient. Scratches and paint blobs are examples of these. *Source inspection* also is done by the individual worker who, instead of checking for defects, checks for errors that will cause defects.

Poka-yoke tries to change either the process or its resources, thus eliminating the need to rely on human experience and knowledge. Examples include the following:

- Use color-coded parts.
- Put a template over an assembled component to show operators where specific parts go.
- Use counters to tell an operator how many operations have been performed.
- Have one prong larger that the other so the electric plug will fit only one way. This is common in electrical wiring.

THE LEAN PRODUCTION ENVIRONMENT

Many elements are characteristic of a lean production environment. They may not all exist in a particular manufacturing situation, but in general they provide some principles to help in the development of a lean production system. These can be grouped under the following headings:

- Flow manufacturing.
- Process flexibility.
- Quality management.
- Total productive maintenance.
- Uninterrupted flow.
- Continuous process improvement.
- Supplier partnerships.
- Total employee involvement.

Flow Manufacturing

The lean production concept was developed by companies such as Toyota and some major appliance and consumer electronic manufacturers. These companies manufacture goods in a repetitive manufacturing environment.

Repetitive manufacturing is the production of discrete units on a flow basis. In this type of system, the workstations required to make the product, or family of products, are located close together and in the sequence needed to make the product. Work flows from one workstation to the next at a relatively constant rate and often with some materials handling system to move the product. Figure 15.2 shows a schematic of flow manufacturing.

These systems are discussed in Chapter 14. They are suitable for a limited range of similar products such as automobiles, televisions, or microwave ovens. Because work centers are arranged in the sequence needed to make the product, the system is not suitable for making a variety of different products. Therefore, the demand for the family of products

WORKSTATIONS

FIGURE 15.2 Flow manufacturing.

FIGURE 15.3 Functional layout.

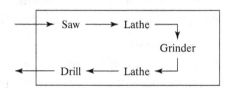

FIGURE 15.4 Work cell layout.

must be large enough to justify economically setting up the line. Flow systems are usually very cost effective.

Work cells Many companies do not have a product line that lends itself to flow manufacturing. For example, many companies do not have sufficient volume of specific parts to justify setting up a line. Companies with this kind of product line usually organize their production on a functional basis by grouping together similar or identical operations. Lathes will be placed together, as will milling machines, drills, and welding equipment. Figure 15.3 shows a schematic of this kind of layout, including routing for a hypothetical product (saw, lathe, grinder, lathe, drill). Product moves from one workstation to the other in lots or batches. This type of production produces long queues, high work-in-process inventory, long lead times, and considerable materials handling.

Usually this kind of layout can be improved. It depends on the ability to detect product flows. This can be done by grouping products together into product families. Products will be in the same family if they use common work flow or routing, materials, tooling, setup procedures, and cycle times. Workstations can then be set up in miniature flow lines or **work cells**. For example, suppose the product flow shown in Figure 15.3 represents the flow for a family of products. The work centers required to make this family can be laid out according to the steps to make that family. Figure 15.4 shows a schematic of such a layout.

Parts can now pass one by one, or in very small lots, from one workstation to the next. This has several benefits:

- Queue and lead times going through the cell are reduced drastically.
- Production activity control and scheduling are simplified. The cell has only one work center to control as opposed to five in a conventional system.
- Floor space needed is reduced.
- Feedback to preceding operations is immediate. If there is a quality problem, it will be found out immediately.

Work cells permit high-variety, low-volume manufacturing to be repetitive. For work cells to be really effective, product design and process design must work together so parts

Flow with Large-Capacity Nondedicated Equipment

Flow with Small-Capacity Dedicated Equipment

FIGURE 15.5 Large versatile equipment versus small dedicated equipment.

are designed for manufacture in work cells. Component standardization becomes even more important. Work cells are sometimes called cellular manufacturing.

Process Flexibility

Process flexibility is desirable so the company can react swiftly to changes in the volume and mix of their products. To achieve this, operators and machinery must be flexible, and the system must be configured to be changed over quickly from one product to another.

Machine flexibility   To achieve **machine flexibility**, it often makes more sense to have two relatively inexpensive general-purpose machines than one large, expensive special-purpose piece of equipment. Smaller general-purpose machines can be adapted to particular jobs with appropriate tooling. Having two instead of one makes it easier to dedicate one to a work cell. Ideally, the machinery should be low-cost and movable. Figure 15.5 illustrates the concept.

Quick changeover   **Quick changeover** requires short setup times. Short setup times also have the following advantages:

- **Reduced economic-order quantity.** The economic lot size depends on the setup cost. If the setup time can be reduced, the lot size can be reduced. For example, if the economic-order quantity is 100 units and the setup can be reduced to 25% of its former value, the economic-order quantity decreases to 50. Inventory is cut in half, and queue and lead times are reduced. Reductions in setup of even greater magnitude are possible. The general opinion is that setup can be cut 50% simply by organizing the work and having the right tools and fixtures available when needed. For example, in one instance, a changeover on a die press was videotaped. The operator doing the changeover was not in view for more than 50% of the time! He was away from the machine getting tools, dies, and so on. One system for setup reduction, called the "four-step method," claims that reductions of 90% can be achieved without major capital expense. This is accomplished by organizing the preparation, streamlining the setup, and eliminating adjustments.
- **Reduced queue and manufacturing lead time.** Manufacturing lead time depends mostly on the queue. In turn, queue depends on the order quantity and scheduling. Reducing setup time reduces the order quantity and queue and lead times.
- **Reduced work-in-process (WIP) inventory.** Work-in-process inventory depends on the number of orders in process and their size. If the order quantity is reduced, the WIP is reduced. This frees up more floor space, allowing work centers to be moved closer together, thus reducing handling costs and promoting the creation of work cells.
- **Improved quality.** When order quantities are small, defects have less time to be buried. Because they are more quickly and easily exposed, their cause will more likely be detected and corrected.

■ **Improved process and material flow.** Inventory acts as a buffer, burying problems in processes and in scheduling. Reducing inventory reduces this buffer and exposes problems in the production process and in the materials control system. This gives an opportunity to correct the problems and improve the process.

Operator flexibility   Flexible machinery and flexible processes need flexible people to operate them. To achieve **operator flexibility**, people should not only be trained in their own jobs but should also be cross-trained in other skills and in problem-solving techniques. Only with well-trained people can the benefits of process flexibility be realized.

Quality Management

Quality management is the subject of Chapter 16. This section will focus on quality from the point of view of manufacturing.

Quality is important for two reasons. If quality is not present in what is supplied to the customer and the product is defective, the customer will be dissatisfied. If a process produces scrap, it creates disrupted schedules that delay supplying the customer, increases inventory or causes shortages, wastes time and effort on work centers, and increases the cost of the product.

Who is the user? Ultimately, it is the company's customer, but the user is also the next operation in the process. Quality at any one work center should meet or exceed the expectations (needs) of the next step in the process. This is important in maintaining the uninterrupted flow of material. If defects occur at one work center and are not detected until subsequent operations, time will be wasted, and the quantity needed will not be supplied.

For manufacturing, quality does not mean inspecting the product to segregate good from bad parts. Manufacturing must ensure that the process is capable of producing the required quality consistently and with as close to zero defects as possible. Manufacturing must do all it can to improve the process to achieve this and then monitor the process to make sure it remains in control. Daily monitoring can best be done by the operator. If defects are discovered, the process should be stopped, and the cause of the defects corrected.

The benefits of a good-quality program are less scrap, less rework, less inventory (inventory just in case there is a problem), better on-time production, timely deliveries, and more satisfied customers.

As the concepts of quality management evolved, several of the concepts were structured, formalized, and enhanced to eventually become six sigma quality. Several of the key aspects of the quality approach are discussed in Chapter 16.

Quality at the source   **Quality at the source** means doing it right the first time and, if something does go wrong, stopping the process and fixing it. People become their own inspectors, personally responsible for the quality of what they produce.

Total Productive Maintenance

Traditional maintenance might be called breakdown maintenance, meaning maintenance is done only when a machine breaks down. The motto of breakdown maintenance is "If it ain't broke, don't fix it." Unfortunately, breakdowns occur only when a machine is in operation, resulting in disrupted schedules, excess inventory, and delayed deliveries. In addition, lack of proper maintenance results in wear and poor performance. For example, if a car is not properly maintained, it will break down, not start, or perform poorly on the road.

For a process to continue to produce the required quality, machinery must be maintained in excellent condition. This can best be achieved through a program of preventive maintenance. This is important for more reasons than quality. Low work-in-process inventories mean there is little buffer available. If a machine breaks down, it will quickly affect other work centers. **Preventive maintenance** starts with daily inspections, lubrication, and cleanup. Since operators usually understand how their equipment should "feel" better than anyone else, it makes more sense to have them handle this type of regular maintenance.

Total productive maintenance takes the ideas of total preventive maintenance one step further. According to the twelfth edition of the *APICS Dictionary*, total productive maintenance is "preventive maintenance plus continuing efforts to adapt, modify, and refine equipment to increase flexibility, reduce material handling, and promote continuous flow." As such, it emphasizes the lean production principle of eliminating waste. Machine operators are typically a major part of a total productive maintenance program. Not only can they be involved with small daily maintenance responsibilities and lower-skilled routine tasks, but they can also assist skilled repair technicians work on the equipment should a breakdown occur. They can also help the skilled technicians on startup and shutdown tasks.

An additional advantage of operator involvement is the reduction on time and work requirements on the skilled technicians, allowing those skilled technicians more time to focus on equipment overhaul and processing improvements.

Uninterrupted Flow

Ideally, material should flow smoothly from one operation to the next with no delays. This is most likely to occur in repetitive manufacturing, where the product line is limited in variety. However, the concept should be the goal in any manufacturing environment. Several conditions are needed to achieve uninterrupted flow of materials: uniform plant loading, a pull system, valid schedules, and linearity.

Uniform plant loading **Uniform plant loading** means that the work done at each workstation should take about the same time. In repetitive manufacturing, this is called **balancing the line**, which means that the time taken to perform tasks at each workstation on the line is the same or very nearly so. The result will be no bottlenecks and no buildup of work-in-process inventory.

Valid schedules There should be a well-planned **valid schedule.** The schedule sets the flow of materials coming into the factory and the flow of work through manufacturing. To maintain an even flow, the schedule must be level. In other words, the same amount should be produced each day. Furthermore, the mix of products should be the same each day. For example, suppose a company makes a line of dog clippers composed of three models: economy, standard, and deluxe. The demand for each is 500, 600, and 400 per week, respectively, and the capacity of the assembly line is 1500 per week. The company can develop the schedule shown in Figure 15.6. This will satisfy demand and will be level based on capacity. However, inventory will build up and, if there is no safety stock, a variation in demand will create a shortage. For example, if there is a surge in demand for the deluxe model in week 1, none may be available for sale in week 2.

An alternate schedule is shown in Figure 15.7. With this schedule, inventory is reduced, and the ability to respond to changes in model demand increases. The number of setups increases, but this is not a problem if setup times are small. The idea can be carried further by making some of each model each day. Now it would mean producing 100, 120, and 80 of each model each day. If the line has complete flexibility, these can be produced

Week	On Hand	1	2	3
Economy	0	1500		
Standard	600		1500	300
Deluxe	800			1200
Total	1400	1500	1500	1500

FIGURE 15.6 Master production schedule.

Week	On Hand	1	2	3
Economy	250	500	500	500
Standard	300	600	600	600
Deluxe	200	400	400	400
Total	750	1500	1500	1500

FIGURE 15.7 MPS leveled by week.

in the following mixed sequence of 15. This is repeated 20 times during the day for a total output of 300:

Sequence: ESD, ESD, ESD, ESD, SES

E: Economy

S: Standard

D: Deluxe

The company makes some of everything each day in the proportions to meet demand. Inventories are at a minimum. If demand shifts between models, the assembly line can respond daily. This is called **mixed-model scheduling.** The schedule is leveled, not only for capacity, but also for material.

Linearity   The emphasis in lean production is on achieving the plan—no more, no less. This concept is called **linearity** and is usually reached by scheduling to less than full capacity. If an assembly line can produce 100 units per hour, it can be scheduled for perhaps 700 units for an eight-hour shift. If there are problems during the shift, there is extra time so the 700-unit schedule can be maintained. If there is time left over after the 700 units are produced, it can be spent on jobs such as cleanup, lubricating machinery, getting ready for the next shift, quality improvements, total productive maintenance activities, process improvements, or solving problems.

Continuous Process Improvement

This topic is an element in both lean production and quality management and was discussed in Chapter 14. Elimination of waste depends on improving processes continuously. Thus continuous improvement is a major feature of lean production.

Supplier Partnerships

If good schedules are to be maintained and the company is to develop a just-in-time environment, it is vital to have good, reliable suppliers. They establish the flow of materials into the factory.

Partnering   **Partnering** implies a long-term commitment between two or more organizations to achieve specific goals. Lean production places much emphasis not only on supplier performance but also on supplier relations. Suppliers are looked on as co-producers, not as adversaries. The relationship with them should be one of mutual trust and cooperation.

There are three key factors in partnering.

1. **Long-term commitment.** This is necessary to achieve the benefits of partnering. It takes time to solve problems, improve processes, and build the relationship need.

2. **Trust.** Trust is needed to eliminate an adversarial relationship. Both partners must be willing to share information and form a strong working relationship. Open and

frequent communications are necessary. In many cases the parties have access to each other's business plans and technical information.

3. **Shared vision.** All partners must understand the need to satisfy the customer. Goals and objectives should be shared so that there is a common direction.

If properly done, partnering should be a win–win situation. The benefits to the buyer include the following:

- The ability to supply the quality needed all the time so there will be no need for inbound inspection. This implies that the supplier will have, or develop, an excellent process quality improvement program.
- The ability to make frequent deliveries on a just-in-time basis. This implies that the supplier will become a just-in-time manufacturer.
- The ability to work with the buyer to improve performance, quality, and cost. For a supplier to become a just-in-time supplier, a long-term relationship must be established. Suppliers need to have that assurance so they can plan their capacity and make the necessary commitment to a single customer.

In return, the supplier has the following benefits.

- A greater share of the business with long-term security.
- Ability to plan more effectively.
- More competitive as a just-in-time supplier.

Supplier selection   Chapter 7 noted that the factors to be considered when selecting suppliers were technical ability, manufacturing capability, reliability, after-sales service, and supplier location. In a partnership there are other considerations based on the partnership relationship. They include the following:

1. The supplier has a stable management system and is sincere in implementing the partnership agreement.
2. There is no danger of the supplier breaching the organization's secrets.
3. The supplier has an effective quality system.
4. The supplier shares the vision of customer satisfaction and delighting the customer.

Supplier certification   Once the supplier is selected, the next step is a certification process that begins after the supplier has started to ship the product. Organizations can set up their own criteria for **supplier certification** or can use one such as what has been developed by the American Society for Quality, whose criterion emphasizes the absence of defects both in product and nonproduct categories (e.g., billing errors) and use of a good documentation system, such as the ISO 9000:2008 system.

Total Employee Involvement

A successful lean production environment can be achieved only with the cooperation and involvement of everyone in the organization. The ideas of elimination of waste and continuous improvement that are central to the lean production philosophy can be accomplished only through people cooperating.

Instead of being receivers of orders, operators must take responsibility for improving processes, controlling equipment, correcting deviations, and becoming vehicles for continuous improvement. Their jobs include not only direct labor but also a variety of traditionally indirect jobs such as preventive maintenance, some setup, data recording, and problem solving. As discussed previously in this chapter, employees must be flexible in the tasks they do. Just as machines must be flexible and capable of quick changeover, so must the people who run them.

The role of management must change. Traditionally, management has been responsible for planning, organizing, and supervising operations. Many of their traditional duties are now done by line workers. In a lean production environment, more emphasis is placed on the leadership role. Managers and supervisors must become coaches and trainers, develop the capability of employees, and provide coordination and leadership for improvements.

Traditionally, staff have been responsible for such things as quality control, maintenance, and record keeping. Under lean production, line workers do many of these duties. Staff responsibilities then become those of training and assisting line workers to do the staff duties assigned to them.

MANUFACTURING PLANNING AND CONTROL IN A LEAN PRODUCTION ENVIRONMENT: JIT PRODUCTION

The philosophy and techniques of lean production discussed in this chapter are related to how processes and methods of manufacture are designed. The major responsibility for designing processes and methods lies with manufacturing and industrial engineering. Manufacturing planning and control are responsible for managing the flow of material and work through the manufacturing process, not designing the process. However, manufacturing planning and control are governed by, and must work with, the manufacturing environment, whatever it is. Figure 15.8 shows the relationship.

This section will study the effect a lean production environment has on manufacturing planning and control. No matter what planning and control system is used, these four basic questions have to be answered:

1. What are we going to make?
2. What do we need to make it?
3. What do we have?
4. What must we get?

The logic of these questions always applies, whether we are going to cook a meal or make a modern jet aircraft. Systems for planning and control vary. The manufacturing planning and control system (manufacturing resource planning) discussed in this text has proved effective in any manufacturing environment. The complexity of the manufacturing process, the number of finished items and parts, the levels in the bill of material, and the lead times have made the planning and control problems either simple or complex. If anything can be done to simplify these factors, the planning and control system will be simpler.

FIGURE 15.8 Lean production.

In general, lean production simplifies these factors, thus making the planning and control problems easier.

The sections that follow will look at how the various parts of the manufacturing planning and control system relate to a lean production environment. In general, lean production does not make the manufacturing planning and control system obsolete but, in some ways, does change the focus. Lean production is not primarily a planning and control system. It is a philosophy and a set of techniques for designing and operating a manufacturing plant. Planning and control are still needed in a lean production environment.

Forecasting

The major effect that lean production has on forecasting is shortened lead time. This does not affect forecasting for business planning or production planning, but it does for master production scheduling. If lead times are short enough that production rates can be matched to sales rates, forecasting for the master production schedule becomes less important.

Production Planning

Lean production emphasizes relationships with suppliers. One purpose of production planning is to arrange for long lead-time purchases. Lean production has the potential for reducing those lead times, but more importantly it provides an environment in which the supplier and buyer can work together to plan the flow of material.

Master Production Scheduling

Several scheduling factors are influenced by lean production and JIT:

1. Master scheduling tries to level capacity, and JIT tries to level the schedule based on capacity and material flow. Figure 15.9 illustrates the difference.

Level Capacity Schedule

Week	1	2	3
Model A	900		
Model B	300	900	
Model C		300	1200
Total	1200	1200	1200

Level Material and Capacity Schedule

Week	1	2	3
Model A	300	300	300
Model B	400	400	400
Model C	500	500	500
Total	1200	1200	1200

FIGURE 15.9 MPS leveled by capacity and by material.

2. The shorter lead times reduce time fences and make the master production schedule more responsive to customer demand. The ideal lead time is so short that the company can respond to actual sales, not to forecast. Whether the company builds to a seasonal demand or to satisfy promotion, a forecast is still necessary. Planning horizons can also be reduced.

3. JIT requires a stable schedule to operate. This principle is supported by using time fences. These are established based on lead times and the commitment of materials and resources. If lead times can be reduced through lean production, the time fences can be reduced.

4. Traditionally, weekly time buckets are used. This gives manufacturing an organizational buffer to plan and organize actual work flow. Because of reduced lead times and schedule stability, it is possible to use daily time buckets in a JIT environment.

Material Requirements Planning

Material requirements planning (MRP) plans the material flow based on the bill of material, lead times, and available inventory. Just-in-time practices may modify this approach in several ways:

- The MRP time buckets are usually one week. As lead times are reduced and the flow of material improved, these can be reduced to daily buckets.

- The MRP netting logic is based on generating order quantities calculated using the planned order releases of the parent, the inventory on hand, and any order quantity logic used. In a pure lean production environment, there is very little or no inventory on hand, and the order quantity logic is to make exactly what is needed. Therefore, there is no netting required. If the lead times are short enough, component production occurs in the same time bucket as the gross requirement, and no offsetting is required.

- Bills of material can frequently be flattened in a lean production and JIT environment. With the use of work cells and the elimination of many inventory transactions, some levels in bills of material become unnecessary.

Both MRP and JIT are based on establishing a material flow. In a repetitive manufacturing environment, this is set by the model mix and the flow rate. The product to be made is decided by the need of the following workstation, which is ultimately the assembly line.

However, many production situations do not lend themselves to level scheduling and the pull system and therefore must rely more heavily on MRP logic. Some examples are as follows:

- Where the demand pattern is unstable.
- Where custom engineering is required.
- Where quality is unpredictable.
- Where volumes are low and occur infrequently.

Capacity Management

Capacity planning's function is to determine the need for labor, equipment, and material to meet the priority plans. Leveling schedules should make the job easier. Capacity control focuses on adjusting capacity daily to meet demand. Leveling should make this task easier, but so will the lean production emphasis on cutting out waste and problems that cause ineffective use of capacity. Linearity, the practice of scheduling extra capacity, will improve the ability to meet priority schedules.

Capacity management in some ways becomes more important in a lean production environment. Since a lean production environment tends to have very low inventory, it becomes critical to have the right capacity at the right time to make the inventory according to customer demand. This also relates to the importance of total productive maintenance, since that approach provides assurance that the process capacity will likely be ready to use when needed.

Inventory Management

Because lean production reduces the inventory in the system, in some respects this should make inventory management easier. However, if order quantities are reduced and annual demand remains the same, more work orders and more paperwork must be tracked, and more transactions recorded. The challenge then is to reduce the number of transactions that have to be recorded. One system used is called **backflushing** or **post-deduct.**

Material flows from raw material to work-in-process to finished goods. In a post-deduct system, raw materials are recorded into work-in-process. When work is completed and becomes finished goods, the work-in-process inventory is relieved by multiplying the number of units completed by the number of parts in the bill of material. In some cases, primarily for those products with short throughput times, material is not moved into work-in-process, meaning it is removed directly from raw material once work is completed. The system works if the bills of material are accurate and if the manufacturing lead times are short.

All of this work on lean production not only reduces waste, which is a major target of lean production, but also establishes an environment that allows for an effective alternative to MRP in the environment.

The Impact on Effective Lot Sizing

MRP is often called a push system, meaning that the material needs are calculated ahead of time (planned order releases) and, assuming there are no significant changes to the plans, pushed out to the production system as a production order. The "trigger" for the entire plan is the projection of the final product need, as represented by the master production schedule (MPS). Part of the difficulty with MRP is that often the plans are not effective because of problems or changes, including

- Changes in customer requirements, both in timing and quantity.
- Supplier delivery problems, including timing, quantity, and quality.
- Inaccurate databases that can make the plans invalid, depending on the nature of the inaccurate data.
- Production problems, including
  - Absenteeism in the workforce.
  - Productivity and/or efficiency problems.
  - Machine downtime.
  - Quality problems.
  - Poor communication.

These problems generally promote an environment that, despite the best-made plans, can allow for ineffective execution and a growth in inventory levels.

The Pull System

The **pull system** was developed as an alternative to classical "push" MRP, and is often identified as the primary aspect of JIT production. The underlying concept is not to preplan and generate schedules but instead to react to the final customer order and produce only what is needed to satisfy demand and also only when it is needed. Essentially, this system is much the same as the basic reorder point system used for independent inventory. If this is the case, why can it work now when it did not work effectively for so many years before MRP? MRP was primarily designed as a more effective alternative to reorder points because reorder points did not work well.

The major reason reorder points normally do not work well in a dependent inventory environment is a significant violation of the assumption of relatively constant demand that allows a reorder point to work well in some independent inventory environments. A simple example may help illustrate the problem.

Suppose the product is a specific model of bicycle. The bicycles are made in batches, which is a typical mode of production for an assemble-to-order environment. The batch size is 200 bicycles.

Now we look at an item of dependent inventory that is one level lower on the bill of materials—the bicycle seat. Suppose it has a lot size of 300, a two-week lead time, and, since we are examining the use of a reorder point, a reorder point of 80.

Example 1—In this case suppose we have an inventory of 290 seats. A new batch of bicycles has just been ordered, requiring us to use 200 of the seats in a very short time. We are left, therefore, with 90 seats—10 above the reorder point. We do not reorder since the reorder point has not been reached. The 90 will stay in inventory until the next order for the bicycles is generated, which may be a significant time. When that order does come to build another 200 bicycles, we can only build 90 because that is the only inventory we have. We need to immediately order another lot of 300, but it will be two weeks before they are available.

Example 2—Now let us assume we have less inventory—enough less that by building the lot of 200 bicycles we will hit the seat reorder point. Suppose we have 270 seats. The order for 200 bicycles comes in, we use 200 seats, and the seat reorder point is reached. That will cause us to immediately reorder. Two weeks later the 300 seats arrive and are added to the 70 left in stock. We now have 370 seats that will stay in inventory (costing a lot of money) until the next time we build the bicycles, which may be a very long time.

As the example illustrates, the lot-sizing problem with dependent inventory often results in either a crisis shortage or a replenishment of stock well before it is actually needed. This example shows that the critical conditions causing the problem are the large lot sizes and the long lead times, both of which are major targets of lean production waste reduction.

First, let us look again at the standard EOQ model that helps determine the most economical lot size. It is, of course, the basic trade-off of inventory holding cost and order cost, as described in detail in Chapter 10.

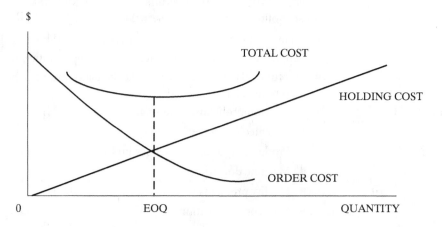

A fundamental assumption of this model is that the two major costs involved are known and relatively fixed. While this is essentially true with holding cost, it is not true with order cost. If the order cost is equipment setup, then a major lean production effort is to reduce this setup cost. If it is a purchased item, the major effort is to work with suppliers to reduce the cost and time of purchase order and delivery. With these efforts, the order cost curve is driven downward and to the left, as in the following figure:

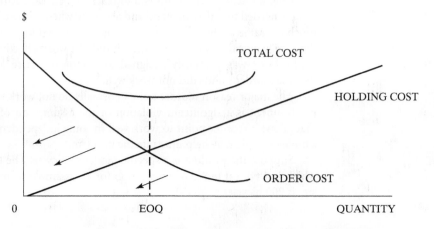

When these actions are taken, a new total cost curve based on the new order cost curve is generated, resulting in a significantly smaller EOQ, as the following figure illustrates:

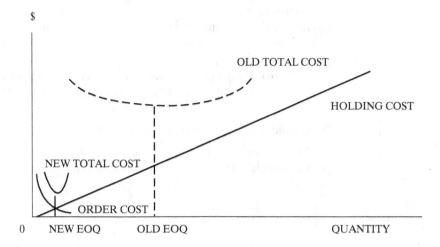

This implies that the economic-order quantities and the reorder points are very small, meaning that we will be ordering frequently but in very small batches. Since the actions are also taken at the final product level, there will be, in the preceding bicycle example, frequent lots of a very small quantity of bicycles built requiring small lots of seats frequently reordered.

If we are to reexamine the scenario with the bicycles and bicycle seats, we now see the impact. The lot size for the bicycles is very small, as is the lot size for the seats. Lead time to replenish the seats, also a target for lean production improvement, has shrunken as well. Suppose the bicycle lot size is now 7 and the seat lot size is 10. The reorder point for the seats is now zero. If we build one lot size of bicycles, we will have not reached the seat reorder point, and it appears as if we do not have enough seats to make another lot of bicycles. With such a small seat lot size, however, we can easily afford to keep two, three, or even more lots on hand (the number being dependent on the new replenishment lead time). We can therefore build the next lot of bicycles with the second lot of seats while the first lot of seats is being replenished.

The downside of the change   While the average inventory is clearly lower in the small lot size scenario, there is a cost involved beyond the one-time cost to reduce the order cost and the lead time. Given that the overall customer demand has not diminished, we will need to order batches to be built much more frequently since each batch is smaller in size. Each time the inventory of a given batch gets close to the reorder point, we risk a stockout if the demand during the replenishment lead time exceeds expectations. The following figure illustrates the condition:

The Kanban System

With shortened lead times a constant goal in lean production, a system is needed to generate the reorder point signal without having to rely on a formal, structured system that could take time to react. The developers of the JIT production concepts utilized a simple card system called **Kanban** (often pronounced *con-bon*), which roughly translated from Japanese means *card* or *ticket*.

The system works very simply. The Kanban signal often a piece of cardboard identifies the material to which it is attached. The information on the Kanban will often include the following:

- Component part number and identification.
- Storage location.
- Container size (if the material is stored in a container).
- Work center (or supplier) of origin.

How it works   The following figures illustrate the use of what is often called a two-card Kanban system. The two types of cards are a production card (authorizing production of whatever part number is identified on the card in the quantity specified) and a withdrawal card (authorizing the movement of the identified material).

At the start of the process there is no movement, since all the cards are attached to full containers. It is only when a card is unattached that activity is allowed. In this way the number of cards will clearly limit the inventory authorized to be at any location.

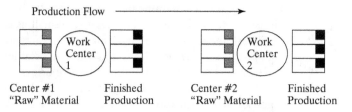

Production Flow ⟶

Center #1 "Raw" Material   Finished Production   Center #2 "Raw" Material   Finished Production

"Steady-State"—no demand and no production

■ PRODUCTION CARD   ■ MOVE CARD

At some point, a downstream process needs some of the parts produced by work center 2 (in its "Finished Production" stock). It takes a container of the material, leaving the work center 2 production card with the center. This illustrates two additional rules of the system—all material movement is in full containers (recall that the container lot size is supposed to be very small) and Kanban cards are attached to a work center. This initial movement is illustrated in the following figure:

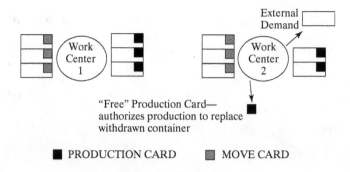

External Demand

"Free" Production Card—authorizes production to replace withdrawn container

■ PRODUCTION CARD   ■ MOVE CARD

The unattached production card is the signal to start the work center 2 production to replace the container that was taken. To do that work they need raw material, which is in the containers in front of the work center with the move cards attached. When that material is used to replace the work center 2 finished material, the raw material container is now empty and the associated move card is unattached, as shown in the following figure:

1. Production container replaced
2. "Free" production card placed on new container
3. Move card on raw material container removed and is now "free"

■ PRODUCTION CARD   ■ MOVE CARD

The unattached move card authorized movement of material to replace the material that was used. That material is found in the "finished goods" section of work center 1. The operator (or material handler) will now move the material and place the move card on the container as proof of the authorization to move the material. Before doing so, however, they must remove the production card that had first authorized its production. That represents another critical rule for Kanban: every container with material must have one, but only one, card attached. Therefore, when the move card is attached the production card must be removed. That is illustrated in the following figure:

1. Full container from Center #1 moved to #2
2. Center #2's move card attached
3. Center #1's production card removed and is now "free"

■ PRODUCTION CARD   ■ MOVE CARD

Now, of course, there is an unattached production card for work center 1, allowing it to produce, using some of the raw material for work center 1 and freeing a move card for that material, as shown in the following figure:

1. Center #1 produces part to refill container
2. Production card attached to container
3. Material usage empties raw material container and "frees" move card that was attached

■ PRODUCTION CARD   ■ MOVE CARD

This process continues upstream even to the suppliers, who can also receive the Kanban move cards as a signal for their next shipment to the facility.

Notice that there are no schedules with this system. Production and movement of material are only authorized purely as a reaction to the utilization of material for production downstream. The production of the final product may be the customer taking material. In some facilities there is a final assembly schedule for customer orders. In those facilities that may be the only formal schedule used.

Also note that the cards only circulate within and between work centers, as shown in the following figure:

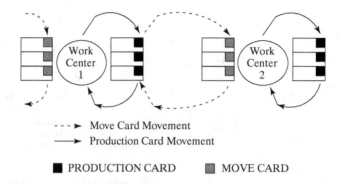

--- ► Move Card Movement
——► Production Card Movement

■ PRODUCTION CARD ■ MOVE CARD

Kanban "rules" Even though there are no formal schedules in a Kanban system, there is a fairly important set of rules—basically a set of constraints under which the Kanban system can most effectively operate. Those rules are summarized here:

- Every container with parts shall have one, but only one, Kanban.
- There will be no partial containers stored. Every container will be filled, empty, or in the process of being filled or emptied. This rule makes inventory accounting easy. You do not need to count parts—only containers and then multiply by the container quantity.
- There will be no production or movement without an authorization in the form of an unattached Kanban card.

Card alternatives Since the development and successful implementation of Kanban systems in many facilities, many alternatives have been designed and implemented. Some of the alternative methods include the following:

- Single card systems. The single card is the production card, with the empty container serving as the move signal.
- Color coding of containers.
- Designated storage spaces.
- Computer systems, often with bar coding serving as the signal generator.

It should be noted that the method used is not important. What is important is that there is a clear reactive signal to generate activity that everyone clearly understands.

Using the Kanban System for Process Improvement

Because the Kanban system allows for a controlled inventory of relatively small containers, there is a great opportunity for using the system to promote continual process improvement. Specifically, whenever the process is working smoothly for an extended period of time, there is a possibility that there actually is too much inventory in the system. The analogy that is often used is a river. If the water level is high enough, it will cover all the rocks in the river and appear to be running smoothly without any obstructions. The water in the analogy is inventory, and the rocks are process problems, including quality problems, worker skills, equipment breakdown, and so forth.

The approach is to gradually remove the water until the first "rock" is exposed, thereby establishing a priority of the most important obstacle to work on. It would be dangerous, of course, to remove too much "water" at a time, because the obstacles may stop the flow altogether. This is where the small lot size of Kanban is a benefit. Removal of one Kanban card will remove one container, and since the containers are small, so too will be the impact of the removal. The important aspect of this is that some process problem will ultimately emerge, signaling the next target for lean production process improvement efforts.

This is not an easy approach to implement. What is implied is that every time a process is working smoothly there may be too much inventory and what is needed is to remove inventory until it "hurts." That is certainly not a natural action for most people, and the performance evaluation system needs to be altered to reflect this type of activity.

Some Additional Lean Production Tools

Value stream mapping   **Value stream mapping** is a tool to map and understand the flow of materials from supplier to customer, focusing on not only understanding the current state of process and flow but also specifying the value-added and non-value-added time of all process steps. This includes all activities, even the in-process storage of inventory and key metrics for the process. This visible understanding of the current flow of activities allows for developing a future state map that will significantly reduce waste, decrease flow time, and make the process flow more efficiently and effectively. Strategies can then be developed for specific actions that will lead the operation toward the future state.

Kaizen   The **kaizen** event usually focuses on a fairly small part of the overall production process to improve that part of the process. It is a structured approach to understand and redesign the process to meet specific process goals that are often part of the overall implementation of a lean production system. Kaizen events are generally considered to be a major part of the overall approach to continuous improvement for an operation. Since kaizen events are generally designed to be accomplished in short periods of time (one to two weeks), the term *kaizen blitz* is frequently used.

Takt time   The **takt time** is sometimes thought of as the heartbeat of the overall process. It is usually defined to be the rate of production that is synchronized with the rate of customer demand. If the production process is well synchronized with demand, the implication is that customer demand will be met with little or no excess inventory or other forms of waste. Takt time is a common metric used to help design a future state process during value stream mapping.

5S approach   While originally developed from a series of Japanese words, a rough English translation is sort, straighten, shine, standardize, and sustain. In general it is a structured approach to organizing the operation for more effectiveness and less waste, which is the overall goal of a lean production system.

- **Sort.** Determine things that are needed and those not needed in the workplace. Remove those that are not needed.
- **Straighten.** Put the necessary things in good order so they may be readily available when needed.
- **Shine.** Clean the area, and keep it clean.
- **Standardize.** Maintain the order and cleanliness that have been developed.
- **Sustain.** Train and develop attitudes to keep the orderliness as an expected and ongoing part of the organization culture.

WHICH TO CHOOSE: MRP (ERP), KANBAN, OR THEORY OF CONSTRAINTS?

As the various systems are developed and promoted, proponents of each claim their favorite to be "the answer" to maximizing service to the customer and minimizing inventory and other process costs. There are, however, certain production and business environments in which one may provide better benefits and another may not work as well. This brings to light the importance of understanding the business environment and developing a specific production strategy to best meet the needs of customers in that environment.

MRP (ERP)

Where it works best   MRP is by its very nature a forward-looking system. Based on the master schedule, it "predicts" when products need to be made and projects the need for component production or purchase at all levels based on a defined set of parameters.

Because of the forward-looking nature of the system, MRP can be very effective in an environment with a great deal of variability and uncertainty. For example, it can handle variability of demand as well as, or better than, most other systems and tends to be quite effective in dealing with product design changes and process changes.

Where it is not as effective   MRP (ERP) has one major disadvantage. It is highly data dependent. It is not only critical to have a lot of data, but the data need to be both accurate and timely on an ongoing basis. The data burden on the infrastructure can be high and costly. If the environment has a great deal of stability in product design, process, and customer demand, the process can often be run just as effectively, or perhaps even more effectively, by using a system such as JIT production that is not so data intensive.

JIT Production (Kanban)

Where it works best   JIT and Kanban are almost the opposite of MRP from the standpoint of the type of preferred environment. In the JIT approach, most of the recommendations fall under the categories of eliminating or reducing the process uncertainties and making production more stable and predictable. This makes sense when it is realized that Kanban is a very reactive system. Very little is planned ahead. Instead, Kanban causes replacement of material used in a totally reactive mode. Changes in product design can cause a real problem in a Kanban system since the system tends to not "look ahead." For these reasons Kanban works best in a highly stable and predictable environment.

Where it is not as effective   Kanban can quickly fail in a highly volatile environment because of the reactive nature of the system. Volatility in customer demand, processing problems, and extensive changes in product designs make it very difficult for a Kanban system to work effectively.

Kanban does not plan production ahead of time but merely provides a signal to replace what has been used. As part of a lean production system, there is also an implication that little excess inventory exists. If there is a change in product design, the reactive part of the system (Kanban) has little advance notice of the change, meaning some inventory of the old design may be left over and demand for the new design can exist before any has been produced in the system. In addition, since the system relies on a fairly small amount of in-process inventory, spikes in demand or even large trends in demand can often run the system out of inventory with little chance to react.

Theory of Constraints (Drum-Buffer-Rope)

Where it works best   Since the TOC system has as its basis the identification and effective management of a constraint (see the discussion on the fundamentals of and approaches to TOC in Chapter 6), it assumes that such a constraint can be identified and will be a constraint long enough to be managed effectively. In operations where that is the case, the concepts of TOC can bring great benefits to managing the process, as has been proved in many operations.

Where it is not as effective   TOC may not be as effective where the constraint cannot be easily identified or managed. If, for example, the product mix for the operation changes in such a way that the constraint may change many times a day, then it may be virtually impossible to effectively manage a constraint, even if it can be identified. Much like JIT and Kanban, TOC probably works more effectively in a more stable demand environment.

Hybrid Systems

As might be expected, some operations have managed to take the best features of each system and combine them into hybrid systems.

Kanban and MRP   The combination of these two systems is becoming quite common. An MRP system is used for advanced planning, including long lead-time purchased materials, adding or changing resources (capacity), and implementing product design changes. Once MRP has the materials and resources "lined up," however, Kanban is used as an execution system, bringing with it the characteristics of rapid response to customer order and reduced inventory levels throughout the process. With this point it should be emphasized that MRP is primarily a planning system and JIT is primarily an execution system. As such they are totally compatible if the MRP system is used to make effective plans in the context of the production plan and master schedule, while using Kanban to execute those plans as customer demand is recognized.

Lean production and TOC   Lean production often promotes process improvements throughout the system, but as TOC teaches, there is almost always one process that constrains the overall throughput. This implies that the TOC approach can help prioritize the areas of improvement, and lean production principles can help with this improvement. In this sense, the TOC concepts can be thought of as an effective approach to implementing the concepts of lean production without trying to change everything at once.

SUMMARY

The lean production philosophy and techniques that seek the elimination of waste and continuous improvement were developed for repetitive manufacturing and are perhaps most applicable there. However, many basic concepts are appropriate to any form of manufacturing organization. They are now also being adapted and adopted by service-oriented operations as well.

As noted in Chapter 14, in intermittent manufacturing, material is processed at intervals in lots or batches, not continuously. It is characterized by large variation in product design, process requirements, and order quantities. In the extreme, every job is made to customer specification, and there is no commonality in product design. General-purpose equipment is used to make products. A contract machine shop is an example. However, many companies make a variety of standard products in small volumes manufactured either to stock or to customer order. Many of these have families of products, and if these can be identified, work cells can be set up.

No matter what the characteristics of the intermittent shop, several lean production principles can be applied:

- Employee involvement.
- Workplace layout.
- Quality control.
- Total productive maintenance.
- Setup time reduction.
- Supplier relations.
- Inventory reduction.

The lean production environment requires a planning and control system. The manufacturing resource planning system is complementary to lean production and JIT production. The way in which some functions are used changes to reflect the differences in the manufacturing environment, but, in general, the functions performed in the MRP II system are those that have to be done in a JIT production.

KEY TERMS

Adding value 341

Backflushing or post-deduct 353

Balancing the line 347

5S approach 359

Kaizen 359

Kanban 356

Lean production 339

Linearity 348

Machine flexibility 345

Mixed-model scheduling 348

Operator flexibility 346

Partnering 348

Poka-yoke 343

Preventive maintenance 346

Process flexibility 345

Pull system 353

Quality at the source 346

Quick changeover 345

Supplier certification 349

Takt time 359

Total productive maintenance 347

Uniform plant loading 347

Valid schedule 347

Value stream mapping 359

Waste 341

Work cells 344

QUESTIONS

1. What is the definition of waste as it is used in this text?

2. What is value to the user? How is it related to quality?

3. What are the elements in a product development cycle? For what is each responsible?

4. Why is product specialization important? Who is responsible for setting the level of product specialization?

5. What is meant by component standardization? Why is it important in eliminating waste?

6. Why is product design important to manufacturing? How can the design add waste in manufacturing?

7. After a product is designed, what is the responsibility of manufacturing engineering?

8. Explain why each of the following are sources of waste:
   a. The process
   b. Methods
   c. Movement
   d. Product defects
   e. Waiting time
   f. Overproduction

9. Explain how inventory affects product improvement, quality, prices, and the ability to respond quickly to the marketplace.

10. What is repetitive manufacturing? What are its advantages? What are its limitations?

11. What is a work cell? How does it operate? What conditions are necessary to establish one? What are its advantages?

12. Why is process flexibility desirable? What two conditions are required?

13. Name and describe five advantages of low setup time.

14. What are the two reasons why quality is important?

15. What is quality for manufacturing? How is it obtained?

16. Why is preventive maintenance important?

17. Describe the differences between preventive maintenance and total productive maintenance.

17. What are the four conditions needed for uninterrupted flow? Describe each.

18. What is the difference between leveling based on capacity and leveling based on material flow?

19. Why would a lean production manufacturer schedule 7 hours of work in an 8-hour shift?

20. Why are supplier relations particularly important in a lean production environment?

21. Why is employee involvement important in a lean production environment?

22. What are the differences in a master production schedule in a lean production environment?

23. What effect does a lean production environment have on MRP?

24. Describe the backflushing or post-deduct system of inventory record keeping.

25. Why is there sometimes difficulty with the MRP system?

26. What is the major difference between the MRP push systems and the pull system?

27. What is the Kanban system? How does it work?

28. What is the difference between production cards and move cards?

29. Where does an MRP system work best?

30. Where does a Kanban system work best?

31. Where does a drum-buffer-rope system work best?

32. Can MRP and Kanban be used at the same time and if so how?

PROBLEMS

15.1. A company carries 10 items in stock, each with an economic-order quantity of $20,000. Through a program of component standardization, the 10 items are reduced to 5. The total annual demand is the same, but the annual demand for each item is twice what it was before. In Chapter 10, we learned that the economic-order quantity varies as the square root of the annual demand. Since the annual demand for each item is now doubled, calculate:

   a. The new EOQ.

   b. The total average inventory before standardization.

   c. The total average inventory after standardization.

15.2. In problem 15.1, if the annual carrying cost is 20% per unit, what will be the annual savings in carrying cost?

15.3. A company has an annual demand for a product of 1000 units, a carrying cost of $20 per unit per year, and a setup cost of $100. Through a program of setup reduction, the setup cost is reduced to $10. Run costs are $2 per unit. Calculate:

   a. The EOQ before setup reduction.

   b. The EOQ after setup reduction.

   c. The total and unit cost before and after setup reduction.

15.4. A company produces a line of golf putters composed of three models. The demand for model A is 500 per month, for B is 400, and for C is 300. What would be the mixed-model sequence if some of each were made each day?

   Answer.   ABC, ABC, ABC, ABA

15.5. The following MPS summary schedule is leveled for capacity. Using the following table, level the schedule for material as well.

Week	1	2	3	4	5
Model A			800	1600	1600
Model B	600	1600	800		
Model C	1000				
Total					

Answer.

Week	1	2	3	4	5
Model A	800	800	800	800	800
Model B	600	600	600	600	600
Model C	200	200	200	200	200
Total					

15.6. Bill builds benches in a small shop and he plans to operate five 8-hour days per week. Each bench has two ends and a top. It takes 5 minutes to cut and sand each end and 3 minutes to make each top. Assembly requires 10 minutes per bench, and painting requires 5 minutes per bench. Bill has one employee who makes the tops and ends. Bill will do the final assembly and painting. He also plans 1 hour per day for setup and teardown for each department.

   a. How many benches should he plan to build per week?

   b. How many hours per week are required for each person?

   c. Suggest ways to increase the number of benches produced per week.

15.7. Parent W requires one of component B and two of component C. Both B and C are run on work center 10. Setup time for B is 2 hours, and run time is 0.1 hour per piece. For component C, setup time is 2 hours, and run time is 0.15 hour per piece. If the rated capacity of the work center is 80 hours, how many Ws should be produced in a week?

   Answer.   190 Ws

15.8. Parent S requires three of component T and two of component U. Both T and U are run on work center 30. Setup time for T is 7 hours, and run time is 0.1 hour per piece. For component U, setup time is 8 hours, and run time is 0.2 hour per piece. If the rated capacity of the work center is 120 hours, how many Ts and Us should be produced in a week?

   Answer.   450 Ts and 300 Us a week

CASE STUDY 15.1

Murphy Manufacturing

When Joe Vollbrach, vice president of operations for Murphy Manufacturing, was given the CEO's directive to investigate the lean production concepts and to implement them if appropriate; he was slightly apprehensive. Everyone knew, he thought, that MRP was the best way to run a manufacturing operation, and they had been pretty successful with their MRP system. Once he read a couple of books and a magazine article or two about JIT and lean production, however, he thought maybe there was something to it and it sure seemed simple enough. Dozens of companies had reported great reductions in inventory cost and other forms of waste, and with Murphy Manufacturing having only five to six inventory turns per year, the prospect of significant inventory reductions was very appealing.

Encouraged with the success stories and very mindful of the CEO directive, Joe wasted no time. He put out the directive to all his people to implement lean production the way it was working in the book examples he had read. A few months later, however, he was beginning to wonder about the truth of the success stories in those books. The following are some of the examples of the complaints he was getting and the problems he was facing.

KAREN, THE PURCHASING MANAGER: "Joe, this JIT and lean production are a disaster for us. It's not only costing us a lot more money, but the suppliers are getting real angry with us. Since our raw material inventory had typically been high, you said we should order smaller quantities and have it delivered just in time for its need. Sure, that cut down on the raw material inventory, but that cost saving has been more than made up for with all the increased cost. First, purchase orders are not cost free, and we're making a lot more of them. That's also taking up a lot more of our buyer's time. Then there's the transportation cost. Since most of the trucking companies charge a lot more for less-than-full truckloads, our costs are going sky-high with more frequent deliveries of smaller loads. Combine that with expediting costs, and it gets really bad. Our schedules are changing even more frequently, and without the raw material the production people are often asking for next-day delivery of material they need for a schedule change. We're flying more parts in, and you know how much that costs!

"That's not all. Our suppliers are really wondering if we know how to run our business. We're changing that schedule to them much more frequently, and the only way they can hope to meet our needs is to keep a lot of our inventory in their finished goods. That's costing them a lot of money in inventory holding costs as well as administrative costs to manage the inventory and to process all our requests. They not only have more requests from us, but it seems like everything is a rush order. They're pressing us hard for price increases to cover their increased cost to keep us as a customer. I've held most of them off for a while but not much longer. Unfortunately, I agree with them, so it's hard for me to make any kind of logical argument to counter their requests for price increases."

OSCAR, SUPERVISOR OF SHIPPING/RECEIVING: "If you're going to keep this up I have to ask for two more truck bays and about four more receiving clerks. There's a lot more trucks making a lot more deliveries. We can't schedule perfectly when a truck will show up, so many times during the day there are several trucks waiting for an open truck bay. Production people are screaming at us because they see a certain truck and they know a critical part is on it, but we have to wait because the trucks currently in the bays being unloaded also have critical parts. It seems like everything is critical these days. A couple more bays with enough people to staff them will help, although it's not the only answer. I figure about a $3 million renovation to the receiving area and an increase in our budget of about $500,000 ought to be about enough to keep us afloat, at least most of the time. Oh, I forgot—better make that $600,000 more. I also need another records clerk to keep up with the big increase in paperwork from all those deliveries."

Joe was just finished taking a couple of aspirin to deal with that headache, when Marsha, a production supervisor, caught up with him:

"Joe, I don't know where you came up with these silly ideas, but you're killing us here. This so-called Kanban system is just plain stupid. It reminds me of the reorder points we used before the MRP system, and we all know how much better MRP made things work. I feel like I just slipped 35 years back in time. We all know our customers are a fickle bunch who are always changing their minds on orders. We used to have visibility with the change when we used MRP, but now all we have is what the final assembly area is working on. That not only causes us big, inefficient downtimes for setup changes but also doesn't give us much time to get the materials we need to make the different parts. When we do figure out what we need, most of the time our suppliers don't have any in raw material stock. Now we have to waste more time and energy to scream at the buyers. What makes it even worse is your directive to eliminate finished goods. We not only don't have material to make what we need half the time, but we're not allowed to make what we can. It would seem that would make sense, so that when a customer does request a certain model we have in stock, at least that order wouldn't end up being a crisis.

"The crisis scenario I just described is what happens when everything else works. When we have some other problems, such as a piece of equipment going down, the real disaster hits. What little order we can force goes out the window and everyone starts really getting uptight. And don't talk about preventive maintenance, either. We need every piece of equipment running as much as we can to even come close to making the orders we need.

"By the way, some of our best people are threatening to quit. Some are being paid on a piece rate, and the lack of material combined with the directive to avoid finished goods has cut seriously into their paychecks. Even the ones on straight hourly pay are unhappy. All we supervisors are being evaluated on labor productivity and efficiency, and our numbers are looking real bad. Naturally, we put the heat on the workers to do better, but I'm not too sure they can do much about it most of the time.

"And another thing while I have your attention—in some of our models we have a lot of engineering design changes. The MRP system used to give us some warning, but now we have none. Suddenly one of the engineers will show up and tell us to use a different part. When we check with purchasing, often they've only just gotten the notification themselves and have only just started to work with the suppliers for the part. Not only do we have to obsolete all the old parts, but also we have to wait for the new ones. The salespeople are even starting to scream at us.

"While I'm on a roll here, you've got to do something with those quality control people. We could deal with some scrap or rejected parts when we had plenty of inventory, but now we need every part in the place. Tell them to quit rejecting parts and let us use them. At least we'll have a better chance of shipping the order, even if it isn't perfect."

Almost as soon as Marsha left, Valorie (the sales manager) came in. Joe braced himself for more of a headache even before she spoke. The expression on her face foreshadowed what she had on her mind:

"Joe, my job is to make sales and keep the customers happy. The sales have been going fine, but our delivery stinks. Our on-time delivery record has fallen from 95% to less than 50% in the past 6 months. Some of our customers are threatening to leave us, and some are pushing for price cuts. According to them, our delivery record is so poor they feel compelled to keep more of our inventory in their raw material stores to account for their lack of faith in our delivery promises. They say that since it's our fault they have increased raw material inventory costs, we should compensate them with a price cut. It's pretty hard to argue with their logic. I'm sure we would do the same with our suppliers if they treated us the way we've been treating our customers lately.

"We all know our customers have to sometimes change orders to reflect what their own customers want. Now, however, the changes are becoming more frequent and radical. It seems since we are so poor in delivery they order more in advance from us to buffer the time for our late deliveries. Ordering further into the future gives them a lot less certainty of what they really need, so naturally they have to change once they do know. I may have to get another order-entry clerk to deal with all the changes, and if I do you better believe I'll let everyone know the extra expense is your fault!

"The bottom line here is simple, Joe. You've got to get after your people to improve the delivery drastically or we may be in big trouble, and soon."

After Valorie left Joe's secretary came in with a rush memo from the CEO:

"I just got the preliminary financial report for the last quarter, and for the first time in over 5 years we show a loss—and it's a big one. That details show sales goals have basically been met. The loss comes from a very large increase in expenses in virtually every area in operations except a modest decrease in inventory cost. I'm calling an emergency staff meeting for two o'clock today. Please be ready to explain the situation completely."

As Joe shut his door to insulate himself from the complaints and to prepare for the meeting, he began to wonder if some of the people who claimed that JIT and lean production were a culturally based system impossible to implement outside of Japan were correct. He knew most of the problems were related to his attempt to implement the new system. What, he wondered, went wrong, and what should he do about it? These were certainly two critical questions that would be major parts of the two o'clock meeting, and he needed good and complete answers. The CEO was reasonable and could deal with the fact that mistakes might have been made, but she would expect a detailed analysis and complete action plan to get things back on track. The aspirin was definitely wearing off, and it was less than an hour ago that he took them!

Assignment

Prepare a complete and comprehensive report for Joe to use for his two o'clock meeting. This should include both the analysis of what went wrong and why, as well as a comprehensive and time-phased plan to implement lean production the correct way. If you do not think lean production is appropriate, explain why in detail and develop a comprehensive alternative plan.

TOTAL QUALITY MANAGEMENT

INTRODUCTION

The quality of a product or service is difficult to define since it is often viewed by people's perceptions and measured against their own experiences. This chapter will cover definitions of quality and how these can be used in the design of products and services to meet customer expectations. Constant improvement in quality is the responsibility of all members of an organization, and this chapter will introduce some management practices such as quality function deployment, ISO 9000:2000 standards, and six sigma, which help to guide an organization in this improvement. Also included is a brief introduction to process variation and its measurement, along with inspection and benchmarking.

WHAT IS QUALITY?

We all know, or think we know, what quality is. But often it means different things to different people. When asked to define quality, people's responses are influenced by personal opinion and perception. Answers are often general or vague, for example, "It's the best there is," "Something that lasts a long time and gives good service," and "Something with style."

While the definitions of **quality** vary, the one we will use contains the most commonly accepted ideas in business today:

*Quality means user satisfaction: that goods or services satisfy
the needs and expectations of the user.*

To achieve quality according to this definition, we must consider quality and product policy, product design, manufacturing, and final use of the product.

Quality and product policy   Product planning involves decisions about the products and services that a firm will market. A product or service is a combination of tangible and intangible characteristics that a company hopes the customer will accept and be willing to pay a price for. Product planning must decide the market segment to be served, the level of performance expected, and the price to be charged, and it must estimate the expected sales volume. The basic quality level of a product is thus specified by senior management according to its understanding of the wants and needs of the market segment.

Quality and product design   A firm's studies of the marketplace should yield a general specification of the product, outlining the expected performance, appearance, price, and volume. Product designers must then build into the product the quality level described in the general specification. They determine the materials to be used, dimensions, tolerances, product capability, and service requirements. If product designers do not do this properly, the product or service will be unsuccessful in the marketplace because it may not adequately satisfy the needs and expectations of the user.

Quality and manufacturing   At the least, manufacturing is responsible for meeting the minimum specifications of the product design. **Tolerances** establish the acceptable limits and are usually expressed as the amount of allowable variation about the desired amount or nominal. For example, the length of a piece of lumber may be expressed as 7'6" ± ⅛". This means that the longest acceptable piece would be 7'6⅛" and the shortest acceptable piece would be 7'5⅞" long. If an item is within tolerance, then the product should perform adequately. If it is not, it is unacceptable. However, the closer an item is to the nominal or target value, the better it will perform and the less chance there is of creating defects.

Quality in manufacturing means that, at a minimum, all production must be within specification limits, and the less variation from the nominal the better the quality. Manufacturing must strive to produce excellent—not merely adequate—products. Every product or service produced will have some form of tolerance expressed. For example, the weight of bars of soap, the frequency response of compact disks, or the time spent waiting in line will all have a plus and (in most cases) a minus tolerance.

Quality and use   To the user, quality depends on an expectation of how the product should perform. This is sometimes expressed as "fitness for use." Customers do not care *why* a product is defective, but they care *if* it is defective.

The customer may need some introduction to the proper use of a product or feature, especially with new products. A good example of this is a feature required on some new cars that turns off the headlight when its adjacent signal is activated. This is a safety feature that improves the visibility of the signal but customers, unaware of that design feature, thought their vehicles had a defect in the lighting. It was recommended that the manufacturer improve the wording in the owner's manual and introduce this improvement to the customer when purchasing the vehicle. If the product has been well conceived, well designed (meets customer needs), well made, well priced, and well serviced, then the quality is satisfactory. If the product exceeds the customer's expectations, that is superb quality.

Figure 16.1 shows the loop formed by product policy, product design, operations, and the user. Quality must be added by each link.

Quality has a number of dimensions, among which are the following:

- **Performance.** Performance is the primary operating characteristic that the customer wants from a product, such as the power of an engine. Performance implies that the product or service is ready for the customer's use at the time of sale. The term *fitness for use*—that the product does what it is supposed to do—is often used to describe this. Three dimensions to performance are important: reliability, durability, and maintainability.

  1. *Reliability* means consistency of performance. It is measured by the length of time a product can be used before it fails.

  2. *Durability* refers to the ability of a product to continue to function even when subjected to hard wear and frequent use.

  3. *Maintainability* refers to being able to return a product to operating condition after it has failed.

- **Features.** Secondary characteristics—little extras, such as remote control on an appliance or entertainment unit.

- **Conformance.** Meeting established standards or specifications. This is manufacturing's responsibility.

- **Warranty.** An organization's public promise to back up its products with a guarantee of customer satisfaction.

FIGURE 16.1 Product development cycle.

- **Service.** An intangible generally made up of a number of things such as the customer service staff's availability, speed of service, courtesy, and competence.
- **Aesthetics.** The product is pleasing to the senses; for example, the exterior finish or the appearance of a product.
- **Perceived quality.** Customers perceive quality not only in the product itself but also in satisfaction based on the complete experience with an organization. Many intangibles, such as a company's reputation or past performance, influence perceived quality.
- **Price.** Customers pay for value in what they buy. Value is the sum of the benefits the customer receives and can be more than the product itself. All the dimensions of quality listed are elements of value.

These dimensions are not necessarily interrelated. A product can be superb in one or a few dimensions and average or poor in others.

TOTAL QUALITY MANAGEMENT

Total quality management (TQM) is an approach to improving both customer satisfaction and the way organizations do business. TQM brings together all of the quality and customer-related process improvement ideas. It is people oriented. According to the twelfth edition of the *APICS Dictionary*, "it is based on the participation of all members of an organization in improving processes, products, services, and the culture they work in."

The objective of TQM is to provide a quality product to customers at a lower price. By increasing quality and decreasing price, profit and growth will increase, which in turn, will increase job security and employment.

TQM is both a philosophy and a set of guiding principles that lead to a continuously improving organization.

Basic concepts   There are six basic concepts in TQM:

1. **A committed and involved management.** Management must direct and participate in the quality program. TQM is a continuous process that must become part of the organization's culture. This requires senior management's absolute commitment.

2. **Focus on the customer.** This means listening to the customer so goods and services meet customer needs at a low cost while including value-adding features. It means improving design and processes to increase value from the customer's point of view and to reduce defects and cost.

3. **Involvement of the total workforce.** Total quality management is the responsibility of everyone in the organization. It means training all personnel in the techniques of product and process improvement and creating a new culture. It means empowering people.

4. **Continuous process improvement.** Processes can and must be improved to reduce cost and increase quality. (This topic was discussed in Chapter 14 and will not be covered in this chapter.)

5. **Supplier partnering.** A partnering rather than an adversarial relationship with suppliers must be established. As discussed in Chapter 15, this should lead to mutual benefit to both parties.

6. **Performance measures.** Improvement is not possible unless there is some way to measure the results.

These basic concepts will be discussed in more detail in the following sections.

Management Commitment

If senior management is not committed and involved, then TQM will fail. These managers must start the process and should be the first to be educated in the TQM philosophy and concepts. The chief executive officer and senior management should form a quality council whose purpose is to establish a clear vision of what is to be done, develop a set of long-term goals, and direct the program.

The quality council must establish core values that help define the culture of the organization. Core values include such principles as customer-driven quality, continuous improvement, employee participation, and fast response. As well, the council must establish quality statements that include a vision, mission, and quality policy statement. The vision statement describes what the organization should become 5 to 10 years in the future. The mission statement describes the function of the organization: who we are, who our customers are, what the organization does, and how it does it. The quality policy statement is a guide for all in the organization about how products and services should be provided. The three statements must be compatible in that the quality policy statement must fulfill the mission statement which in turn should support the vision statement. Finally, the quality council must establish a strategic plan that expresses the TQM goals and objectives of the organization and how it plans to achieve them.

Customer Focus

Total quality management implies an organization that is dedicated to delighting the customer by meeting or exceeding customer expectations. It means not only understanding present customer needs but also anticipating customers' future needs.

A customer is considered to be a person or organization who receives products or services. There are two types of customers: external and internal. *External customers* exist outside the organization and purchase goods or services from the organization. *Internal customers* are persons or departments who receive the output from another person or department in an organization. Each person or operation in a process is considered a customer of the preceding operation. If an organization is dedicated to delighting the customer, internal suppliers must be dedicated to delighting internal customers.

Customers have six requirements of their suppliers:

1. High quality level.
2. High flexibility to change such things as volume, specifications, and delivery.
3. High service level.
4. Short lead times.
5. Low variability in meeting targets.
6. Low cost.

Customers expect improvement in all requirements. These requirements are not necessarily in conflict. Low cost and high flexibility, for example, do not have to be trade-offs if the process is designed to provide them.

Employee Involvement

TQM is organization-wide and is everyone's responsibility. In a TQM environment, people come to work not only to do their jobs but also to work at improving their jobs. Motivating employees to improve their jobs needs employee commitment to the organization. To encourage this commitment through TQM, requires the following:

1. **Training.** People should be trained in their own job skills and, where possible, cross-trained in other related jobs. As well, they should be trained to use the tools of continuous improvement, problem solving, and statistical process control. Training provides the tools for continual people-driven improvement.
2. **Organization.** The organization must be designed to put people in close contact with their suppliers and customers, internal or external. One way is to organize into customer-, product-, or service-focused cells or teams.
3. **Local ownership.** People should feel ownership of the processes they work with. This results in a commitment to make their processes better and to continuous improvement. They should be empowered.

Empowerment means giving people the authority to make decisions and take action in their work areas without getting prior approval. For example, a customer service representative can respond to a customer's complaint on the spot rather than getting approval or passing the complaint on to a supervisor. Giving people the authority to make decisions motivates them to take ownership of their jobs to accomplish the goals and objectives of the organization.

Teams A team is a group of people working together to achieve common goals or objectives. Good teams can move beyond the contribution of individual members so that the sum of their total effort is greater than their individual efforts. Working in a team requires skill and training, and to work in teams is part of total quality management.

Continuous Process Improvement

This topic, an element in both lean production and TQM, was discussed in Chapter 14. Quality requires continuous process improvement. If a product is excellent in one dimension, such as performance, then improved quality in another dimension should be sought.

Supplier Partnerships

Supplier partnerships are very important in both lean production and total quality management. This topic was discussed in some detail in Chapter 15.

Performance Measures

"What gets measured gets done" is a recurring quote from Tom Peters which illustrates management's need for quantifiable measures. To determine an organization's performance, its progress must be measured. Performance measures can be used to

- Discover which process(es) need(s) improvement.
- Evaluate alternative processes.
- Compare actual performance with targets so corrective action can be taken.
- Evaluate employee performance.
- Show trends.

It is really not a question of whether performance measures are necessary but of selecting appropriate measures. There is no point in measuring something that does not give valid and useful feedback on the process being measured. There are many basic characteristics that can be used to measure the performance of a particular process or activity, such as the following:

- **Quantity.** For example, how many units a process produces in a period of time. Time standards measure this dimension.
- **Cost.** The amount of resources needed to produce a given output.
- **Time/delivery.** Measurements of the ability to deliver a service or product on time.
- **Quality.** There are three dimensions to quality measurements:
  1. **Function.** Does the product perform as specified?
  2. **Aesthetics.** Does the product or service appeal to customers? For example, the percentages of people who like certain features of a product.
  3. **Accuracy.** This measures the number of nonconformances produced. For example, the number of defects or rejects, or the ability to meet specifications.

Performance measures should be simple, easy for users to understand, relevant to the user, visible to the user, preferably developed by the user, designed to promote improvement, and few in number.

Measurement is needed for all types of processes. Some of the areas and possible measurements are as follows:

- **Customer.** Number of complaints, on-time delivery, dealer or customer satisfaction.
- **Production.** Inventory turns, scrap or rework, process yield, cost per unit, time to perform operations.

- **Suppliers.** On-time delivery, rating, quality performance, billing accuracy, continuous improvement.
- **Sales.** Sales expense to revenue, new customers, gained or lost accounts, sales per square foot.

QUALITY COST CONCEPTS

Quality costs fall into two broad categories: the cost of failure to control quality and the cost of controlling quality.

Costs of Failure

The costs of failing to control quality are the costs of producing material that does not meet specification. They can be broken down into the following:

- **Internal failure costs** are the costs of correcting problems that occur while the goods are still in the production facility. Such costs are scrap, rework, and spoilage. These costs would disappear if no defects existed in the product before shipment.
- **External failure costs** are the costs of correcting problems after goods or services have been delivered to the customer. They include warranty costs, field servicing of customer goods, and all the other costs associated with trying to satisfy customer complaints. External failure costs can be the most costly of all if the customer loses interest in a company's product. These costs would also disappear if there were no defects.

Costs of Controlling Quality

The costs of controlling quality can be broken down into the following:

- **Prevention costs** are the costs of avoiding trouble by doing the job right in the first place. (Remember the old adage, "An ounce of prevention is worth more than a pound of cure.") They include training, statistical process control, machine maintenance, design improvements, and quality planning costs.
- **Appraisal costs** are the costs associated with checking and auditing quality in the organization. They include product inspection, quality audits, testing, and calibration.

Investment in prevention will improve productivity by reducing the cost of failure and appraisal. Figure 16.2 shows the typical pattern of quality costs before and after a quality

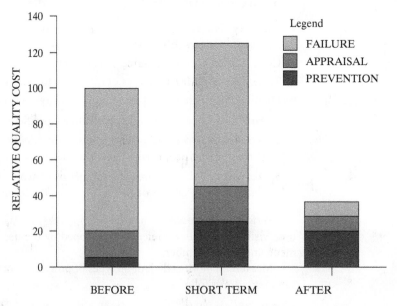

FIGURE 16.2 Impact of quality improvement on quality-related costs. Note that the increased effort put into prevention results in a reduction in both failure costs and appraisal costs.

improvement program. Investing in prevention will increase total costs in the short run, but in the long run prevention will eliminate the causes of failure and reduce total quality costs.

VARIATION AS A WAY OF LIFE

Variability exists in everything—people, machines, or nature. People do not perform the same task in exactly the same way each time, nor can machines be relied upon to perform exactly the same way each time. In nature no two leaves are alike. It is really a question of how much variability there is.

Suppose that a lathe made 100 shafts with a nominal diameter of 1 inch. If we measured those shafts we would find that, while the diameters tended to cluster about 1 inch, some shafts were smaller and some bigger. If we plotted the number of shafts of each diameter, we would probably get a distribution as shown in Figure 16.3; this forms a histogram.

Chance variation   In nature or any manufacturing process, we can expect to find a certain amount of **chance variation** that is inherent in the process. This variation comes from everything influencing the process but is usually separated into the following six categories.

1. **People.** Poorly trained operators tend to be more inconsistent compared with well-trained operators.

2. **Machine.** Well-maintained machines tend to give more consistent output than a poorly maintained, sloppy machine.

3. **Material.** Consistent raw materials give better results than poor quality, inconsistent or ungraded materials.

4. **Method.** Changes in the method of doing a job will alter the quality.

5. **Environment.** Changes in temperature, humidity, dust, and so on can affect some processes.

6. **Measurement.** Measuring tools that may be in error can cause incorrect adjustments and poor process performance.

Dividing all possible variations into these six smaller categories makes it easier to identify the source of variation occurring in a process. If a connection can be found between variation in the product and variation in one of its six sources, then improvements in quality are possible.

There is no way to alter chance variation except to change the process.
If the process produces too many defects, then it must be changed.

FIGURE 16.3 Frequency distribution (histogram) of shaft diameters.

Assignable variation   Chance is not the only cause of variation. A tool may shift, a gauge may move, a machine may wear, or an operator may make a mistake. There is a specific reason for these causes of variation, which is called **assignable variation**.

Statistical control   As long as only chance variation exists, the system is said to be in **statistical control**. If there is an assignable cause for variation, the process is not in control and is unlikely to produce a good product. As will be shown later in this chapter, the objective of statistical process control is to detect the presence of assignable causes of variation. Statistical process control, then, has two objectives:

■ To help select processes capable of producing the required quality with minimum defects.
■ To monitor a process to be sure it continues to produce at the required quality and no assignable cause for variation exists.

Patterns of Variability

The output of every process has a unique pattern that can be described by its **shape**, **center**, and **spread**.

Shape   Suppose, instead of measuring the diameters of 100 shafts, we measured the diameters of 10,000 shafts. If we plotted the distribution of the diameters of the 10,000 shafts, the results in Figure 16.3 would be smoothed out and we would have a curve as shown in Figure 16.4. This bell-shaped curve is called a *normal curve* and is commonly encountered in manufacturing processes that are running under controlled conditions. This curve exists in virtually all natural processes, from the length of grass on a lawn, to the heights of people, to student grades.

Center   We can see from Figure 16.4 that the normal distribution has most results clustered near one central point, with progressively fewer results occurring away from this center. The **center** of the distribution can be calculated as follows:

Let:

$$\Sigma x = \text{sum of all observations}$$
$$n = \text{number of observations}$$
$$\mu = \text{arithmetic mean (average or center)}$$

Then:

$$\mu = \frac{\Sigma x}{n}$$

In the example we are using:

$$\Sigma x = 10,000$$
$$n = 10,000$$
$$\mu = \frac{10,000}{10,000} = 1 \text{ inch}$$

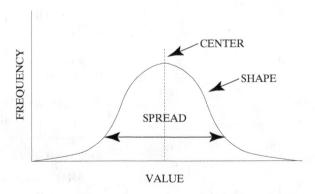

FIGURE 16.4 Normal distribution.

Spread   To evaluate a process, we must know not only what the center of the distribution is but also something about the **spread** or variation. In statistical process control there are two methods of measuring this variation: the range and the standard deviation.

- **Range.** The range is simply the difference between the largest and smallest values in the sample. In the example shown in Figure 16.3, the largest value was 1.003 inches and the smallest was 0.997 inch. The range would be 1.003 inch − 0.997 inch = 0.006 inch.

- **Standard deviation.** The standard deviation (represented by the Greek letter σ or sigma) may be thought of as the "average spread" around the center. A distribution with a high standard deviation is "fatter" than one with a low standard deviation. Higher-quality products have little variation (a low standard deviation). The measurement of the standard deviation was discussed in Chapter 11 in the section on determining safety stock. We know that

$$\mu \pm 1\sigma = 68.3\% \text{ of observations}$$
$$\mu \pm 2\sigma = 95.4\% \text{ of observations}$$
$$\mu \pm 3\sigma = 99.7\% \text{ of observations}$$

where

μ = mean or average

σ = standard deviation

We can use the standard deviation to estimate the amount of variation (quality) in a product. Suppose in our example of the shafts that

$$\mu = 1.000 \text{ inches}$$
$$\sigma = 0.0016 \text{ inch}$$

Applying standard deviation to the previous example we know that

68.3% of the shafts will have a diameter of 1 inch ± 0.0016 inch (1σ)

95.4% of the shafts will have a diameter of 1 inch ± 0.0032 inch (2σ)

99.7% of the shafts will have a diameter of 1 inch ± 0.0048 inch (3σ)

PROCESS CAPABILITY

Tolerances are the limits of deviation from perfection and are established by the product design engineers to meet a particular design function. For example a shaft might be specified as having a diameter of 1 inch ± 0.005 inch. Thus, any shaft having a diameter between 0.995 inch and 1.005 inches would be within tolerance. In statistical process control 0.995 inch is called the **lower specification limit (LSL)** and is the minimum acceptable level of output. Similarly 1.005 inches is called the **upper specification limit (USL)** and is defined as the maximum acceptable level of output. *Both the USL and the LSL are related to the product specification usually determined by the customer and are independent of any process.* The distance between the upper and lower specifications is often called the specification doorway. The doorway is analogous to a tunnel with a vehicle (the process) passing through it. Parts of the vehicle that are wider than the doorway will represent defective product or scrap. In this example it is not possible to change the width of the tunnel. Specifications are set by designers and ultimately by the customer and are normally not challenged. It is up to the producer to keep the spread of the process output well within these limits. Figure 16.5 illustrates this. One process, having a narrow spread (low sigma), will produce product within the specification limits. The other process, having a wide spread (high sigma), will produce defects. The first process is said to be capable, the second is not.

Besides spread, there is another way a process can produce defects. If there is a shift in the mean (average), defects will be produced. Figure 16.6 illustrates the concept.

In summary,

- The capability of the process is a measure of the process spread compared to the specification limits.

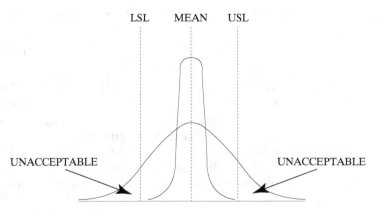

FIGURE 16.5 Effect of process spreads.

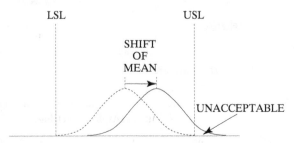

FIGURE 16.6 Effect of shift in mean.

- A process must be selected that can meet the specifications.
- Processes can produce defects in two ways: by having too big a spread (sigma) or by a shift in the mean (average).

Process Capability Index, C_p

The **process capability index** combines the process spread and the tolerance into one index making it easier for operators and managers to quickly determine the capability of a process. It assumes that the process is centered between the upper and lower specification limits—that there has been no shift of the mean. As well, the index assumes that processes are 6σ wide, representing 99.7% of the output of a normal process. If the 6σ process spread is smaller than the specification doorway then the process is said to be capable.

$$C_p = \frac{\text{USL} - \text{LSL}}{6\sigma}$$

In the example used under process spread, the tolerance was 1.000 inch ± 0.005 inch, and the standard deviation of the process (σ) was 0.0016 inch.

$$C_p = \frac{1.005 - 0.995}{6 \times 0.0016} = 1.04$$

In this example the C_p is slightly greater than 1.00 so the process is said to be capable. If the capability index is greater than 1.00, the process is capable of producing 99.7% of parts within tolerance and is said to be capable. If C_p is less than 1.00, however, the process is said to be not capable. Because processes tend to shift back and forward, a C_p of 1.33 has become a standard of process capability. Some organizations use a higher value such as 2 for their quality standards. The higher the capability index, the fewer the rejects and the greater the quality. Figure 16.7 shows the concept of the capability index for the above example.

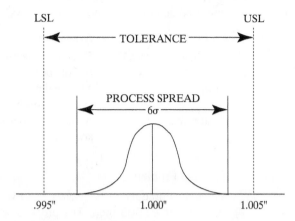

FIGURE 16.7 C_p index greater than 1.

Example Problem

The specification for the weight of a chemical in a compound is 10 ± 0.05 grams. If the standard deviation of the weighing scales is 0.02, is the process considered capable?

ANSWER

$$C_p = \frac{10.05 - 9.95}{6 \times 0.02} = 0.83$$

The C_p is less than 1, and the process is not considered capable.

The process capability index indicates whether process variation is satisfactory, but it does not measure whether the process is centered properly. Thus it does not protect against out-of-specification product resulting from poor centering. In some cases this is important to know.

C_{pk} Index

This index measures the effect of both center and variation at the same time. The philosophy of the C_{pk} **index** is that if the process distribution is well within specification on the worst-case side, and is capable according to the C_p then it is sure to be acceptable for the other specification limit. Figure 16.8 illustrates the concept.

The C_{pk} index is the lesser of

$$\frac{USL - Mean}{3\sigma} \quad or \quad \frac{Mean - LSL}{3\sigma}$$

The greater the C_{pk}, the further the 3σ limit is from the specification limits and the fewer rejects there will be.

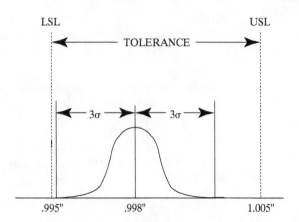

FIGURE 16.8 C_{pk} index.

Interpretation of the C_p index is as follows.

C_{pk} Value	Evaluation
Less than +1	Unacceptable process. Part of process distribution is out of specification.
+1 to +1.33	Marginal process. Process distribution barely within specification.
Greater than 1.33	Acceptable process. Process distribution is well within specification.

Example Problem

A company produces shafts on a lathe with a nominal diameter of 1 inch and a tolerance of ±0.005 inch. The process has a standard deviation of 0.001 inch. For each of the following cases, calculate the C_{pk} and evaluate the process capability.

a. A sample has an average diameter of 0.997 inch.

b. A sample has an average diameter of 0.998 inch.

c. A sample has an average diameter of 1.001 inches.

ANSWER

a. $C_{pk} = \dfrac{1.005 - 0.997}{3 \times 0.001} = 2.67$ or $= \dfrac{0.997 - 0.995}{3 \times 0.001} = 0.667$

$C_{pk} = 0.667$ which is less than 1. Process is not capable.

b. $C_{pk} = \dfrac{1.005 - 0.998}{3 \times 0.001} = 2.33$ or $= \dfrac{0.998 - 0.995}{3 \times 0.001} = 1.00$

C_{pk} is 1. Process is marginally capable.

c. $C_{pk} = \dfrac{1.005 - 1.001}{3 \times 0.001} = 1.33$ or $=$ or $\dfrac{1.001 - 0.995}{3 \times 0.001} = 2$

C_{pk} is 1.33. Process is capable.

Note that the lower C_{pk} is always used in each of the above calculations.

Example Problem

A sample has been taken from a recent shipment of laptop hinge pins and the following readings of pin lengths have been recorded:

2.01   2.02   1.99   2.01   2.01   2.00   2.03   2.02   2.01   2.00

a. A specification of 2.00" ± 0.05" is required for the pins. Sketch the data and enter the specification limits.

ANSWER:

b. Calculate the standard deviation of the data, the C_p, and the C_{pk}.

ANSWER: Sigma for the data = 0.01095; average = 2.01

$$C_p = \frac{2.05 - 1.95}{6 \times 0.01095} \qquad C_{pk} = \frac{2.01 - 1.95}{3 \times 0.01095} \qquad C_{pk} = \frac{2.05 - 2.01}{3 \times 0.01095}$$
$$= 1.52 \text{ Capable} \qquad = 1.83 \text{ Capable} \qquad = 1.21 \text{ Marginal}$$

The data shows that the pins are slightly oversized since the average is above the nominal specification of 2.00". With a C_{pk} of 1.21 the process is marginally capable but would improve if the average was moved to 2.00. The supplier should adjust their equipment to reduce the length of the pins by 0.01 inch. Making the suggested improvement to the average, even though no parts out of specification were found is an example of continuous process improvement.

PROCESS CONTROL

Process control attempts to prevent the production of defects by showing that when the standard deviation increases or when there is a significant change in the average there is an *assignable* cause for variation.

We have seen that variation exists in all processes and that the process must be designed so the spread will be small enough to produce a minimum number of defects. Variation will follow a stable pattern as long as the system of chance causes remains the same and there is no assignable cause of variation. Once a stable process is established, the limits of the resulting pattern of variation can be determined and will serve as a guide for future production. When variation exceeds these limits, it shows a high probability that there is an assignable cause which needs to be corrected.

We have also seen that a process can produce defects if the spread is too great or if the center or the average is not correct. Some method is needed to measure these two characteristics continually so we can compare what is happening to the product specification. This is done using the $\overline{X}$ (X bar) and R control chart.

Control Charts

Run charts Suppose a manufacturer was filling bottles and wanted to check the process to be sure the proper amount of liquid was going into each. Samples are taken every half hour and measured. The average of the samples is then plotted on a chart as shown in Figure 16.9. This is called a **run chart**. While it gives a visual description of what is happening with the process, it does not distinguish between system (chance) variation and assignable cause variation.

FIGURE 16.9 Run chart.

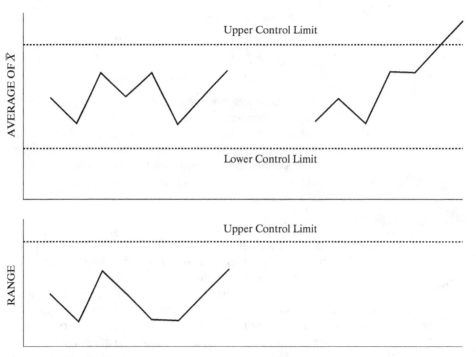

FIGURE 16.10 An $\overline{X}$ and R control chart.

$\overline{X}$ **(X bar) and R Chart**   A control chart for averages and ranges ($\overline{X}$ **and R chart**) tracks the two critical characteristics of a frequency distribution—the center and the spread. Small samples (typically three to nine pieces) are taken on a regular basis over time and the sample averages and range plotted. The range is used rather than the standard deviation because it is easier to calculate. Samples are used in control charts rather than individual observations because average values will indicate a change in variation much faster. Figure 16.10 shows an example of an $\overline{X}$ and R chart.

Control Limits

Figure 16.10 also shows two dotted lines, the upper control limit (UCL) and the lower control limit (LCL). These limits are established to help in assessing the significance of the variation produced by the process. *They should not be confused with specification limits*, which are permissible limits of each unit of product (tolerances). Specification limits are generally established by the customer and have nothing to do with the process. Showing specification limits on control charts is not recommended.

Control limits are set so that there is a 99.7% probability that if the process is in control, the sample value will fall within the control limits. When this situation occurs, the process is considered to be in statistical control and there is no assignable cause of variation. The process is stable and predictable. This is shown on the left portion of the chart in Figure 16.10. All the points lie within the limits and the process is in statistical control. Only chance variation is affecting the process. However, when assignable causes of variation exist, the variation will be excessive and the process is said to be out of control. This is shown on the right portion of the chart, which indicates something has caused the process to go out of control.

As explained, two types of changes can occur in a process:

- **A shift in the mean or average.** This might be caused by a worn tool or a guide that has moved. This will show up on the $\overline{X}$ portion of the chart.
- **A change in the spread of the distribution.** If the range increases but the sample averages remain the same, we might expect this kind of problem. It might be caused by a gauge or tool becoming loose or by some part of the machine becoming worn. This will show up on the R portion of the chart.

The $\overline{X}$ and R chart is used to measure variables, such as the diameter of a shaft, which can be measured on a continual scale. Operators should construct and monitor their own control charts as a way of taking ownership of their jobs. They are the most likely person to know what changes are affecting their process. In practice, operators readily interpret changes in the mean or spread and can quickly take corrective action with the process, often before defects are produced.

Control Charts for Attributes

An attribute refers to quality characteristics that either conform to specification or do not, for example, visual inspection for color, missing parts, and scratches. A go–no-go gauge is a good example. Either the part is within tolerance or it is not. These characteristics cannot be measured, but they can be counted. Attributes are usually plotted using a proportion defective or *p*-chart.

Other Quality Control Tools

In addition to some of the previously discussed tools such as histograms (page 473), run charts (page 481), and *X* bar and *R* charts (page 481), there are five other simple tools that are commonly used. These include the following:

1. **Pareto diagrams.** These diagrams are merely histograms that are reorganized in such a way as to show the highest bar first and all others in descending order from high to low. This approach allows one to easily focus on the most important issues and was discussed in Chapter 14 under continuous process improvement.

2. **Checksheets.** These represent a very simple method to collect data. Once an issue of interest has been determined (e.g., customer complaints about some product or service), the sources of the complaints are listed as they occur. Whenever a complaint reason is repeated, a check is put beside the reason. Over time the number of checks should show clearly the major source of complaint, thereby allowing action to focus on that major source.

3. **Process flow diagrams.** These diagrams (discussed in Chapter 14) show in detail the steps required to produce a product or service. Once the specific tasks are identified, data can be collected about these tasks to determine bottlenecks or other types of problems that can be corrected to improve the process.

4. **Scatterplots.** These merely show the relationship between two variables of interest. For example, a bank may want to know whether there is a relationship between how long people have to wait in line and how satisfied they are with their service by the bank. For each customer, they would obtain a measure of the wait time and their satisfaction. They could then plot each person's score with the wait time on the horizontal axis and the satisfaction index on the vertical axis. Plotting many customer scores would then provide an indication of whether there is a relationship and also the possible strength of that relationship.

5. **Cause-and-effect (fishbone) diagrams.** These diagrams (discussed in Chapter 14) are used to plot out all the potential causes for an identified problem (effect). As specific problems are branched out from the major effect area, the result appears something like a fishbone. The potential causes can then be researched to find the root cause and correct it. Figure 16.11 shows the structure:

FIGURE 16.11 The structure for a cause-and-effect diagram.

SAMPLE INSPECTION

Statistical process control monitors the process and detects when the process goes out of control, thus minimizing the production of defective parts. Traditional inspection methods inspect a batch of parts after it is made and, on the basis of the inspection, accepts or rejects the batch. There are two inspection procedures: 100% and acceptance sampling.

A **100% inspection** means testing every unit in the lot. This is appropriate when the cost of inspection is less than the cost of any loss resulting from failure of the parts—for example, when inspection is very easy to do or the inspection is part of the process. A light bulb manufacturer could easily build a tester to see if every light bulb lights, or a baker could visually inspect all products prior to packaging them. In cases in which the cost of failure is exceptionally high, 100% inspection is vital. Products for the medical and aerospace industry may be checked many times because of the importance of product performance or the high cost of failure.

Acceptance sampling consists of taking a sample of a batch of product and using it to estimate the overall quality of the batch. Based on the results of the inspection a decision is made to reject or accept the entire batch. There is a chance that a good batch will be rejected or a bad batch will be accepted. Sampling inspection is necessary under some conditions.

Reasons for sampling inspection   There are four reasons for using sample inspection.

1. **Testing the product is destructive.** The ultimate pull strength of a rope or the sweetness of an apple can be decided only by destroying the product.

2. **There is not enough time to give 100% inspection to a batch of product.** On Election Day, newscasters are eager to get coverage. Once a small percentage of the votes are in, a guess is made of the final outcome, usually with some estimate of the error (say 19 times out of 20).

3. **It is too expensive to test all of the batch.** Market sampling is an example of this, as are surveys of public attitude.

4. **Human error is estimated to be as high as 20% when performing long-term repetitive testing.** There are good reasons to have a representative sample taken of a batch rather than to hazard this high an error.

Conditions necessary for sampling inspection   The use of statistical sampling depends on the following conditions:

- **All items must be produced under similar or identical conditions.** Sampling the incoming produce to a food-processing plant would require separate samples for separate farmers or separate fields.
- **A random sample of the lot must be taken.** A random sample implies that every item in the lot has an equal chance of being selected.
- **The lot to be sampled should be a homogeneous mixture.** This means that defects will occur in any part of the batch. (The apples on the top should be the same quality as the apples on the bottom!)
- **The batches to be inspected should be large.** Sampling is rarely performed on small lots and is much more accurate in very large samples.

Sampling Plans

Sampling plans are designed to provide some assurance of the quality of goods while taking costs into consideration. Lots are defined as good if they contain no more than a specified level of defects, called the acceptable quality level (AQL). A plan is designed to have a minimum allowable number (or %) of defects in the sample in order to accept the lot. Above this level of defects, the lot will be rejected.

Selecting a particular plan depends on three factors:

Consumer's risk   The probability of accepting a bad lot is called the **consumer's risk**. Since sampling inspection does not produce results with 100% accuracy, there is always

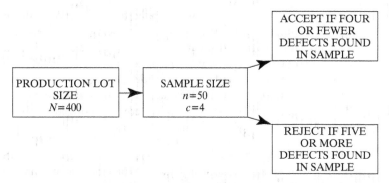

FIGURE 16.12 Sampling plan.

a risk that a lot containing more than the desired number of defects will be accepted. The consumer will want to be sure that the sampling plan has a low probability of accepting bad lots.

Producer's risk The probability of rejecting a good lot is called the **producer's risk**. Since sampling involves probabilities, there is a chance that a batch of good products will be rejected. The producer will want to ensure that the sampling plan has a low probability of rejecting good lots.

Cost Inspection costs money. The objective is to balance the consumer's risk and the producer's risk against the cost of the sampling plan. The larger the sample, the smaller the producer's and consumer's risks and the more the likelihood that good batches will not be rejected and poor batches will not be accepted. However, the larger the sample size, the greater the inspection cost. Thus there is a balance between the producer's and consumer's risks and the cost of inspection.

Example For simplicity, a single sampling plan will be considered (there are others). The plan will specify the sample size (n)—the number of randomly selected items to be taken—from a given size of production lot (N). These will be inspected for some known characteristic, and the plan will set a maximum allowable number of defective products in the sample (c). If more than this number of defectives is found in the sample, the entire lot is rejected. If the allowable number of defects, or fewer, are found in the sample the lot is accepted. Figure 16.12 illustrates an example of a single sampling plan.

The larger the sample, the smaller the producer's and consumer's risk and the more the likelihood that good batches will not be rejected and poor batches accepted. However, the larger the sample size, the greater the inspection cost. Thus there is a trade-off between the producer's and consumer's risks and the cost of inspection.

ISO 9000:2008

The International Organization for Standardization (ISO) has issued a series of standards; the most recent version is **ISO 9000:2008**. Established in 1947, ISO continues to be a nongovernmental organization based in Geneva, Switzerland. The acronym (ISO) is derived from the Greek *isos* meaning equality, and it is used in many languages. The European Community (EC) has accepted the ISO standards, and they are becoming universally accepted, especially in North America. Besides being a requirement for doing business in Europe, customers throughout the world have come to expect a quality standard and to demand ISO certification of their suppliers.

The two categories of ISO standards are technical standards and management standards. Technical standards allow interchanging of parts such as light bulbs, nuts and bolts, tire sizes, and electrical connectors. As discussed in Chapter 14, standardizing parts has many advantages to the production and marketing of products. ISO 9000:2008 is a management standard that defines how a company conducts its business, which helps it work and understand its suppliers and customers.

The standards are intended to prevent nonconformities during all stages of business functions, such as purchasing, invoicing, quality, and design. Originally, they were written for contractual situations between suppliers and customers in which the supplier would develop a quality system that conformed to the ISO standards and was satisfactory to the customer. The customer would then audit the system for acceptability. This resulted in multiple audits for different suppliers and different customers. Because of this, a third-party registration system was created to avoid duplicate work and to ensure consistency for all supplier–customer situations.

Third-party registration system   A third party called a registrar assesses the adequacy of the supplier's quality system. When the system conforms to the registrar's interpretation of the applicable ISO 9000 standard, the registrar issues a certificate of registration. The registrar continues to survey the supplier and makes full reassessment every three or four years. The registrar is a "qualified" certifying agent who has usually been accredited by the Registrar Accreditation Board, which is affiliated with the American Society for Quality (ASQ). The third-party registration system ensures customers that a supplier has a quality system in place and that the latter is monitored, thus eliminating the need for audits for each customer.

ISO 9000:2008 is designed around a process approach to management and is based on eight principles that are closely aligned with total quality management:

1. **Customer focus.** Understanding customer needs, striving to exceed customer expectations.
2. **Leadership.** Establishing direction, unity of purpose, and a supportive work environment.
3. **Involvement of people.** Ensuring that all employees at all levels are able to fully use their abilities for the organization's benefit.
4. **Process approach.** Recognizing that all work is done through processes and managed accordingly.
5. **System approach to management.** Expands on the previous principle in that achieving any objective requires a system of interrelated processes.
6. **Continual improvement.** As a permanent organizational objective, recognizing and acting on the fact that in all cases further improvement is possible.
7. **Factual approach to decision making.** Acknowledging that sound decisions must be based on analysis of factual data and information.
8. **Mutually beneficial supplier relationships.** Synergy can be found in such relationships.

A common misconception about ISO 9000:2008 is that it applies only to the manufacturing sector. ISO's intent, however, is that the standard be applied to any business. An indication of this in the most recent version is the use of the term *product realization*. Product realization refers to all the processes that are used to bring products into being. This is an update to the previously used term *production system* and can now include service activities such as giving information, diagnosing a patient, or designing a building. Examples of services where ISO 9000:2008 can be applied follow:

hospitality	communications	health care
maintenance	government	trading
financial	professional	administration
purchasing	transportation	scientific
utilities	technical	education

Documentation

ISO does not provide the documentation but specifies generic requirements for management that are typically grouped into four levels: policies (quality manual), procedures, practice, and proof, as shown in Figure 16.13. Policies define what management wants to accomplish. Procedures are established and closely linked to the policies to ensure that policies are incorporated in the activities of the organization. Practice is the demonstration

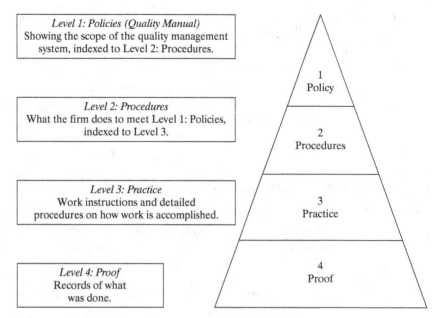

FIGURE 16.13 ISO 9000:2008 documentation pyramid.

of procedures, and documentation is the proof that the procedures have been carried out. Auditors closely monitor all these documented activities to ensure that they are being followed. An example of a policy in a retail environment may be the statement "Customers will be satisfied with the quality of our products." The resulting procedure could then be "A full refund will be issued, provided proof of purchase, and the approval of the department supervisor." The practice would involve giving the department supervisor the authority to issue the refund, and the proof would be documented by the proper filing of receipts and returns.

ISO 9000:2008 covers all aspects of managing a business, including operations, administration, sales, and technical support. It puts in place a process approach for all the day-to-day activities of generating products or services. Customers and suppliers to an ISO-certified organization can be assured that consistent management processes are in place, providing stability and continuous improvement in products and services.

BENCHMARKING

Benchmarking is a systematic method by which organizations can compare their performance in a particular process to that of a "best-in-class" organization, finding out how that organization achieves those performance levels and applying them to their own organization. Continuous improvement, as discussed in Chapter 14, seeks to make improvement by looking inward and analyzing current practice. Benchmarking looks outward to see what competitors and excellent performers outside the industry are doing.

The steps in benchmarking are these:

1. **Select the process to benchmark.** This is much the same as the first step in the continuous improvement process.

2. **Identify an organization that is best in class in performing the process you want to study.** This may not be a company in the same industry. The classic example is Xerox using L. L. Bean, a mail order sales organization, as a benchmark when studying its own order entry system.

3. **Study the benchmarked organization.** Information may be available internally, may be in the public domain, or may require some original research. Original research includes questionnaires, site visits, and focus groups. Questionnaires are useful when information is gathered from many sources. Site visits involve meeting with the best-in-class organization. Many companies select workers to be on a benchmark team that

meets with counterparts in the other organization. Focus groups are panels that may be composed of groups such as customers, suppliers, or benchmark partners, brought together to discuss the process.

4. **Analyze the data.** What are the differences between your process and the benchmark organization? There are two aspects to this. One is comparing the processes and the other is measuring the performance of those processes according to some standard. The measurement of performance requires some unit of measure, referred to as metrics. Typical performance measures are quality, service response time, cost per order, and so forth.

SIX SIGMA

Modern equipment is becoming increasingly complex, often involving thousands of components that must work reliably to ensure that the entire system does not fail. Bill Smith, a reliability engineer at Motorola Corporation, found that to function properly the company's complicated systems required individual component failure rates approaching zero. These extremely low rates were beyond the ability of inspectors to measure, and Smith worked with others to develop the **Six Sigma** Breakthrough Strategy aimed at defect rates of 3.4 parts per million:

- **Scope.** Systematic reduction of process variability.
- **Quality definition.** Defects per million possibilities.
- **Purpose.** Improve profits by reducing process variation.
- **Measurement.** Defects per million possibilities.
- **Focus.** Locating and eliminating sources of process error.

Six sigma, however, is about more than just measurements of parts production. It encourages companies to focus on improving all business processes. Process improvements result in reduced waste, costs, and lost opportunities, which all lead to higher profits for the producer and benefits to the customer. The six sigma methodology must be initiated by upper management since it sets the business goals of the company and guides the actions of all employees. Middle management is tasked with translating the business goals into process goals and measures. Six sigma is a highly focused system of problem solving with two main elements: projects and project managers. Figure 16.14 illustrates the eight essential

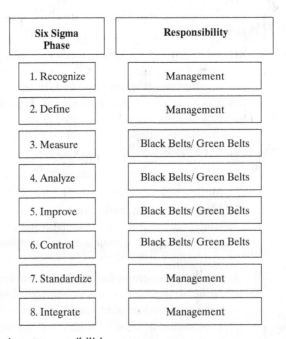

Six Sigma Phase	Responsibility
1. Recognize	Management
2. Define	Management
3. Measure	Black Belts/ Green Belts
4. Analyze	Black Belts/ Green Belts
5. Improve	Black Belts/ Green Belts
6. Control	Black Belts/ Green Belts
7. Standardize	Management
8. Integrate	Management

FIGURE 16.14 Six sigma responsibilities.

FIGURE 16.15 Six sigma occurs when the process doorway is twice the process spread:

$$C_p = \frac{USL - LSL}{6\sigma} > 2$$

phases and responsibilities of six sigma projects, which may be expressed as DMAIC (design, measure, analyze, improve, and control).

When the project has been selected:

1. Select the appropriate metrics or key performance output variables.
2. Determine how the metrics will be tracked over time.
3. Determine the current project baseline performance.
4. Determine the input variables that drive the key performance output variables.
5. Determine what changes need to be made to the input variables to positively affect the key performance output variables.
6. Make the changes.
7. Determine if the changes positively affect the key performance output variables.
8. If the changes positively affect the key performance output variables, establish controls of the input variables at the new levels. If they do not, return to step 5.

From a technical perspective, six sigma is achieved when the process capability, C_p, is equal to 2 or greater. That is, the specification doorway is twice the width of the six sigma process spread, and the long-term failure rate would be 3.4 parts per million. With good controls in place the minor shifts in the process will be detected prior to any defective parts being produced. Figure 16.15 shows this concept graphically. Note that the process is well centered.

The experience and abilities of project managers are designated by terms from karate. "Green Belts" have a specified amount of training and are required to complete a cost-saving project of approximately $10,000. Black Belts have extensively more training and are expected to implement projects with savings in excess of $100,000. Master Black Belts have even further training and usually have completed large-scale projects with savings of $1,000,000. Most often Black Belts also require a master's degree from an accredited university. Only a small portion of a company's managers will attain Master Black Belt status, and they are tasked with the training and guidance of trainees.

The six sigma method is an extension to other business processes of basic statistical process control and can be compared to other quality initiatives, such as continuous process improvement or ISO 9000. It does encourage companies to take a customer focus and improve business processes through a series of well-defined steps and responsibilities. Process improvement of any kind will lead to reduced waste, decreased costs, and improved opportunities. It is the customer who ultimately enjoys lower costs and enhanced quality.

QUALITY FUNCTION DEPLOYMENT

Quality function deployment or QFD is a decision-making technique used in the development of new products or the improvement of existing products, which helps ensure that the wants, needs, and expectations of the customer are reflected in a company's designs. Organizations that ignore the relationship between what is provided in their products and what a customer wants will not remain competitive. QFD was originally developed in the

1960s by Dr. Yoji Akao and Dr. Shigeru Mizuno and has been adopted by notable U.S. manufacturers, including GM, Ford, Daimler Chrysler, IBM, Raytheon, Boeing, Lockheed Martin, and their suppliers. As defined in the twelfth edition of the *APICS Dictionary*, QFD is "a methodology designed to ensure that all the major requirements of the customer are identified and subsequently met or exceeded through the resulting product design process."

QFD works as follows. The needs of the customer are gathered using various survey methods or by comparing a company's own products against the competition's. These wants are referred to as the **voice of the customer** or VOC, which must be translated into engineering specifications through a series of well-defined steps. A House of Quality, as shown in Figure 16.16, is used to sort all the data into a structured process that takes the customer requirements, prioritizes them, and sets the engineering target values for the new design.

The House of Quality in Figure 16.16 is a simple example used for the design of an insulated travel mug. On the left-hand side is a list of all the features that the customer feels are important in the design of the travel mug. On the right-hand side is an evaluation of how the sample mug holds up against the competition, listed from low to high and showing where the sample and the competition rank in each of the identified customer needs. In this example it seems the mug has a well-fitting lid and customers like the handle design. However, the mug spills easily, is not very durable, does not hold enough liquid, and does not insulate well. These are considered the "wants" of the customer. The "hows" of meeting these wants are listed near the top of the house with such features as the thickness of the material used and the volume and stability of the mug. The "roof" of the house is used to show the interaction of the features, and in this case only strong negatives and positives are shown. A strong positive, such as the thickness of

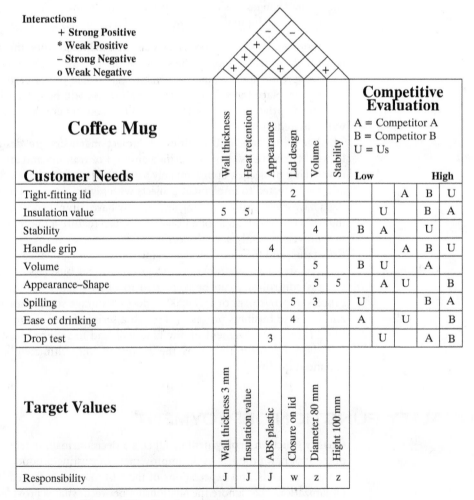

FIGURE 16.16 House of Quality for a travel mug.

the wall and the heat retention, shows that they are closely related to each other and that an increase in the wall thickness leads to an increase in the insulation value. Increasing the wall thickness, however, has a negative affect on the volume. In the center of the house, priorities are set by management showing where improvements should be made and their relative importance. Technical specifications to meet the desired features and priorities are entered at the bottom of the house along with a responsibility code showing which department or person will work on the design of the final product. In this case the design of our new product will call for a short (100 mm) and stout (80 mm) mug made of ABS plastic. The handle will also be of ABS plastic, which can be molded from the same plastic as the mug. The new design must make sure that any of the negative interactions such as wall thickness and volume are considered.

When QFD is properly administered and good group decision making is used, it will ensure that design targets and features will reflect the needs of the customers and will avoid adding costs and features that are not required.

LEAN PRODUCTION, TQM AND MRP

Although the purposes of MRP, Lean Production, and TQM are different, there is a close relationship among them. Lean Production is a philosophy that seeks to eliminate waste and focuses on decreasing non-value-added activities by improving processes and reducing lead time. TQM places emphasis on customer satisfaction and focusing the whole company to that end. While Lean Production seems to be inward looking (the elimination of waste in the organization and lead time reduction) and TQM outward looking (customer satisfaction), they both have many of the same concepts. Both emphasize management commitment, continuous process improvement, employee involvement, and supplier partnerships. Performance measurement is necessarily a part of process improvement in both Lean Production and TQM. Lean Production places emphasis on quality as a means of reducing waste and thus embraces the ideas of TQM. TQM is directed to satisfying the customer, which is also an objective of JIT.

Lean Production and TQM are mutually reinforcing. They should be considered two sides of the same coin—providing customers what they want at low cost.

MRP is primarily concerned with managing the flow of materials into, through, and out of an organization. Its objectives are to maximize the use of the organization's resources and provide the required level of customer service. It is a planning and execution process that must work with existing processes, be they good or bad. Lean Production is directed toward process improvement and lead time reduction, and TQM is directed toward customer satisfaction. Thus both Lean Production and TQM are part of the environment in which MRP II must work. Improved processes, better quality, employee involvement, and supplier partnerships can only improve the effectiveness of MRP. Figure 16.17 illustrates the relationship graphically.

FIGURE 16.17 MRP, Lean Production, and TQM. *Source:* Adapted from *Basics of Supply Chain Management*, APICS-The Ed. Soc. For Res. Mgt., Falls Church, VA, 1997. Reprinted with permission.

SUMMARY

As the last chapter in this text we come to the conclusion that quality of both products and services is ultimately established by the customer and the customer is continuously setting higher and higher standards. A company's commitment to quality must start with top management to ensure the entire company works towards improvements. A commitment to quality determines everything from the design policies of products and services, to the design of the production processes, to the quality of suppliers and finally to the end use by the consumer. Worker involvement is essential since they have direct knowledge of the processes used and are the first to be aware of any changes.

The technical aspects of quality focus on reducing variation and the factors that cause variation both common cause and assignable cause. Statistical tools are readily available to study variation and calculators and computers take a lot of the drudgery out of the calculations. Where possible it is important to control the process rather than the product itself. Sampling plans test products after they are produced and do not directly improve the quality of products. But sampling is still necessary when the costs of failure are high in industries such as pharmaceuticals and aerospace.

Management can follow many accepted programs such as ISO standards, Six Sigma or QFD to drive quality improvements. High quality is a necessary part of lean production as we work with lower inventories and faster product flows which has been the topic of all previous chapters in this book.

KEY TERMS

Acceptance sampling 382	Performance 368
Aesthetics 369	Prevention costs 372
Appraisal costs 372	Price 369
Assignable variation 374	Process capability index 376
Cause-and-effect (fishbone) diagrams 381	Producer's risk 383
Center 374	Quality 367
Chance variation 373	Quality function deployment 387
Checksheets 381	Run chart 379
Conformance 368	Scatterplots 381
Consumer's risk 382	Service 369
Control limits 380	Shape 374
C_{pk} index 377	Six sigma 386
Empowerment 371	Spread 375
External failure costs 372	Statistical control 374
Features 368	Third-party registration system 384
100% inspection 382	Tolerances 367
Internal failure costs 372	Upper specification limit (USL) 375
ISO 9000:2008 383	Voice of the customer 388
Lower specification limit (LSL) 375	Warranty 368
Pareto diagrams 381	(X bar) and R chart 380
Perceived quality 369	

QUESTIONS

1. What is the definition of quality?
2. In which four areas must quality be considered? How do they interrelate?

3. Name and describe the eight dimensions to quality.

4. What is total quality management, and what are its objectives?

5. What are the six basic concepts of TQM?

6. What does *customer focus* mean? Who is the customer?

7. What is empowerment, and why is it important in TQM?

8. What are the three key factors in supplier partnerships?

9. What is the purpose of performance measurement?

10. Quality costs fall under two categories. Name each category and think of an example to illustrate the category.

11. What is chance variation? What are its causes? How can it be altered?

12. What is assignable variation?

13. What is a normal distribution? Why is it important in quality control?

14. What is the arithmetic mean or average?

15. What is meant by *process spread*? What are the two measures of it?

16. What percentage of the observations will fall within 1, 2, and 3 standard deviations of the mean?

17. In which two ways can a process create defects?

18. What is tolerance, and how does it relate to the USL and LSL?

19. What is the purpose of the process capability index C_p and the C_{pk}? How do they differ?

20. What is the purpose of process control? What kind of variation does it try to detect?

21. What is a run chart?

22. What is an $\overline{X}$ and R chart?

23. What are upper and lower control limits?

24. What is the difference between variables and attributes?

25. When is it appropriate to use 100% inspection?

26. What is acceptance sampling? When is it appropriate to use?

27. What are the consumer's risk and the producer's risk?

28. Why was the third-party registration system established for ISO 9000 certification?

29. What is benchmarking, and how is it different from continuous improvement?

30. What is the first step in Quality Function Deployment? What is the output from QFD?

31. List three similarities and three differences between Lean Production and TQM.

32. What does the acronym *VOC* stand for?

33. What technique is used to organize the VOC?

PROBLEMS

16.1. The specification for the length of a shaft is 12 inches ± 0.001 inch. If the process standard deviation is 0.00033, approximately what percentage of the shafts will be within tolerance?

Answer. There are approximately 99.7% of shafts within tolerance.

16.2. In problem 16.1, if the tolerance changes to +0.0007 inch, approximately what percentage of the shafts will be within tolerance?

16.3. The specification for the thickness of a piece of steel is 0.5 inch ± 0.05 inch. The standard deviation of the band saw is 0.015. Using C_p, calculate whether the process is capable or not.

Answer. $C_p = 1.11$. Process is marginally capable.

16.4. The specification for the weight of a chemical in a compound is ±0.05. If the standard deviation of the weighing scales is 0.02, is the process considered capable?

16.5. The specification for the diameter of a hole is 0.75 inch ± 0.015 inch. The standard deviation of the drill press is 0.007 inch. Using C_p, calculate whether the process is capable or not.

16.6. If, in problem 16.5, the process is improved so the standard deviation is 0.0035, is the process capable now?

Answer. Process is capable.

16.7. In problem 16.6, what is the C_{pk} when

a. The process is centered on 0.75? Is the process capable?

b. The process is centered on 0.74? Is the process capable?

Answer. a. $C_{pk} = 1.43$. Process centered on 0.75. The process is capable.

b. $C_{pk} = 0.24$. Process centered on 0.74. The process is not capable

16.8. A company fills plastic bottles with 8 ounces of shampoo. The tolerance is ±0.1 ounce. The process has a standard deviation of 0.02 ounce. For the following situations, calculate the C_{pk} and evaluate the process capability.

a. A sample has an average of quantity of 7.93 ounces.

b. A sample has an average of quantity of 7.98 ounces.

c. A sample has an average of quantity of 8.04 ounces.

16.9. Create a House of Quality for a product familiar to you and complete the House of Quality form. Pick at least three different brands of the product to make the competitive comparison. List at least three customer needs inherent in the products and three features that deliver these needs. Identify the interactions among the features and establish target values for your new and improved product.

16.10. A pallet manufacturer has measured the output of a board cutting operation. The boards have a specification of 24 inches plus or minus ½ inch. A sample of the boards is shown below. Calculate the capability of the board cutting operation. What suggestions would you make to the operator?

24.1 24.2 24.3 24.2 24.1 24.0 23.9 24.2

24.1 24.3 24.2 24.0 24.4 24.1 24.3 24.2

CASE STUDY 16.1

Accent Oak Furniture Company

Accent Oak Furniture Company has been in business for more than 30 years, serving customers in Chicago and the surrounding area. The business consists of three different divisions: a custom furniture division that manufactures such crafted items as dining room suites, a kitchen cabinet division and a banister division that manufactures and installs quality oak railings.

Each division reports to a vice president who in turn reports to Frank Johnson, the president and founder of the company. Total sales for all three divisions are projected to reach $8 million for the current fiscal year.

Figure 1 Installation Department Monthly Report—August 8.				
Job#	Crew#	Budget $	Actual $	Comments
7156	1	1,100	1,127	Waited 1/2 hr for customer
7157	2	985	1,154	Fit problem with spindles
7158	5	1,200	996	
7160	4	1,500	1,854	Recalled for loose spindle
7163	2	850	865	Two split spindles
7166	5	1,200	1,385	Fit problem with spindles
7167	1	1,450	1,620	Customer changed design refit
7168	4	1,800	2,254	Spindle shims needed
7169	5	1,100	1,080	
7171	2	980	1,200	Handrail rough finish
7172	4	1,560	1,860	Loose spindles
7174	1	1,200	1,650	Not to drawings
7175	2	975	1,320	Handrail cracked
7177	4	1,400	1,875	Fit problem spindles
7179	3	2,250	3,200	Recalled for loose bannister
7181	5	1,900	2,520	Fit problem spindles
7182	3	1,800	2,260	Fit problem spindles
7184	3	1,750	1,780	Customer changed design
TOTAL		$25,000	$30,000	

Frank has been quite pleased with the performance of the custom furniture division and the kitchen cabinet division, which together account for more than 85% of the sales revenue. He does, however, have some concerns about the banister division based on last year's profit performance and the first week of August's sales report for the installation crews as indicated in the Installation Department Monthly Report.

It is now the second week of August and the new installation market is just starting up. s are installed in new homes in the fall when the homes are nearly finished and ready for sale. There is some demand for s throughout the year for renovations. However, this business is concentrated in the fall and quickly dies off before Christmas. Any problems with the banisters should be resolved before the peak season begins.

On Monday, Frank met with Tom Smythe, the vice president of the division, and voiced his concerns. Frank suggested that they meet again on Friday to discuss some further actions to get back on track. Tom felt the concerns were a bit premature but agreed grudgingly. Tom felt that some of his key people should attend, so Brian Coulter, the sales manager; Pete Harburg, who was in charge of the five two-man installation crews and Hank Strong, the manufacturing supervisor, were invited to attend.

During the meeting, Tom asked each one of his people to describe their individual concerns about the past week's installation report.

Hank began by giving a brief outline of the manufacturing process that he was responsible for in the plant.

Handrail Area

1. The oak was purchased in 16-foot lengths and inspected for any flaws or excessive knots to ensure it was #1 grade.

2. Any rejects were sent to the cabinet division to be used for interior shelves or to make spindles.

3. The approved boards were run through a multihead mill that planed the bottom side and shaped the top and sides of the handrail.

4. They were inspected again for rough grain and any knots that could cause quality problems. Any rejects were then cut into shorter usable lengths for shorter handrails or spindles.

5. The handrails were then sent to the drilling machine where the holes were automatically spaced and drilled by the operator on an industrial quality drill press.

6. Occasionally the operator inspects the dimensions of the holes using a dual purpose go–no-go gauge. On one end of the gauge is a metal rod that is inserted in the hole to measure the depth. The rod has a hatchmarked area that has PASS stamped into the metal. If the top of the hole is in the PASS area, then the hole dimension is considered okay. The other end of the gauge is long and round and has three steps cut into the circumference. This makes the rod get bigger around at about ¼ from the end and ½ from the end. If the first part goes into the hole but not the middle, the hole is undersized. If the second step but not the third enters the hole, the hole is of the correct diameter. The third step indicates oversize.

7. The handrails are then sent for sanding and varnishing. A final inspection is performed for appearance and finish. The handrail sections are then sorted by length for full size and shorts.

Spindle Area

1. Oak is purchased, inspected, and cut to length. Approximately 5% also comes from the handrail area.

2. Sections are placed on a planer and run through twice to give the square end dimensions. Pieces are then placed into a pattern lathe, which provides the product with the spindle design and tapered top end. The operator also lightly sands the spindle while it is on the lathe.

3. An occasional inspection is performed using a go–no-go gauge. The inspection procedure requires the operator to fit over the end of a spindle a gauge, which is an aluminum bar with a specified hole size. The spindle will pass inspection if ¼ to ½ inch of spindle protrudes through the gauge. The gauge is actually marked with red paint outside the limits to assist the operator when inspecting.

4. The operator sets the preangled cutter to maintain the desired size of the spindle end.

5. The approved spindles are then sent to final sanding and varnishing and final inspection.

Hank felt that his people did the best job possible given the wood and machinery available.

Brian Coulter, the sales manager, felt that his people were certainly doing their jobs since sales had increased at a rate of 15% over the last 3 years. One major concern that Brian did have was the increased number of complaints from his major customer, Lincoln Homes, for the quality of the installations. They have already told Brian they will take their business elsewhere if the quality does not improve immediately.

Pete was the most vocal of the group, since his area was always getting the flack. He felt his crews were being pushed as hard as possible but just couldn't keep on plan. Accent Oak banisters are designed to be easily installed in the field even for custom work. However, crews seem to have to refit every other piece and spend time chasing defects. Pete recently started having his crew keep track of reasons why they were over or under budget on each job.

Frank angrily told everyone that he didn't care whose fault the problems were, he just wanted them fixed yesterday and stomped out of the room.

Tom and his group had just recently completed a quality management course, and all agreed that they might as well see if it could help them solve the problem and get Frank off their backs.

Inspection Report—Spindle

The following figure shows the specified depth and allowable tolerance for the pilot study on spindle fit using the knife-edge gauge designed for this purpose.

Figure 2

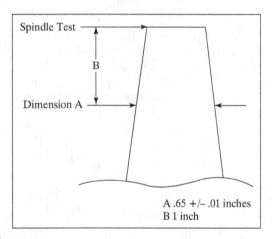

The following 50 readings have been taken and recorded as of August 14.

Figure 3									
Spindle Widths—Inches									
.60	.63	.60	.62	.60	.59	.61	.67	.57	.61
.62	.59	.61	.64	.67	.66	.69	.63	.69	.68
.61	.67	.68	.67	.60	.61	.68	.60	.62	.60
.66	.60	.63	.62	.68	.67	.62	.70	.67	.68
.58	.68	.67	.69	.58	.69	.65	.68	.59	.64

Figure 4

Hole Diameters—Inches									
.57	.56	.58	.59	.57	.58	.56	.58	.56	.58
.58	.59	.60	.55	.61	.60	.58	.57	.58	.60
.56	.61	.57	.59	.58	.57	.55	.57	.59	.57
.60	.58	.56	.60	.56	.62	.59	.58	.62	.59
.57	.62	.59	.61	.63	.59	.64	.60	.61	.63

Case Analysis

1. Analyze the customer complaints using Pareto analysis to identify the largest cause of complaints.
2. Construct histograms of the spindle and hole data to see if there is an assignable cause to the problem.
3. Complete the following three office memos to show how the Hank Strong could implement your recommendations.

INTEROFFICE MEMO
TO: Lead Hand—Handrail   DATE: August 17
FROM: Hank Strong
SUBJECT: Customer Complaints—s

INTEROFFICE MEMO
TO: Lead Hand—Spindle Department   DATE: August 17
FROM: Hank Strong
SUBJECT: Customer Complaints—s

INTEROFFICE MEMO
TO: Tom Smythe   DATE: August 17
FROM: Hank Strong
SUBJECT: Customer Complaints—s

READINGS

CHAPTER 1

Buffa, E. S., and R. K. Sarin, *Modern Production / Operations Management*, 8th ed., Chap. 2. India: Wiley, 2010.

Hill, T. E. *Manufacturing Strategy*, 3rd ed. New York: McGraw-Hill, 2000.

Reid, R. D., Sanders, N. R., *Operations Management*, 4th ed., New York, Wiley: 2009

CHAPTER 2

Fogarty, D. W., Blackstone, J. H., and T. R. Hoffmann, *Production and Inventory Management*. Cincinnati, OH: South-Western, 1990.

Ling, R. C., and W. E. Goddard, *Orchestrating Success*. New York: John Wiley & Sons, 1988.

Plossl, G. W., *Production and Inventory Control, Principles and Techniques*, 2nd ed., Chap. 7. Englewood Cliffs, NJ: Prentice Hall, 1985.

Vollmann, T. E., W. L. Berry, D. C. Whybark, and F. R. Jacobs, *Manufacturing Planning and Control Systems for Supply Chain Management*, 5th ed. New York: McGraw-Hill, 2005.

Wallace, T. F., and R. A. Stahl, *Sales and Operations Planning: The Executive's Guide*. Cincinnati, OH: T. F. Wallace & Company, 2006.

CHAPTER 3

Fogarty, D. W., Blackstone, J. H., and T. R. Hoffmann, *Production and Inventory Management*. Cincinnati, OH: South-Western, 1990.

Mather, H., *Competitive Manufacturing*. Englewood Cliffs, NJ: Prentice Hall, 1988.

Plossl, G. W., *Production and Inventory Control, Principles and Techniques*, 2nd ed., Chap. 7. Englewood Cliffs, NJ: Prentice Hall, 1985.

Schonberger, R. J., and E. M. Knod, *Operations Management: Serving the Customer*, 3rd ed., Chap. 6. Plano, TX: Business Publications, 1988.

Vollmann, T. E., W. L. Berry, D. C. Whybark, and F. R. Jacobs, *Manufacturing Planning and Control Systems for Supply Chain Management*, 5th ed. New York: Irwin, 1992.

CHAPTER 4

Buffa, E. S., and R. K. Sarin, *Modern Production Operations Management*, 8th ed., Chap. 6. New York: Wiley, 1987.

Fogarty, D. W., Blackstone, J. H., and T. R. Hoffmann, *Production and Inventory Management*. Cincinnati, OH: South-Western, 1990.

Garwood, D., *Bills of Material: Structured for Excellence*. Marietta, GA: Dogwood Publishing, 1988.

Mather, H., *Bills of Materials, Recipes and Formulations*. Atlanta, GA: Wright Publishing, 1982.

Orlicky, J., *Material Requirements Planning*. New York: McGraw-Hill, 1975.

Plossl, G. W., *Production and Inventory Control, Principles and Techniques*, 2nd ed., Chap. 6. Englewood Cliffs, NJ: Prentice Hall, 1985.

Vollmann, T. E., W. L. Berry, D. C. Whybark, and F. R. Jacobs, *Manufacturing Planning and Control Systems for Supply Chain Management*, 5th ed. New York: Irwin, 1992.

CHAPTER 5

Blackstone, J. H., Jr., *Capacity Management*. Cincinnati, OH: South-Western, 1989.

Fogarty, D. W., Blackstone, J. H., and T. R. Hoffmann, *Production and Inventory Management*. Cincinnati, OH: South-Western, 1990.

Plossl, G. W., *Production and Inventory Control, Principles and Techniques*, 2nd ed., Chap. 9. Englewood Cliffs, NJ: Prentice Hall, 1985.

Vollmann, T. E., W. L. Berry, D. C. Whybark, and F. R. Jacobs, *Manufacturing Planning and Control Systems for Supply Chain Management*, 5th ed. New York: Irwin, 1992.

CHAPTER 6

Fogarty, D. W., Blackstone, J. H., and T. R. Hoffmann, *Production and Inventory Management*. Cincinnati, OH: South-Western, 1990.

Goldratt, E. M., and J. Cox, *The Goal*, rev. ed. Croton-on-Hudson, NY: North River Press, 1986.

Goldratt, E. M., and R. E. Fox, *The Race*. Croton-on-Hudson, NY: North River Press, 1992.

Pinedo, Michael L., *Planning and Scheduling in Manufacturing and Services*, New York: Springer Publishing 2005

Plossl, G. W., *Production and Inventory Control, Principles and Techniques*, 2nd ed., Chaps. 10–12. Englewood Cliffs, NJ: Prentice Hall, 1985.

Vollmann, T. E., W. L. Berry, D. C. Whybark, and F. R. Jacobs, *Manufacturing Planning and Control Systems for Supply Chain Management*, 5th ed. New York: Irwin, 1992.

CHAPTER 7

Chopra, S., Meindl, P., *Supply Chain Management*, 4th ed., Englewood Cliffs NJ: Prentice Hall, 2010

Johnson, P. F., Leenders, M., Flynn, A., *Purchasing and Supply Management* 14th ed., Whitby ON: McGraw Hill Ryerson, 2011.

CHAPTER 8

Buffa, E. S., and R. K. Sarin, *Modern Production Operations Management*, 8th ed., Chap. 4. New York: Wiley, 1987.

Fogarty, D. W., Blackstone, J. H., and T. R. Hoffmann, *Production and Inventory Management*. Cincinnati, OH: South-Western, 1990.

Plossl, G. W., *Production and Inventory Control, Principles and Techniques*, 2nd ed., Chaps. 4 and 5. Englewood Cliffs, NJ: Prentice Hall, 1985.

Schonberger, R. J., and E. M. Knod, *Operations Management: Serving the Customer*, 3rd ed., Chap. 4. Plano, TX: Business Publications, 1988.

Vollmann, T. E., W. L. Berry, D. C. Whybark, and F. R. Jacobs, *Manufacturing Planning and Control Systems for Supply Chain Management*, 5th ed. New York: Irwin, 1992.

CHAPTER 9

Buffa, E. S., and R. K. Sarin, *Modern Production Operations Management*, 8th ed., Chap. 5. New York: Wiley, 1987.

Fogarty, D. W., Blackstone, J. H., and T. R. Hoffmann, *Production and Inventory Management*. Cincinnati, OH: South-Western, 1990.

Plossl, G. W., *Production and Inventory Control, Principles and Techniques*, 2nd ed., Chap. 2. Englewood Cliffs, NJ: Prentice Hall, 1985.

Schonberger, R. J., and E. M. Knod, *Operations Management: Serving the Customer*, 3rd ed., Chap. 7. Plano, TX: Business Publications, 1988.

Vollmann, T. E., W. L. Berry, D. C. Whybark, and F. R. Jacobs, *Manufacturing Planning and Control Systems for Supply Chain Management*, 5th ed. New York: Irwin, 1992.

CHAPTERS 10 AND 11

Buffa, E. S., and R. K. Sarin, *Modern Production Operations Management*, 8th ed., Chap. 5. India: Wiley, 2010.

Fogarty, D. W., Blackstone, J. H., and T. R. Hoffmann, *Production and Inventory Management*. Cincinnati, OH: South-Western, 1990.

Martin, A. J., *Distribution Resource Planning*. Essex Junction, VT: Oliver Wight Publications, 1995.

Plossl, G. W., *Production and Inventory Control, Principles and Techniques*, 2nd ed., Chap. 3. Englewood Cliffs, NJ: Prentice Hall, 1985.

Reid, R. D., Sanders, N. R., *Operations Management,* 4th ed., New York, Wiley: 2009

Summers, Donna C. S. *Quality,* 4th ed. Upper Saddle River, NJ: Pearson, 2006.

CHAPTERS 12 AND 13

Ballou, Ronald H., *Business Logistics / Supply Chain Management,* 5th ed. Englewood Cliffs, NJ: Prentice Hall, 2004.

Bowersox, D. J., P. J. Calabro, and G. D. Wagenheim, *Introduction to Transportation.* New York: Macmillan, 1981.

Bowersox, D. J., D. J. Closs, and M. B. Cooper, Supply Chain *Logistics Management,* 3rd ed. Whitby, ON: McGraw Hill, 2010

Coyle, J. J., Bardi, E. J., Novack, R., Gibson, B., *Transportation a Supply Chain Perspective,* 7th ed., Toronto ON: Nelson, 2011

Coyle, J. J., Bardi, E. J., Novack, R., Gibson, B., *The Management of Business Logistics,* 7th ed., Oklahoma City OK: South-Western , 2009

Murphy, P. R. Jr., Wood, D., *Contemporary Logistics,* 10th ed., New Jersey: Prentice Hall, 2011

CHAPTER 14

Arnold, J. R., and L. M. Clive, *Introduction to Operations Management.* Qualicum Beach, BC: J. R. Arnold & Associates Ltd., 1996.

Chase, R. B., and N. J. Aquilano, *Production and Operations Management.* Chicago: Richard D. Irwin, 1995.

Schonberger, R. J., and E. M. Knod, *Operations Management.* Chicago: Richard D. Irwin, 1995.

Starr, M. K., *Operations Management.* Danvers, MA: Boyd & Fraser Publishing, 1996.

Turner, W. C., et al. *Introduction to Industrial and Systems Engineering.* Englewood Cliffs, NJ: Prentice Hall, 1993.

CHAPTER 15

Dennis, Pascal, *Lean Production Simplified,* 2nd Edition. Boca Raton, FL: CRC Press, 2007.

Goddard, W. E., *Just-in-Time: Surviving by Breaking Tradition.* Essex Junction, VT: Oliver Wight Publications, 1986.

Hall, R. W., *Zero Inventories.* Homewood, IL: Dow Jones-Irwin, 1983.

Hall, R. W., *Attaining Manufacturing Excellence.* Homewood, IL: Dow Jones-Irwin, 1987.

Schonberger, R. J., *Japanese Manufacturing Techniques: Nine Hidden Lessons in Simplicity.* New York: Free Press, 1982.

Schonberger, R. J., *World Class Manufacturing: The Lessons of Simplicity Applied.* New York: Free Press, 1986.

Suzaki, K., *The New Manufacturing Challenge: Techniques for Continuous Improvement.* New York: Free Press, 1987.

Wemmerlöv, U., *Production Planning and Control Procedures for Cellular Manufacturing.* Falls Church, VA: American Production and Inventory Control Society, 1988.

Womack, J. P., and D. T. Jones, *Lean Thinking.* New York: Simon & Schuster, 1996.

CHAPTER 16

Arnold, J. R., and Clive L. M., *Introduction to Operations Management.* Qualicum Beach, BC: J. R. Arnold & Associates Ltd., 1996.

Besterfield, D. H., C. Besterfield-Michna, G. H. Besterfield, and M. Besterfield-Sacre, *Total Total Quality Management.* Englewood Cliffs, NJ: Prentice Hall, 2003.

Juran, J. M., and A.B. Godfrey, Juran's *Quality Handbook,* 5th ed. New York: McGraw-Hill Professional, 1998.

Reid, R. D., Sanders, N. R., *Operations Management,* 4th ed., New York, Wiley: 2009

Schonberger, R. J., and E. M. Knod, *Operations Management.* Chicago: Richard D. Irwin, 2001.

Summers, Donna C. S., *Quality,* 4th ed. Upper Saddle River, NJ: Pearson, 2006.

INDEX

A

A items, 210
ABC inventory control, 207–210
    classification of, 210
    steps in, 208–210
Acceptance sampling, 382
Accessibility, 264
Accounting equation, 204
Action bucket, 76
Adding value, 340–341
Aesthetics, 369
Aggregate inventory management, 196
Airways, 290
Allocate, 74
Anticipation inventories, 198
Anticipation inventory, 228
APICS (Association for Operations Management), 4
Appraisal costs, 372
Approving payment, 150
Assemble-to-order, 3, 31, 47
Asset, 203
Assignable variation, 374
Association for Operations Management (APICS), 4
ATP (Available to promise), 50
Available facilities, 12
Available time, 103
Available to promise (ATP), 50
Average, 241–242
Average cost, 207
Average demand, 173

B

Backflushing, 353
Backlog, 31
Back scheduling, 107–108
Backward scheduling, 124
Balance sheet, 203–204
Balancing the line, 347
Bar codes, 273
Bar coding, 262
Basic MRP record, 76
Bell curve, 241
Benchmarking, 385–386
Bias, 180–181
Bill of material, 12
    indented bill, 69, 120
    multilevel bills, 66
    multiple bill, 66
    parent-component relationship, 66
    pegging report, 70
    planning bills, 69–70
    processor, 64
    product tree, 65
    single-level bill, 66–68

    summarized parts list, 69
    where-used report, 70
Bottlenecks, 128–129
    definition of, 128
    managing, 129
    principles, 128–129
    throughput, 128
Bottom-up replanning, 83
Boundary spanners, 5
Break-bulk, 297
Break-even point, 158
Bullwhip effect, 163
Buyer specifications, 153
Buyer-developed specifications, 153

C

C items, 210
Calculated or rated capacity, 103
Capacity, 16
Capacity-associated costs, 203
Capacity available, 102–104
Capacity control, 99
Capacity management, 20, 98–99, 352
    available time, 103
    back scheduling, 107–108
    calculated or rated capacity, 103
    capacity available, 102–104
    capacity control, 99
    capacity planning, 99–100
    capacity required (load), 98, 105–107
    capacity requirements planning (CRP), 99–100, 100–102
    definition of capacity, 98–99
    demonstrated (measured) capacity, 103, 104
    determining capacity available, 103–104
    efficiency, 104
    inputs, 100–101
    lead time, 101
    levels of capacity, 103
    load, 98, 105–106
    measuring capacity, 102–103
    move time, 101
    open order file, 101
    planned order releases, 101
    queue time, 101
    rated capacity, 104
    resource planning, 99
    rough-cut capacity planning, 99
    routing file, 101
    scheduling orders, 107–108
    shop calendar, 101–102
    standard time, 103
    units of output, 102–103
    utilization, 103
    wait time, 101

Capacity management (*continued*)
    work center file, 101
    work center load report, 106–107
Capacity planning, 99–100
Capacity required (load), 98, 105–107
Capacity requirements planning (CRP), 76, 99–100, 100–102
Capital, 204
Card alternatives, 358
Carriage, costs of, 369289
Carriage, legal types of, 290–291
Carrying costs, 201–202
Cash flow analysis, 205
Cause-and-effect diagram, 325–326
Cause-and-effects (fishbone) diagram, 381
Center, distribution, 374
Centralized system, 252
Central storage, 266
CEP (Cost equalization point), 321–322
Chance variation, 373
Chase (demand matching) strategy, 26
Chase strategy, 30
Checksheets, 381
Classes of activity, 327
Common carriers, 291
Competition, 2
Competitive bidding, 158–159
Component items, 66
Component standardization, 341
Concurrent engineering, 314
Conformance, 368
Constraints, theory of, 130–132
Consumer's risk, 382–383
Continuous manufacturing, 119, 318
Continuous process improvement (CPI), 322–332, 371
    analysis, 327
    cause-and-effect diagram, 325–326
    classes of activity, 327
    developing solutions, 330
    economic considerations, 324
    human and environmental factors, 331
    human factor, 324
    learning curve, 331
    maintenance, 331
    motion economy, principles of, 330
    operations process charts, 327
    Pareto diagrams, 324–325
    people involvement, 323
    process flow diagrams, 327, 329
    productivity, improving, 323
    record, 326–327
    root cause, finding the, 329–330
    steps of, 323
    teams, 323
Contract buying, 160
Contract carriers, 291
Control, 118, 133–138
Control charts, 379–380
Control files, 121
Control limits, 380–381
Conveyors, 303
Cost equalization point (CEP), 321–322
Cost of goods sold, 205

Costs, 201–203
Costs of failure, 372
Cost trade-off, 286
Count frequency, 272–273
CPI (Continuous process improvement), 322–332, 371
C_{pk} index, 377–379
CR (critical ratio), 137
Cranes and hoists, 303
Critical ratio (CR), 137
CRM (customer relationship management), 164
CRP (capacity requirements planning), 76, 99–100, 100–102
Cube utilization and accessibility, 264–265
Cumulative variance, 134
Customer focus, 370
Customer relationship management (CRM), 162
Cycle counting, 271–272
Cycle stock, 199
Cycle time, 123

D
Data collection and preparation, 171–172
Data requirements, 120–121
Days of supply, 29, 206
Decentralized system, 252
Decline phase, 311
Delivery lead time, 3–4
Demand forecasting, 168
    average demand, 175
    bias, 180–181
    characteristics of demand, 168–170
    data collection and preparation, 171–172
    demand lead time, 185
    dependent *versus* independent demand, 170
    deseasonalized demand, 177, 178–179
    economic indicators, 172
    exponential smoothing, 175–176
    extrinsic forecasting techniques, 172
    forecast error, 180–181
    intrinsic forecasting techniques, 172–176
    mean absolute deviation (MAD), 181–184
    moving average, 173–175
    normal distribution, 182–183
    P/D ratio, 184–185
    principles of, 170–171
    production lead time, 184
    qualitative techniques, 172
    random variation, 169, 181
    seasonal forecasts, 178
    seasonal index, 176–177
    seasonality, 169, 176–179
    smoothing constant, 175
    stable *versus* dynamic, 170
    tracking signal, 183–184
    trend, 169
Demand lead time, 185
Demand management, 167–168
Demand time fence, 52, 54
Demonstrated (measured) capacity, 103, 104
Density, 294
Dependent *versus* independent demand, 170
Deseasonalized demand, 177, 178–179

Determining capacity available, 103–104
Differing forecast and lead-time intervals, 247
Dispatching, 136–138
Dispersion, 242
Distribution channel, 282–284
Distribution inventories, 198, 251–254
Distribution requirements planning, 252–254
Distribution warehouse, 296
Drum-Buffer-Rope, 130, 131, 360
Dynamic, 170

E
Economic indicators, 172
Economic-order quantity (EOQ), 219–223
EDI (electronic data interchange), 160
Effective lot sizing, 353
Efficiency, 104
Electronic data interchange (EDI), 160
Employee empowerment, 331
Empowerment, 371
Engineer-to-order, 3, 48
Enterprise resource planning (ERP), 23–24
Environmentally responsible purchasing, 161
EOQ (economic-order quantity), 219–223
ERP (enterprise resource planning), 23–24
Error management, 54
Exception messages, 81
Expenses, 204
Exploding and offsetting, 71
Exponential smoothing, 175–176
External failure costs, 372
Extranet, 161
Extrinsic forecasting techniques, 172

F
Fair price, 157
FAS (final assembly schedule), 47–48
Features, 368
FIFO (first in first out), 207
Final assembly schedule (FAS), 47–48
Financial statements and inventory,
    203–207
Finished goods, 197
Finite loading, 124–125
Firm planned orders, 81
First in first out (FIFO), 207
Fishbone diagrams, 381
5S approach, 359
Fixed costs, 157, 289, 320
Fixed-location system, 266
Fixed-order quantity, 218–219
Floating-location system, 266
Flow manufacturing, 119, 343–344
Flow of material, 197–198
Flow processing, 318
Fluctuation inventory, 198
FOB (freight on board), 294
Focused factory, 312–313
Forecast error, 180
For hire carrier, 291
Forward scheduling, 123, 124
Freight on board (FOB), 294

Frozen zone, 54
Functional specifications, 151, 152–154

G
Gateway operation, 129
General and administrative expenses, 205
General-purpose machinery, 317
General warehouse, 296
Global distribution, 286–287
Green production, 22
Green reverse logistics 284
Gross and net requirements, 72–74
Growth phase, 310

H
Hedge inventory, 199
Hoists, and cranes, 303
Human factor, 324
Hybrid strategy, 28
Hybrid systems, 360–361

I
Implementation and control, 11
Income, 204
Income statement, 204–205
Incoterms, 287
Indented bill, 69, 87
Industrial trucks, 303
Infinite loading, 124
Input/output control, 134–136
Input/output report, 134–135
Inputs, 100–101
100% inspection, 382
Installation, of new method, 331
Interfaces, 287–288
    marketing, 287–288
    production, 288
Intermittent manufacturing, 119, 318–319
Internal failure costs, 372
International Commercial Terminology (Incoterms), 295–296
Internet, role of, 161
Intranet, 161
Intrinsic forecasting techniques, 172–176
Introduction phase, 310
Inventory
    ABC inventory, 207–210
    anticipation inventories, 198
    average cost, 207
    capacity-associated costs, 203
    carrying costs, 201–202
    costs, 201–203
    cycle stock, 199
    days of supply, 206–207
    distribution inventories, 198
    financial statements and inventory, 203–207
    first in first out (FIFO), 207
    flow of material, 197–198
    fluctuation inventory, 198
    functions of, 198–199
    hedge inventory, 199
    inventory turns, 206
    item cost, 201

Inventory (*continued*)
    landed price, 201
    last in first out (LIFO), 207
    lot-size inventories, 199
    maintenance, repair, and operational supplies (MROs), 198, 199
    movement inventories, 199
    objectives of, 199–201
    ordering costs, 202–203
    Pareto's law, 208
    physical control and security, 267–268
    pipeline inventories, 199
    record accuracy, 268–273
    safety stock, 198
    standard cost, 207
    stockout costs, 203
    supply and demand patterns, 198
    transportation inventories, 199
Inventory-carrying cost, 303–304
Inventory management, 11, 353
Inventory record file, 64
Inventory records, 64
Inventory turns, 206
ISO 9000:2008, 383–385
Item cost, 201
Item inventory management, 196–197
Item master file, 120

J
Job design, 331
Job enlargement, 331
Job enrichment, 331
Job rotation, 331
Just-in-time capabilities, 155
Just-in-time environment, 348
Just-in-time manufacturing, 348
    adding value, 340–341
    backflushing, 353
    balancing the line, 347
    capacity management, 352
    card alternatives, 358
    component standardization, 341
    continuous process improvement, 330, 371
    effective lot sizing, 353
    flow manufacturing, 343–344
    inventory management, 353
    just-in-time environment, 348
    Kanban system, 356–358, 358–359
    lean production tools, 359
    linearity, 348
    machine flexibility, 345
    manufacturing planning and control, 350–359
    master production scheduling, 351–352
    materials requirements planning, 352, 389
    mixed-model scheduling, 348
    objectives, 340
    operator flexibility, 346
    partnering, 348–349
    poke-poke (fail safe), 343
    post-deduct, 353
    process flexibility, 345–346
    production planning, 352
    pull system, 347, 353–355
    quality at the source, 346
    quick changeover, 345–346
    supplier partnerships, 348–349
    supplier selection and certification, 349
    total employee involvement, 349–350
    total productive maintenance, 346–347
    total quality management (TQM), 369–372, 389
    uniform plant loading, 347
    uninterrupted flow, 347–348
    valid schedule, 347–348
    waste, 341–343
    work cells, 344–345

K
Kaizen, 359
Kanban system, 248, 356–358, 358–359, 360
Kanban system and MRP, 360

L
Laid-down cost (LDC), 299
Landed price, 201
Last in first out (LIFO), 207
LDC (laid-down cost), 299
Lead time, 71, 101, 237
Lean production, 339
Lean production tools, 359
Learning curve, 331, 332
Level production plan, 29–30, 31–32
Liabilities, 204
LIFO (last in first out), 207
Limited access, 268
Linearity, 348
Line-haul costs, 292–293
Line-haul cost per hundredweight, 292
Linkages to other planning and control functions, 63–64
Liquid zone, 54
Little's Law, 329
Load, 98, 105–106
Load leveling, 127
Location audit system, 273
Lost capacity cost, 202
Lot-for-lot, 218
Lot-size decision rules, 218–219
Lot-size inventories, 199
Low-cost processing, 313
Lower specification limit (LSL), 375
Low-level code, 76
Low-level coding and netting, 76–78
LSL (lower specification limit), 375
Lumpy demand, 228

M
Machine flexibility, 345
MAD (mean absolute deviation), 181–184
Maintenance, repair, and operational supplies (MROs), 198, 199
Make-to-order production plan, 3, 31–32, 47
Make-to-stock production plan, 3–4, 28–30
Make-to-stock products, 47
Manufacturing capability, 155
Manufacturing lead time (MLT), 122–123

Manufacturing planning and control, 11–12, 17–20, 350–359
Manufacturing resource planning (MRP II), 22–23, 359–360
Manufacturing strategy, 3–4
Manufacturing systems, 119–120
Market boundary, 298–300
Mass customization, 315
Master production schedule (MPS), 17, 19, 41, 64
 available to promise (ATP), 50
 delivery promises, and, 50–52
 demand time fence, 52
 development of, 44–49
 differences, resolution of, 47
 error management, 54
 planning horizon, 48–49
 preliminary master production schedule, 44–45
 production plan, relationship to, 42–44
 projected available balance (PAB), 52–53
 rough-cut capacity planning, 45–46
 scheduled receipt, 50
 time fences, 53–54
Master scheduling, 41–42
Material requirements planning, impact of, 159–161
Materials handling, 302–303
Materials handling costs, 285, 304
Materials management definition, 9–10
Material requirements plan (MRP), 19, 62–84
 action bucket, 76
 basic MRP record, 76
 bills of material (See Bills of material)
 bottom-up replanning, 83
 capacity requirements planning, 76
 exception messages, 81
 exploding and offsetting, 71
 factors in managing, 82
 firm planned orders, 81
 gross and net requirements, 72–74
 inventory record file, 64
 inventory records, 64
 JIT, TQM and, 389
 lead time, 71
 linkages to other planning and control
  functions, 63–64
 low-level coding and netting, 76–78
 management of, 82–84
 multiple bills of material, 78–81
 nature of demand, 62–63
 net requirements, 75–76
 objectives of, 63
 offsetting, 71
 open orders, 75
 planned order receipt, 72
 planned order release, 72
 planned orders, 72, 81
 planning factors, 63–64
 planning horizon, 76
 priority, 82
 process of, 71–81
 released orders, 81
 releasing orders, 74
 scheduled receipts, 74–75
 system nervousness, reducing, 83
 time buckets, 76

 transaction messages, 82
 use of, 81–84
Maturity or saturation phase, 311
Maximum-level inventory, 250–251
Mean, 241–242
Mean absolute deviation (MAD), 181–184
Metrics, 7–8
Minimum order, 228
Min-max system, 218
Mixed-model scheduling, 348
MLT (manufacturing lead time), 122–123
Modularization, 312
Monetary unit lot size, 223
Motion economy, principles of, 330
Movement inventories, 199
Move time, 101, 122
Moving averages, 173–175
MPS (master production schedule), 17, 19, 41, 64
MROs (maintenance, repair, and operational supplies),
 198, 199
MRP (material requirements plan), 19, 62–84
MRP II (manufacturing resource planning), 22–23, 359–360
Multilevel bills, 66
Multiple bill, 66
Multiple bills of material, 78–81
Multiple sourcing, 154
Multi-warehouse systems, 303–305

N
Nature of demand, 62–63
Need for new products, 310–311
Nesting, 315
Net requirements, 75–76
Non-instantaneous receipt model, 224
Normal curve, 241
Normal distribution, 182–183, 240, 241

O
Offsetting, 71
Open order file, 101
Open orders, 75
Operation overlapping, 125–126
Operation sequencing, 136–138
Operations management, 1–4
Operation splitting, 126–127
Operations process charts, 327
Operator flexibility, 346
Ordering costs, 202–203
Order picking and assembly, 266–267
Order point, 237
Order point system, 237–239
Order preparation, 121–122
Order processing, 286, 168
Order qualifiers, 2–3
Order quantities
 economic-order quantity (EOQ), 219–223
 fixed-order quantity, 218–219
 just-in-time and, 229
 lot-for-lot, 218
 lot-size decision rules, 218–219
 min-max system, 218
 monetary unit lot size, 223

Order quantities (*continued*)
    noninstantaneous receipt model, 224
    order n periods supply, 219
    period-order quantity (POQ), 226–229
    quantity discounts, 224–225
    relevant costs, 220–221
    stock-keeping unit (SKU), 218
    time between orders, 227
    trial-and-error method, 221–222
    unknown costs, products with, 221–222
Order winners, 2–3
Owners' equity, 204

P

PAB (projected available balance), 52–53
PAC (purchasing and production activity control), 19–20
Packaging, 294, 301–302
Packaging costs, 304
Pallet, 301
Pallet positions, 264
Parent, 66
Parent-component relationship, 66
Pareto analysis, 324
Pareto diagrams, 381
Pareto diagrams, 324–325
Pareto's law, 208
Partnering, 348–349
P/D ratio, 184–185
Pegging report, 70
People involvement, 323
Perceived quality, 369
Performance, 368
Performance measure, 7
Performance standards, 7–8
Periodic (annual) inventory, 271
Periodic review system, 249–251
Period-order quantity (POQ), 226–229
Perishability, 294
Permanent or static information, 248
Perpetual inventory record, 248–249
Physical control and security, 267–268
Physical distribution, 282–305
    activities, 285–286
    billing and collection costs, 293
    common carrier, 291
    contract carriers, 291
    distribution channel, 282–284
    global distribution, 286–287
    for hire carrier, 291
    interfaces, 287–288
    line-haul costs, 292–293
    materials handling, 302–303
    multi-warehouse systems, 303–305
    packaging, 301–302
    physical supply, 282
    pickup and delivery costs, 293
    private carriers, 290, 291
    reverse logistics, 284–285
    terminal-handling costs, 293
    total-cost concept, 286
    total transportation costs, 293–294
    transaction channel, 282–284

    transportation, 288–290
    transportation cost elements, 291–296
    warehousing, 296–300
Physical supply, 282
Physical supply/distribution, 12–13
Pickup and delivery costs, 293
Pipelines, 290
Pipeline inventories, 199
Planned order receipt, 72
Planned order releases, 72, 101
Planned orders, 72, 81
Planner/buyer concept, 159–160
Planning bills, 69–70
Planning factors, 63–64
Planning files, 120–121
Planning horizon, 48–49, 76
Planning time fence, 54
Point-of-use storage, 266
Poke-poke (fail safe), 343
POQ (period-order quantity), 226–229
Post-deduct, 353
Postponement, 4
Preliminary master production schedule, 44–45
Prevention costs, 372
Preventive maintenance, 346
Price, 155–156, 369
Price, determining, 150, 157–159
Price negotiation, 159
Priority, 16, 82
Private carriers, 290, 291
Processes, 315
Process capability, 375–379
Process capacity index (C_p), 376–377
Process control, 379–381
Process design, 315, 316–317
Process flexibility, 345–346
Process flow diagrams, 327, 329, 381
Process focus, 312
Processing equipment, 317
Process specifications, 12
Producer's risk, 383
Product and market focus, 312
Product description, 12
Product development principles, 311–313
Product groups, establishing, 24–25
Production activity control, 117–139
    backward scheduling, 124
    bottlenecks, 128–129
    constraints, theory of, 130–132
    continuous manufacturing, 119
    control, 118, 133–138
    control files, 121
    critical ratio (CR), 137
    cumulative variance, 134
    cycle time, 123
    data requirements, 120–121
    dispatching, 136–138
    Drum-Buffer-Rope, 130, 131
    finite loading, 124–125
    flow manufacturing, 119
    forward scheduling, 123, 124
    implementation, 118, 132–133

infinite loading, 124
input/output control, 134–136
input/output report, 134–135
intermittent manufacturing, 119
item master file, 120
load leveling, 127
managing bottlenecks, 129
manufacturing lead time (MLT), 122–123
manufacturing systems, 119–120
move time, 122
operation overlapping, 125–126
operation sequencing, 136–138
operation splitting, 126–127
order preparation, 121–122
overview, 117
planning, 118
planning files, 120–121
production reporting, 138
product structure file (bill of material file), 120
project manufacturing, 120
queue time, 122
repetitive manufacturing, 119
routing file, 120–121
run time, 122
scheduling, 122–127
setup time, 122
shop order detail file, 121
shop order master file, 121
throughput, 128
throughput time, 123
wait time, 122
work center master file, 121
Production control costs, 202
Production lead time, 184–185
Production leveling, 26–27
Production plan, relationship to, 42–44
Production planning, 11, 19, 351
    assemble-to-order, 31
    backlog, 31
    characteristics, 25
    chase (demand matching) strategy, 26
    chase strategy, 30
    hybrid strategy, 28
    level production plan, 29–30, 31–32
    make-to-order production plan, 31–32
    make-to-stock production plan, 28–30
    product groups, establishing, 24–25
    production leveling, 26–27
    resource planning, 32–33
    subcontracting, 27–28
Production reporting, 138
Productivity, improving, 323
Product layout, 318
Product mixing, 297
Product tracking, 139
Products
    concurrent engineering, 314
    continuous manufacturing, 318
    decline phase, 311
    flow processing, 318
    focused factory, 312–313
    general-purpose machinery, 317

    growth phase, 310
    intermittent manufacturing, 318–319
    introduction phase, 310
    low-cost processing, 313
    mass customization, 315
    maturity or saturation phase, 311
    modularization, 312
    need for new products, 310–311
    nesting, 315
    process design, 315, 316–317
    processes, 315
    process focus, 312
    processing equipment, 317
    product and market focus, 312
    product development principles, 311–313
    product layout, 318
    project (fixed position) processes, 319
    repetitive manufacturing, 318
    simplification, 311
    simultaneous engineering, 314–315
    specialization, 312–313
    special-purpose machinery, 317
    specification and design, 313–315
    standardization, 311–312
Product structure file (bill of material file), 120
Product tree, 65
Profit leverage, 147–148
Projected available balance (PAB), 52–53
Project (fixed position) processes, 319
Project manufacturing, 120
Protective packaging, 285
Pull system, 347, 353–357
Purchase order, issuing a, 150
Purchase order cost, 202
Purchasing
    approving payment, 150
    buyer specifications, 153
    competitive bidding, 158–159
    contract buying, 160
    environmentally responsible, 161–162
    expansion of, 162–163
    functional specifications, 151, 152–154
    material requirements planning, impact of, 159–161
    multiple sourcing, 154
    objectives, 148
    organizational implications and, 163–164
    planner/buyer concept, 159–160
    price, determining, 150, 157–159
    price negotiation, 159
    profit leverage, and, 147–148
    purchase order, issuing a, 150
    purchasing cycle, 149–150
    quotations, requesting, 149–150
    ranking method, 156
    receiving and accepting goods, 150
    receiving and analyzing purchase requisition, 149
    reduce, reuse, recycle, 161, 162
    single sourcing, 154
    sole sourcing, 154
    sourcing, 154
    specifications, establishing, 150–152

Purchasing (*continued*)
  standard specifications, 153–154
  suppliers, selecting, 149, 154–157
  supply chain management, and, 162
  value analysis, 152
Purchasing and production activity control (PAC),
  19–20
Purchasing cycle, 149–150

Q
QFD (quality function deployment), 387–389
Qualitative techniques, 172
Quality, 367–369
Quality at the source, 346
Quality control tools, 381
Quality function deployment (QFD), 387–389
Quantity discounts, 224–225
Quantities required, 12
Queue time, 101, 122
Quick changeover, 345–346
Quotations, requesting, 149–150

R
Radio frequency identification (RFID), 262, 273–274
Railways, 289
Random variation, 169, 181
Ranking method, 156
Rated capacity, 104
Raw materials, 197
R chart, 380
Receiving and accepting goods, 150
Receiving and analyzing purchase requisition, 149
Record, 326–327
Record accuracy, 268–273
Reduce Reuse Recycle, 161
Reducing system nervousness, 83
Released orders, 82
Releasing orders, 74
Relevant costs, 220–221
Reliability, 155
Repetitive manufacturing, 119, 318
Reserve stock, 266
Resource bill, 32
Resource planning, 32–33, 99
Retained earnings, 204
Revenue, 204
Reverse logistics, 284–285
RFID (radio frequency identification), 262, 273–274
Road transport, 289
Root cause, finding the, 329–330
Rough-cut capacity planning, 45–46, 99
Routing file, 101, 120–121
Run charts, 379–380
Run time, 122

S
Safety factor, 244–245
Safety lead time, 239
Safety stock, 198, 239–245
Sales and operations planning (SOP), 20–22
Scatterplots, 381
Scheduled receipts, 50, 74–75

Scheduling, 107, 122–127
Scheduling orders, 107–108
Seasonal forecasts, 178
Seasonal index, 176–177
Seasonality, 169, 176–179
Self-check, 343
Self-directed teams, 331
Service, 369
Service, after-sales, 155
Service levels, determining, 245–246
Setup and teardown costs, 202
Setup time, 101
Shape, 374
Shop calendar, 101–102
Shop floor control, 11
Shop order detail file, 121
Shop order master file, 121
Simplification, 311
Simultaneous engineering, 314–315
Single-level bill, 66–68
Single sourcing, 154
Six Sigma, 386–387
SKU (stock-keeping unit), 218
Slushy zone, 54
Smoothing constant, 175
Sole sourcing, 154
SOP (sales and operations planning), 20–22
Source inspection, 343
Sourcing, 154
Specialization, 312–313
Special-purpose machinery, 317
Specification and design, 313–315
Specifications, establishing, 150–152
Spread, 375
SRM (supplier relationship management), 163
Stable *versus* dynamic, 170
Standard, 311
Standard cost, 207
Standard deviation (Sigma), 242–243
Standardization, 311–312
Standard specifications, 153–154
Standard time, 103
Statistical control, 374
Stock-keeping unit (SKU), 218
Stock location, 265–266
Stockout, 198
Stockout costs, 203
Strategic business plan, 18, 20–22
Subcontracting, 27–28
Successive check inspection, 343
Summarized parts list, 69
Supplier certification, 349
Supplier flexibility and reliability, 160
Supplier location, 155
Supplier partnerships, 348–349, 371
Suppliers, selecting, 149–150, 154–157
  factors in, 155–156
  final selection of, 156–157
  sources, 154
Supplier relationship management (SRM), 163
Supplier selection, 349
Supply and demand patterns, 198

Supply chain management, 4–9
    conflicts, 8–9
    factors, 4
    growth of, 5–6
    historical perspective, 5
    organizational implications, 163–164
Supply chain metrics, 7–8
System nervousness, reducing, 83
System service capability, 304–305

T
Takt time, 359
Target-level inventory, 250–251
Teams, 323, 371
Technical ability, 155
Technology applications, 273–274
Terminal-handling costs, 293
Terminals, 289
Theory of constraints, 130–132, 360
Third party logistics (3PLs) providers, 287
Third-party registration system, 384
Throughput, 128
Throughput time, 123
Time between orders, 227
Time buckets, 76
Time fences, 53–54
Time needed to perform operations, 12
Tolerance, 269–270, 367
Total cost, 286
Total-cost concept, 286
Total employee involvement, 349–350
Total line-haul cost, 292
Total productive maintenance, 346–347
Total quality management (TQM), 369–372
    assignable variation, 374
    benchmarking, 385–386
    chance variation, 373
    concepts, 369–372
    continuous process improvement, 371
    costs of failure, 372
    customer focus, 370
    defining quality, 367–369
    employee involvement, 370–371
    empowerment, 371
    ISO 9000:2000, 383–385
    JIT, MRP and, 389
    management commitment, 369–370
    performance measures, 371–372
    process capability, 375–379
    process control, 379–381
    quality, controlling, 372–373
    quality control tools, 381
    quality function deployment (QFD), 387–389
    sample inspection, 382–383
    Six Sigma, 386–387
    statistical control, 374
    supplier partnerships, 371
    teams, 371
    variation, 373–375
Total system cost, 304
Total transportation costs, 293–294
TQM (total quality management), 369–372

Tracking signal, 183–184
Transaction channel, 283
Transaction messages, 82
Transportation, 288–290
Transportation consolidation, 297
Transportation costs, 303
Transportation cost elements, 291–296
Transportation inventory, 199, 228
Transportation terms, 294–295
Trend, 169
Trial-and-error method, 221–222
Two-bin system, 248

U
Uniform plant loading, 347
Uninterrupted flow, 347–348
Unitization, 301–302
Unit loads, 301
Units of output, 102–103
Unknown costs, products with, 225–226
Upper specification limit (USL), 375
USL (upper specification limit), 375
Utilization, 103

V
Valid schedule, 347–348
Value, 294
Value analysis, 152
Value stream mapping, 359
Variability, patterns of, 374–375
Variable costs, 157, 289, 320–321
Variable or dynamic information, 249
Variation, 373–375
Vehicles, 289
Vendor-managed inventory, 160–161
Voice of the customer, 388

W
Wait time, 101, 122
Warehouses (distribution centers), 285
Warehousing, 296–300
    costs, 304
    effect on transportation costs of, 300
    market boundaries, 298–300
    role of, 297
    transportation costs and, 297–298
Warehousing management, 262–274
    accessibility, 264
    activities, warehouse, 263
    central storage, 266
    cube utilization and accessibility, 264–265
    fixed-location system, 266
    floating-location system, 266
    order picking and assembly, 266–267
    pallet positions, 264
    point-of-use storage, 266
    reserve stock, 266
    stock location, 265–266
    working stock, 265
    working stock and reserve stock,
        265–266, 267
Warranty, 368

Waste, 341–343
Waterways, 290
Ways, 289
Where-used report, 70
WIP (work-in-process), 11, 197
Work cells, 344–345
Work center file, 101
Work center load report, 106–107
Work center master file, 121

Working stock, 265
Working stock and reserve stock, 265–266, 267
Work-in-process (WIP), 11, 197

X
X bar, 380

Z
Zone method, 273